MW00845533

Laser Cutting Guide for Manufacturing

Laser Cutting Guide for Manufacturing

Charles L. Caristan

Society of
Manufacturing
Engineers

Association for
Forming & Fabricating
Technologies of SME

Dearborn, Michigan

987654321

Library of Congress Catalog Card Number: 2003109758
International Standard Book Number: 0-87263-686-0

Additional copies may be obtained by contacting:
Society of Manufacturing Engineers
Customer Service
One SME Drive, P.O. Box 930
Dearborn, Michigan 48121
1-800-733-4763
www.sme.org

SME staff who participated in producing this book:
Rosemary Csizmadia, Editor/Production Supervisor
Frances Kania, Administrative Coordinator

Printed in the United States of America

Cover photo courtesy of Alabama Laser

ABOUT THE SOCIETY OF MANUFACTURING ENGINEERS (SME)

The Society of Manufacturing Engineers is the world's leading professional society supporting manufacturing education. Through its member programs, publications, expositions, and professional development resources, SME promotes an increased awareness of manufacturing engineering and helps keep manufacturing professionals up to date on leading trends and technologies. Headquartered in Michigan, SME influences more than half a million manufacturing engineers and executives annually. The Society has members in 70 countries and is supported by a network of hundreds of chapters worldwide. Visit us at www.sme.org.

ABOUT AFFT/SME

The Association for Forming & Fabricating Technologies of SME (AFFT/SME) focuses on the technologies and processes that efficiently make products from metal sheet, coil, plate, tube, or pipe stock. Typical industries served are automotive, off-highway, aerospace, defense, appliance, furniture, and consumer electronics products. Core processes include general pressworking—stamping, drawing, forming, bending, and shearing, for example—as well as the fabricating technologies of punching, cutting, sawing, welding, and others. Many AFFT/SME members are manufacturing, tool, or process engineers specializing in keeping production forming or fabricating technologies current for their companies; general stamping, fabricating, welding, and assembly managers responsible for overseeing plant operations; and owners, partners, proprietors, and other company officials of relevant job shops. AFFT/SME membership allows such people to more quickly identify innovations that can lower costs while increasing product quality and yield. The AFFT/SME community also fosters learning among members to better manage their businesses and interact with customers, suppliers, and industry partners.

Table of Contents

Part II: Outputs

Preface and Acknowledgments

"Scientific truth is signaled by coherence and efficiency. Poetic truth is signaled by beauty."

—Aimé Césaire

As I began this endeavor to write a book on laser cutting, I had no doubt that I was up to the task, as I am a firm believer of the lesson from Henry Ford: "whether you think that you can, or that you can't, you are usually right." Over the long course of completing this manuscript, I was reminded with humility that, in the words of the great philosopher Alain, also known as Emile Chartier, it is a difficult art to express in writing thoughts that you usually verbalize without needing to think about them. Thank God, I was supported and had been prepared by great family and friends. Among them, I am especially grateful to my wife Lisa for her judicious proofreading and our sons Adrien and Alex for their patience. My mother Marguerite and sister Helene shared their brilliance and wisdom. My Ph.D. advisers, Prof. Jean-Pierre Martin of CNRS Laboratory EM2C at Ecole Centrale de Paris and Prof. William Rich of the Ohio State University in Columbus, Ohio were my models for the thought process and inspired my passion for discovery.

I am deeply indebted to five experts for their informative reviews that helped make this book a reality: Dr. Richard Martukanitz, Head of the Laser Processing Division of the Applied Research

Laboratory at Penn State University; Prof. Dr. Rer. Nat. Reinhardt Poprawe and Dr. Rer. Nat. Dirk Petring of the Fraunhofer Institute for Laser Technologies at The University of Aachen in Germany; Dr. Norio Karube, President and CEO of LEMI Ltd. in Japan; and Dr. Joachim Berkmanns, Senior Program Manager, Laser Gases and Laser Applications, AGA Gas, Inc. in Michigan.

I also thank Professor Charles Townes of the University of California at Berkeley for his kind response to my communication.

This book would not have been possible without the illustrations supplied by various organizations; I am grateful for their support. They are:

AGA Gas, Inc., a member of the Linde Group
Air Liquide America LP
Alabama Laser
Amada
Cincinnati, Inc.
Fraunhofer Institute for Laser Technologies
GSI Lumonics
Haas Laser Technologies
Lasercut, Inc.
Rofin-Sinar
Strippit-LVD
Trumpf, Inc.

To the readers, whether students, experts, or neophytes, may this book provide the information, tools, ideas, and motivation for which you are looking. In many instances I chose to maintain a high level of detail that may appear to some overwhelming and repetitive. I ask for your indulgence as many of those instances are motivated by my personal experiences. Metaphorically speaking, readers familiar with the 1974 book, *The Gulag Archipelago*, by Alexander Solzhenitsyn, can appreciate how for some, cutting bread in slanted slices rather than vertical slices, is a detail far more important than having bread at all.

In this guide, I have broken down scientific concepts into simplified explanations so they could be understood by all, without hopefully stripping out totally the science foundation behind the art of laser cutting of metals. Some of the assertions in this guide may have derived from hypotheses that do not necessarily describe everyone's specific situation and circumstances. However, in the words written by Gaston Bachelard in 1938, "the goal of a hypothesis is not to be true or false; it is to help arrive at a true or false result." Translating this true scientific spirit into pragmatic manufacturing engineering, the relationship between hypothesis and result is inherent in the dichotomy of this book—"Part I—Laser Cutting Inputs" and "Part II—Laser Cutting Outputs." All efforts were made to jell these two parts with a cohesive combination of experience, expertise, and education. "Education is what remains after one has forgotten what one has learned in school," said Albert Einstein. After reading this book, my friends may argue that I forgot a lot. I hope that all others credit it with some contribution to the teaching of laser cutting processes, lasers, and optics.

In conclusion, I will risk another attempt at a long-loved poetry hobby with inclusion of these verses that I wrote in praise of the invention and teaching of lasers. They are inspired by a notorious poem by Victor Hugo. Far from rivaling Hugo's prowess, may you find it an entertaining mnemotechnic means of remembering the decimal digits of a famous real number so irrational, yet so useful to the wise . . . up to the 30th decimal place.

To Laserfacturers

And I love a sound knowledge of lasers grown,
Via world teachers, engineers, artists, Internets!

Set on lit coherent wave, gleams of wisdom sown,
For all revealed, fix pi numeral alphabets.

——Charles L. Caristan

Introduction

"Where there is much light, the shadows are deepest."

—Johann W. Von Goethe

Judging by the fast rise of laser cutting's popularity in the world market, it can no longer be considered a high-tech science reserved for a few specialists. Market data from the Laser Systems Product Group of the Association for Manufacturing Technology (AMT) shows that among all industrial laser applications, laser-cutting systems have solidly earned their rank as first, representing about 10% of the sale of all machine tools in North America. The quarterly growth index for laser-cutting systems parallels that of the U.S. machine-tool industry since at least 1999. Laser cutting of thick metal plates and thin sheet metal has become common practice equally popular in the small so-called "Mom and Pop" shops as on the plant floors of large fabricator companies. In fact, laser cutting has expanded beyond prototype application roles into outright volume production in all segments of sheet-metal fabrication in the automotive, aerospace, appliance, shipyard, and electronics industries.

To support the successful transition from laboratory development to the industrial manufacturing world, a practical reference manual is essential to offer guidance from a modern quality manufacturing perspective. This transition started less than 10 years after the invention of lasers in the early 1960s and promises a bright future, particularly in the metal industry. A book on laser cutting targeted to this industry that addresses the manufacturing challenges is long due.

Rather than duplicating academic reviews on the subject, a manufacturing perspective is presented here to provide complementary practical information and guidance for successful establishment of a laser metal-cutting business. This guide is designed to deliver essentials for a roadmap to develop, implement, operate, maintain, and even benchmark a laser-cutting manufacturing enterprise. It distinguishes itself from other publishing efforts in that it remains focused in its unbiased practical presentation.

The scope of the book encompasses common metal cutting of flat parts, roll-formed parts, hydroformed parts, and 3-D shaped stampings. The intent is to present today's reality of the technical, engineering, and business challenges of laser cutting metals. Following the fishbone diagram of *Figure P-1*, it is organized to support the development, implementation, operation, and maintenance of laser-cutting activity. It is written in simple terms familiar to a shop-floor operator. The targeted audience for this practical guide also includes owners and their management teams; engineers from production, quality, service and maintenance teams; product engineers and industrial process engineers; and students in search of information on manufacturing with lasers.

"Part I—Laser Cutting Inputs" includes Chapters 1 through 8. Chapter 1, "Overview of Metal Laser-cutting Applications," describes various laser-cutting applications in metal forming and fabrication. It also provides a perspective of special applications and, in particular, an alternative to traditional die blanking that high-speed laser cutting presents to the automotive industry. Chapter 2, "Market for Laser Cutting," summarizes market surveys published by independent and government entities. It places laser cutting in a wider machine-tool industry business context. Technology trends follow with insight to the ever-evolving state of the art. Chapters 3 through 8 describe laser cutting's specific key process input variables (KPIVs) within each of the "6M" categories: material, machine, method, man, measurement, and Mother Nature.

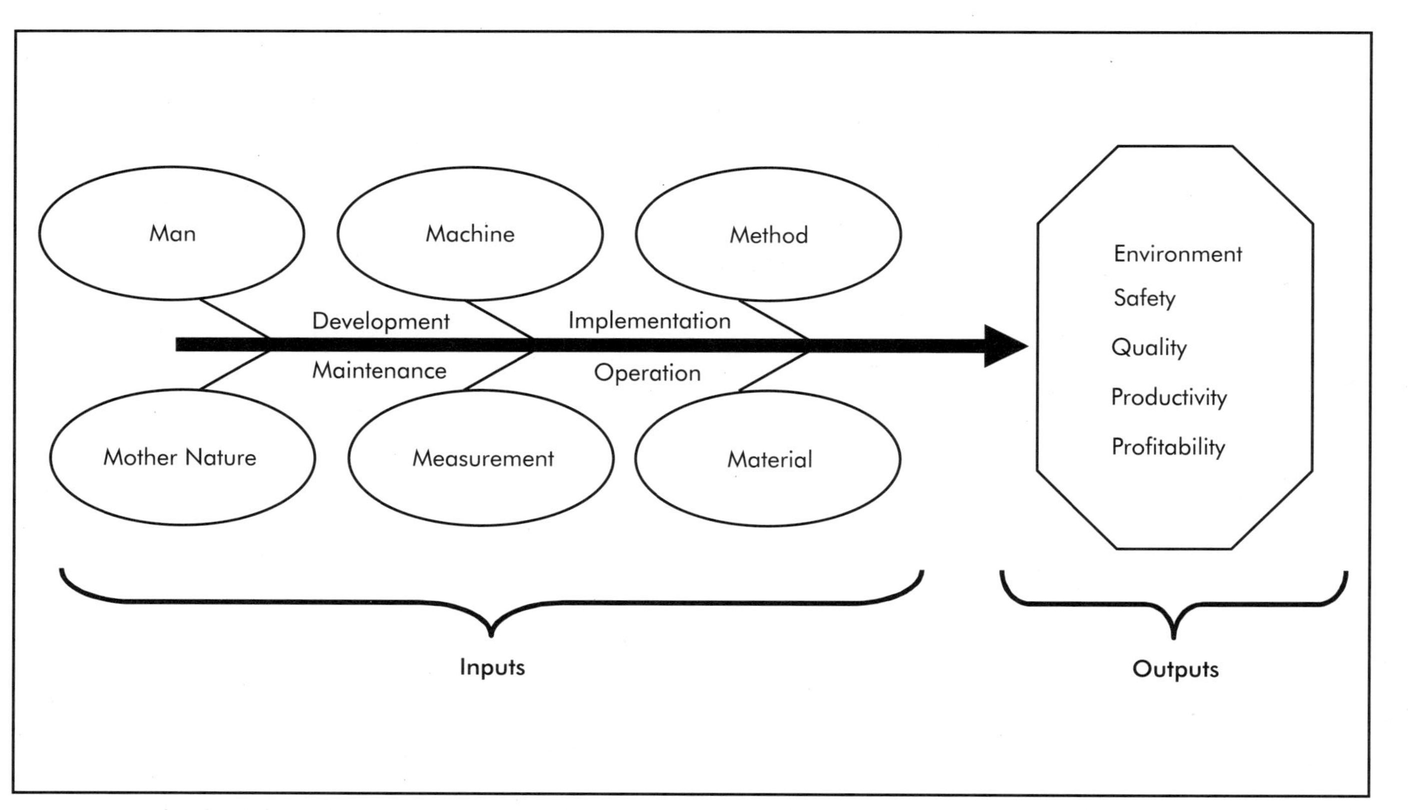

Figure P-1. This high-level Ishikawa fishbone diagram helps visualize influential inputs and key outputs for industrial laser cutting of metal sheets and plates.

"Part II—Laser Cutting Outputs" includes Chapters 9 through 13. It extensively details laser cutting's specific key process output variables (KPOVs) for a laser operation. Each KPOV appears as a customer-driven, critical-to-quality specification and is categorized into one of five main areas: quality, productivity, profitability, environment, and safety. The influences of the KPIVs on the KPOVs are exposed. Chapter 13, "The Six-sigma Approach," explains the methodology as it relates to the design, verification, and control phases in a continuous-improvement cycle. The chapter defines defects and opportunities for defects, and explains process mapping, measurement and analysis, and how to rank critical-to-quality (CTQ) specifications.

For more in-depth study, three appendices explain the customization of tools specific to laser cutting that can be helpful for design and implementation, troubleshooting, operation, and maintenance. Appendix A reviews the basics of lasers with a historical perspective. Appendix B develops beam-propagation tools practical for many realistic beam-delivery-system designs. Appendix C provides information on compressible gas dynamics for laser cutting.

Part I: Inputs

Overview of Laser-cutting Applications

"Any sufficiently advanced technology is indistinguishable from magic."

—Arthur C. Clark

INTRODUCTION

The art and science of laser cutting applies in almost all aspects of metal cutting, for consumer products and industrial work-in-process. Most alloys and product designs lend themselves to this thermal-cutting process. This book focuses on the most developed and successful laser-cutting applications for thin and thick flat sheet metals made from cold- and hot-roll mills and the shaped products of roll-forming, hydroforming, and stamping operations. Materials range from ferrous alloys like mild steel and stainless steel, to aluminum, brass, copper, titanium, and nickel alloys.

Why use laser cutting and what are the alternatives? It is true that lasers are not indispensable to metal cutting. Mechanical cutting could be performed roughly with a saw. Milling yields exceptionally great cut-edge quality at the expense of severe cutting-speed reduction. Turret and punch press use is widespread, as is die blanking and die trimming with presses. Thermal processes, such as flame cutting and plasma cutting are still widely in operation today as the heavy metal industry is a haven for traditional processes; sometimes due to unexpected controlling influences, such as insurance companies in the shipyard and aerospace industries. Waterjet cutting also is a viable metal-removal cutting method, particularly for product designs that do not tolerate heat-affected-zone metallurgical transformation. Wire electrical discharge machining (EDM) is a thriving industry for small, intricate, and precise feature cutting.

Laser cutting is receiving much attention and continuously winning market share away from traditional processes. Various explanations can be offered for the justification of this success. However, it appears that they all point to the mystic force of light radiation. In that regard, the laser industry may owe Hollywood director George Lucas as much as Nobel Prize of Physics laureates Charles H. Townes of the U.S. and A. M. Prokhorov and N.G. Basov of the USSR. These physicists were recognized for their work leading to the 1960 invention of the LASER (light amplified by stimulated emission of radiation). How much did the 1977 epic movie *Star Wars* promote the use of lasers in manufacturing? The imagination sparked in many by this movie has equated high-power lasers with superior cutting power that can be used to slice and dice even mighty steel. As with most forces, good comes from correct usage and bad results from abusive and careless practice. The purpose of this book is to help improve practices and render laser use easy, efficient, and productive.

Within a year from the release of the first *Star Wars* episode, the first flatbed laser-cutting machine was introduced commercially in the U.S. in 1978 by Strippit, Inc., of Buffalo, New York. It was a combination punch/laser-cutting machine as illustrated in *Figure 1-1*. This machine featured a traditional turret punch and new laser-cutting head, which shared the same base, numerical controls, and workpiece-motion system. The optics were stationary, while the workpiece was moved in the *X* and *Y* directions. *Figures 1-2a* and *b* show close-up views illustrating the impressive improvement of the laser-cut-edge finish over the traditional turret-punch finish. The difference in the mechanical design complexity of the two technologies is equally striking. This combination is indicative of the early appeal of lasers for their ability to cut clean and be flexible. It is also indicative of its early disadvantage of

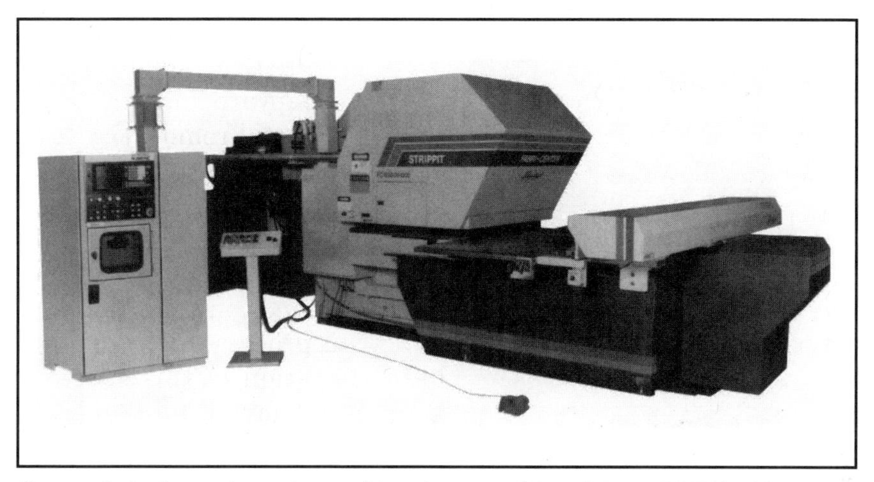

Figure 1-1. Laser/punch combination machine (circa 1978). (Courtesy Strippit-LVD)

cutting slower than traditional mechanical processes; in fact too slow as a stand-alone cutting machine. Since then, 1-kW laser resonators utilizing 35 ft^2 (3.3 m^2) of industrial floor space (including laser power supply and laser controls), have been replaced at the 20th century's end by laser sources five times more powerful, twice as reliable, twice as compact, and nearly twice as efficient.

COST OF CHANGE

There is a perpetual question behind progress—what is the cost of a change in process? Some might answer that the cost of status quo is even greater. It should be recognized that the road to change is not without problems for laser cutting. More than ever, manufacturing changes involve complex, nontechnical considerations, including purchasing strategies, commercial objectives, and government policies. Development costs and time, along with initial installation cost (implementation), are difficult to forecast with great precision and represent a serious impediment to new technologies. Even when financial savings are clearly identified and quantified, fear of out-of-control initial installation and learning-curve costs often are large enough disadvantages to stall decision-making, particularly when more business decisions depend heavily

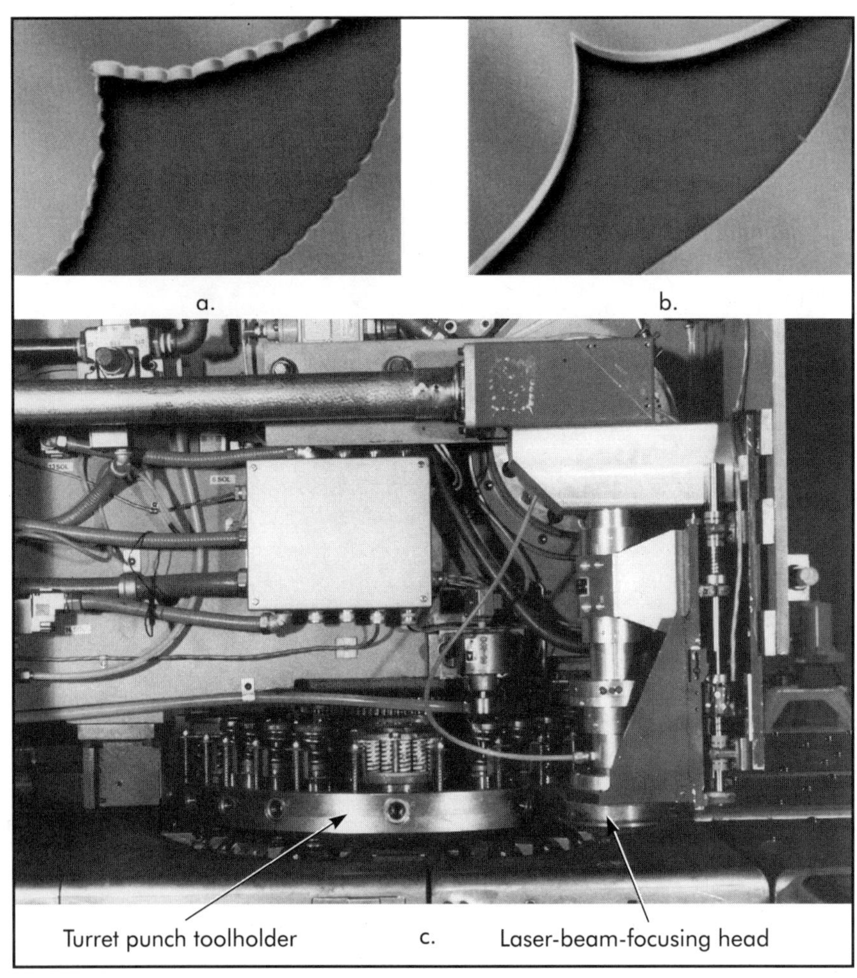

Figure 1-2. (a) Traditional turret-punch cut-edge finish; (b) laser-cut-edge finish. The difference between a nibbled edge and a laser finish is obvious. (c) The laser-beam-focusing head stands in striking simplicity adjacent to the complex mechanical assembly of the turret punch toolholder. (Courtesy Strippit-LVD)

on short-term quarterly outlook. It is fair to say that laser manufacturing processes in general cut through the traditional cost and pricing matrix. A shift of benefit from just processing service replacement to added value in material savings, leaner manufacturing, reduction in tooling expenditures and maintenance, added flexibility, and opening of new product-design opportunities makes traditional cost-estimation methods inadequate. Purchasing practices must also demonstrate flexibility and adapt to new processes to account for "outside-the-box" benefits.

Market Demands

While it may not be indispensable, the market is making the case that laser cutting is necessary to adapt to the highly flexible, environmentally friendly, lean manufacturing era. Some are working diligently to make lasers sufficient to perform most manufacturing cutting jobs. They are helped by the fact that, in essence, all metals can be cut with lasers. Carbon, stainless, and alloy steels are finding their way into automobile bodies, appliances, medical devices, and off-road and farm vehicles. More aluminum is being used in powertrain components. The aerospace industry is a large user of aluminum and its alloys and grades, as well as titanium, nickel-based Inconel®, and ceramics. The electronics industry consumes copper and copper alloys and a large quantity of steel and stainless-steel casings. Magnesium, tin, precious metals such as gold, special applications metals such as magnetically soft electrical steel, and structural alloys are specified for sub-zero temperature applications. Corrosion-resistant metals also come in various forms, from wire, bars, and slabs, to sheets, tubes, pipes, and plates. All can be cut with lasers.

Gantry versus Articulated Robot Systems

General guidelines for cutting metals can be applied to standard flatbed, 3-axis gantry systems as illustrated in *Figure 1-3*, as well as 6-axis systems for 3D parts processing (*Figure 1-4*), whether a gantry servo-driven system or a less accurate, less precise, slower but lower-cost standard articulated robot is used. The robot in *Figure 1-4* is located within reach of the workpiece. A yttrium-aluminum-garnet (YAG) laser (not shown) is placed in a remote area of the factory. The flexibility of the fiberoptic-beam delivery simplifies integration with a robot, almost to a plug-and-play level.

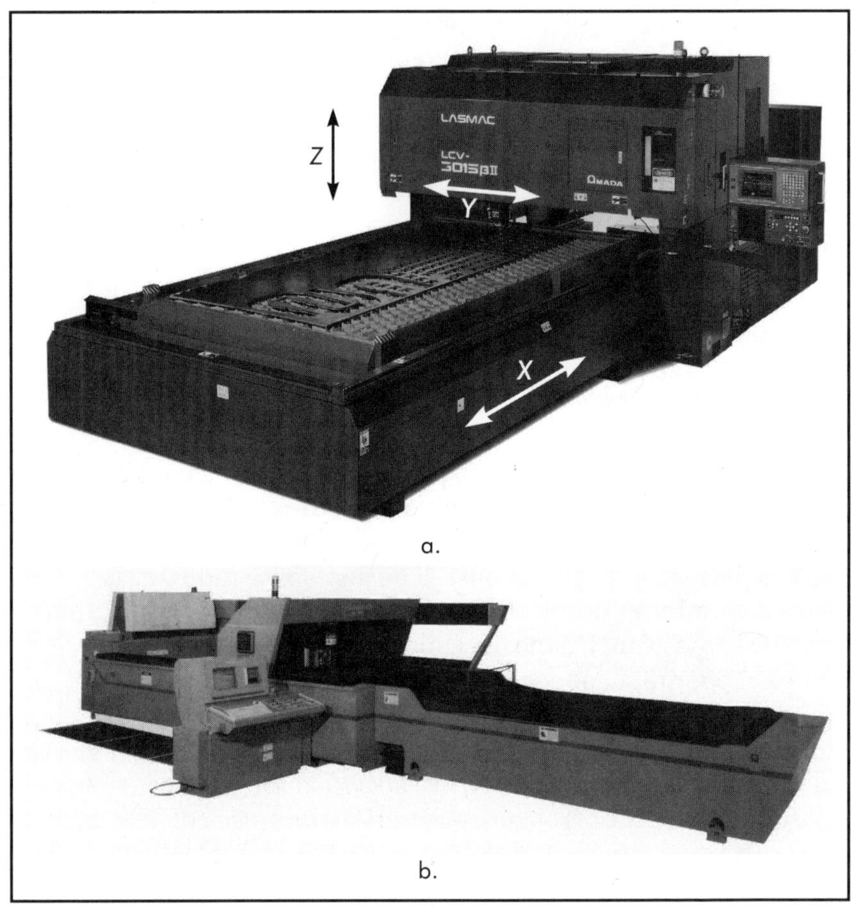

Figure 1-3. Examples of machine motion system configurations: (a) hybrid flatbed laser-cutting sytem, in which the workpiece moves in the X direction while the processing head moves in the Y and Z directions (Courtesy Amada, Inc.); *(b) a flying optics machine, in which the workpiece is stationary and the processing head moves across the entire work envelope.* (Courtesy Cincinnati, Inc.)

Finishing to Specifications

The shaped parts resulting from forming operations often need recutting and retrimming as finishing processes before final assembly to bring them within dimensional accuracy and precision specifications. These shaped parts can be die-formed from a flat

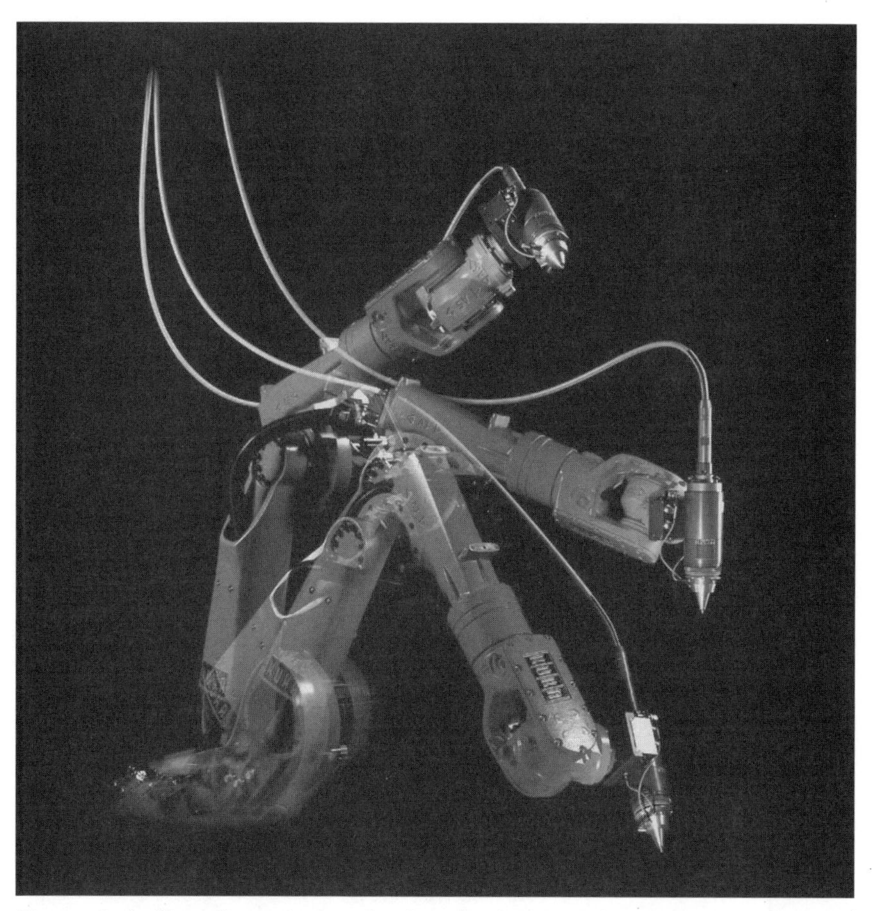

Figure 1-4. Six-axis, articulated robot for laser-cutting systems, equipped with fiberoptic-beam delivery and a cutting/welding head for 3D parts processing. (Courtesy Trumpf, Inc.)

sheet in a stamping or punch press. They can even be profiled from continuous roll-forming operations from coils, such as for rails, tube, and pipe products. In some cases, the profiled tubes undergo an additional shaping operation step, known as hydroforming. *Hydroforming* deforms a straight section of tube into a 3D closed-section structure. This deformation process is as severe as some deep-drawing stamping operations, so internal and peripheral trimming is necessary to finish the part to within dimensional accuracy specifications for final assembly, as illustrated in *Figures 1-5* and *1-6*. *Figure 1-6* illustrates the laser cutting of tubes and 3D-shaped, hydroformed, closed sections such as the ones assembled in automotive underbody frames. This is the fastest growing volume production application of laser metal cutting.

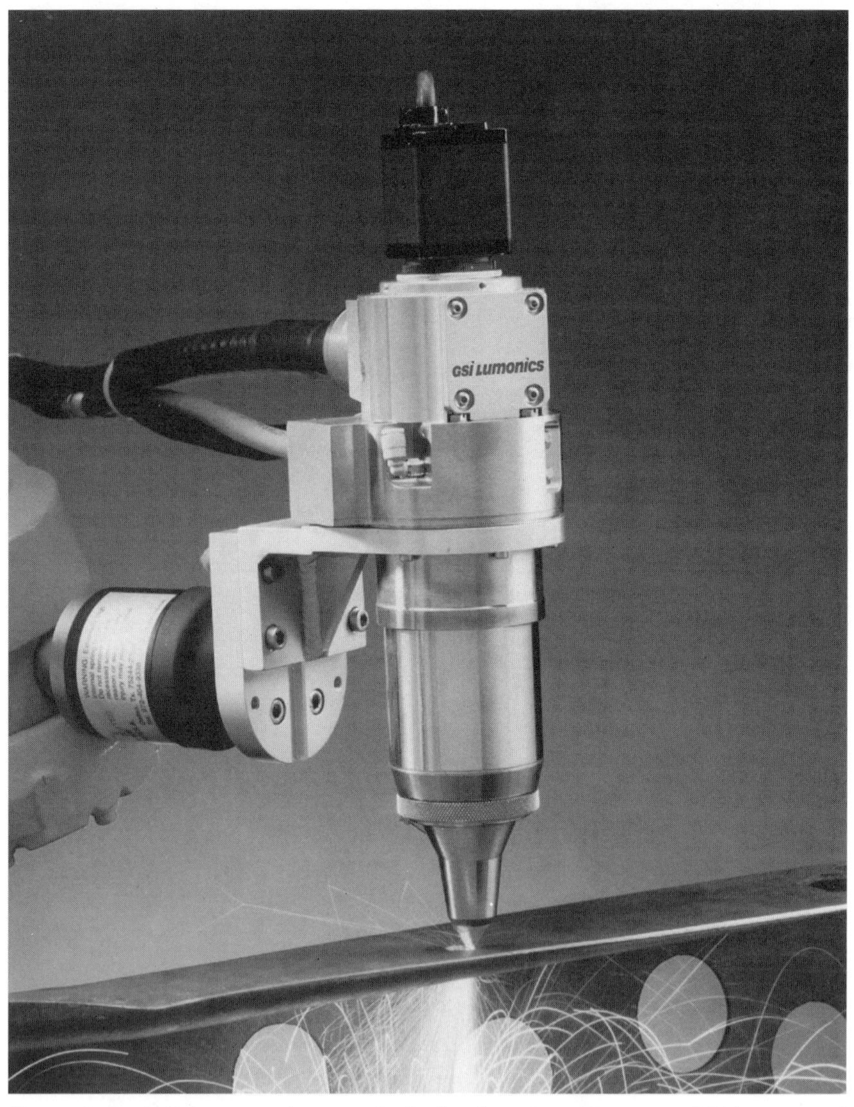

Figure 1-5. YAG laser cutting applied after forming. (Courtesy GSI Lumonics)

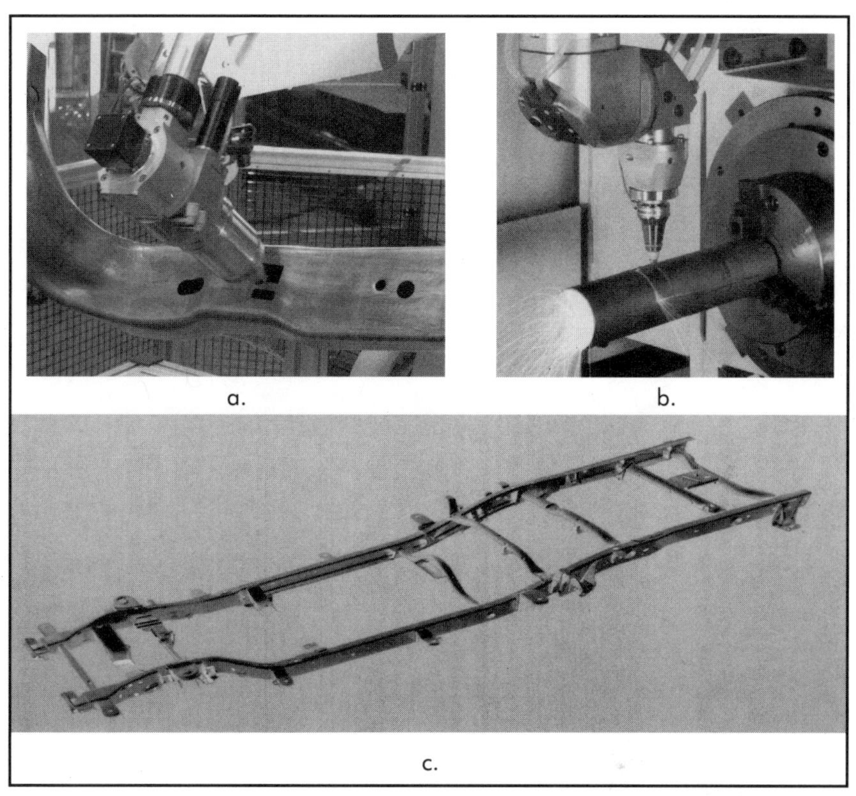

Figure 1-6. (a) YAG laser cutting of hydroformed tube with 6-axis robot and fiberoptic delivery (Courtesy GSI Lumonics)*; (b) CO_2 laser cutting of tube with 5-axis gantry machine* (Courtesy Trumpf, Inc.)*; (c) truck underbody frame assembled from hydroformed closed sections.* (Courtesy Trumpf, Inc.)

FLAT PRODUCTS

Flat products start the chain of metal manufacturing. They are often stored in thick, rectangular slab form or thinner-gage coil form. In most applications, coils are unwound and sheared into flat sheets or plates with rectangular, trapezoidal, or contoured configurations. The purpose of cutting at an upstream stage is to produce a part with the configured contour geometry for a subsequent forming operation. For example, if the part is destined for final assembly without subsequent shaping, then the cuts can be final internal trims as well as final peripheral contours. However, if the cut contour (internal or peripheral) is to be shaped in a subsequent forming operation, it is expected that the contours and trims also will be deformed in a controllable fashion, as illustrated in *Figure 1-7*, and sometimes with dimensional accuracy suffering from out-of-specification variations.

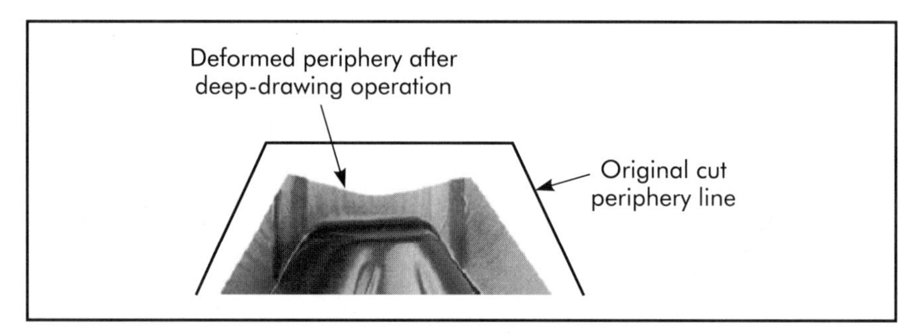

Figure 1-7. Deep-drawing forming operations deform cut contours; straight-cut segments before forming become curvilinear contours after forming.

The vast majority of sheet metals used in fabrication are supplied in the form of cold-rolled products. Steel sheets may have galvanizing zinc- or aluminum-based coatings, particularly used in large volume by the automotive and appliance industries. In general, cold-rolled sheets are relatively thin, generally less than 0.250 in. (6.35 mm) and more than 0.010 in. (0.25 mm) thick. Plates are generally hot-rolled products thicker than 0.230 in. (5.84 mm) (American Society for Metals 1985). Most steel plates consumed in the United States are as wide as 120 in. (3 m) with slab thicknesses of 0.187–8.000 in. (4.75–203.20 mm). Currently up to 1.25-in. (31.8-mm) thick plates are laser cut for off-road automotive machines, such as farm and earth-moving equipment. For even thicker plates, alternative processes, such as flame cutting, plasma cutting, sawing, and milling, are being used.

Cutting flat products is usually done on a flatbed machine with work envelopes typically of 4 × 8 ft (1.2 × 2.4 m), 5 × 10 ft (1.5 × 3.0 m), and 6 × 12 ft (1.8 × 3.7 m). Larger plates are accommodated by a flatbed cutter with an envelope as wide as 120 in. (3 m) and length of 100 ft (30 m) or longer. CO_2 lasers with average power ranging from 1–6 kW are used almost exclusively. Very few multikilowatt YAG laser-cutting systems are used on flatbed metal-cutting machines.

Each laser-power range enables a maximum cutting thickness and processing speed, which is largely dependent on the workpiece material and thickness. For metal cutting, most is done with an O_2 assist-gas for mild steel, N_2 for stainless steel, and air for aluminum. For other metals, neutral gas, such as N_2, or more expensive inert gases, such as argon and even hydrogen diluted in a mix, are commonly used. Typical maximum thickness cutting capability for the aforementioned three metals is illustrated in *Figure 1-8*. Only a range of guidelines is provided, since capability is dependent on more than just laser power. For a given increase in laser power, the corresponding increase in cutting speed of thick-gage material is disappointing when operating in pulse mode with O_2 assist-gas. Most of the benefits of higher power come in the form of maximum-thickness cutting capability enhancement and improvement of cut-edge quality. The design of a beam-delivery system also is an equally important determining factor of cutting capability.

When processing mild steel with oxygen assist-gas, speed is not directly proportional to power. Speed reaches saturation at about 400 in./min (10 m/min), beyond which clean cutting can no longer occur. However, when operating in continuous-wave (CW) mode with neutral gas, speed becomes proportional to laser power up to a much higher saturation point, which is determined by plasma absorption of the laser beam just above the workpiece's surface. To lift this plasma obstacle, appropriate assist-gas possessing a plasma-shielding effect is recommended. Neutral gases such as N_2, inert gases such as Ar or He, or gases such as H_2 and combinations of these have proven to enable and enhance high-speed cutting at high power.

Figure 1-9 illustrates examples of various flat-sheet laser-cutting applications from the electronic, telecommunication, aerospace, automotive, appliance, and off-road machinery industries.

FORMED AND SHAPED PRODUCTS

In some applications where openings are designed in a 3D-shaped part, it is preferable not to cut interior pierces and trims

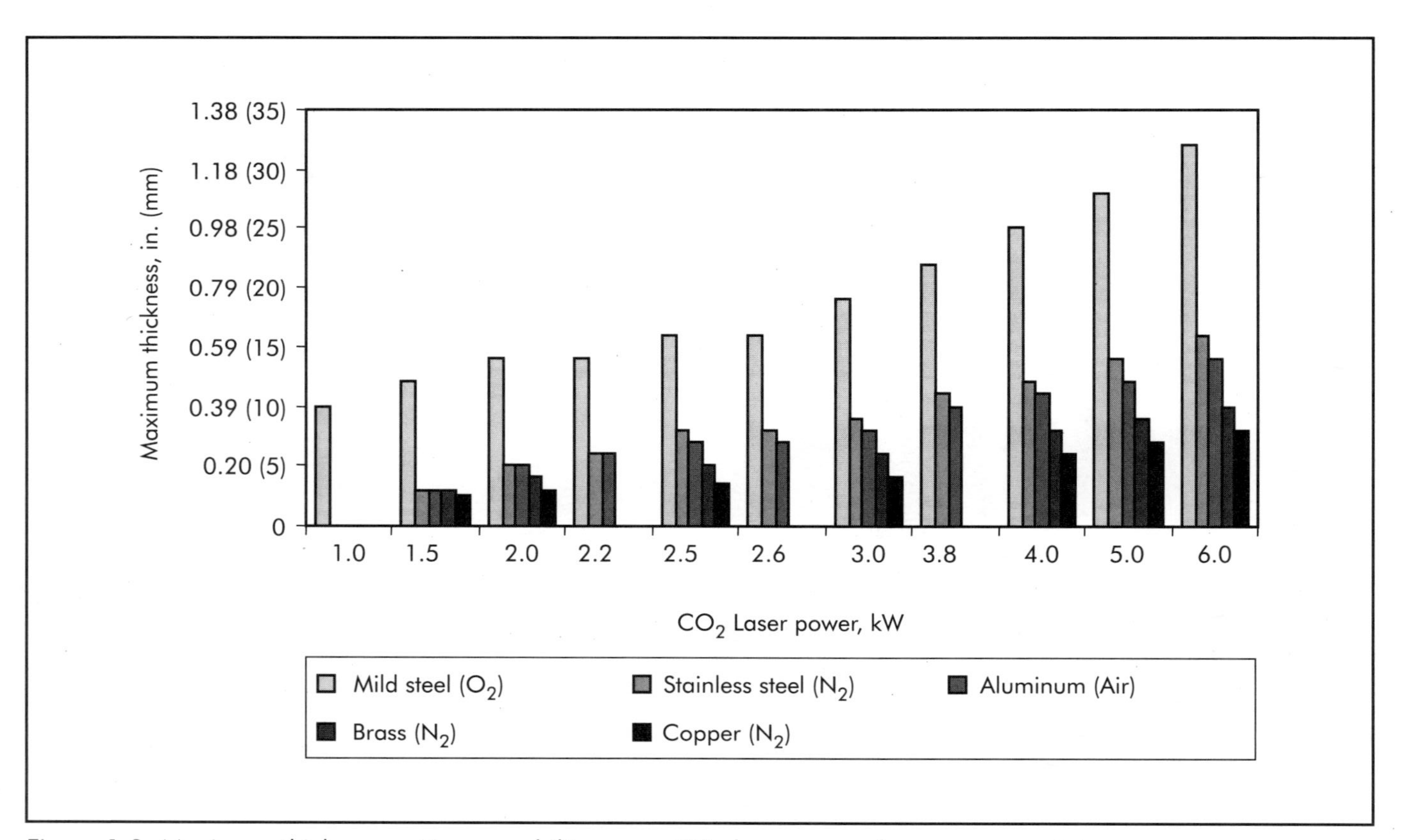

Figure 1-8. Maximum-thickness cutting capability versus CO_2 laser power for common metals.

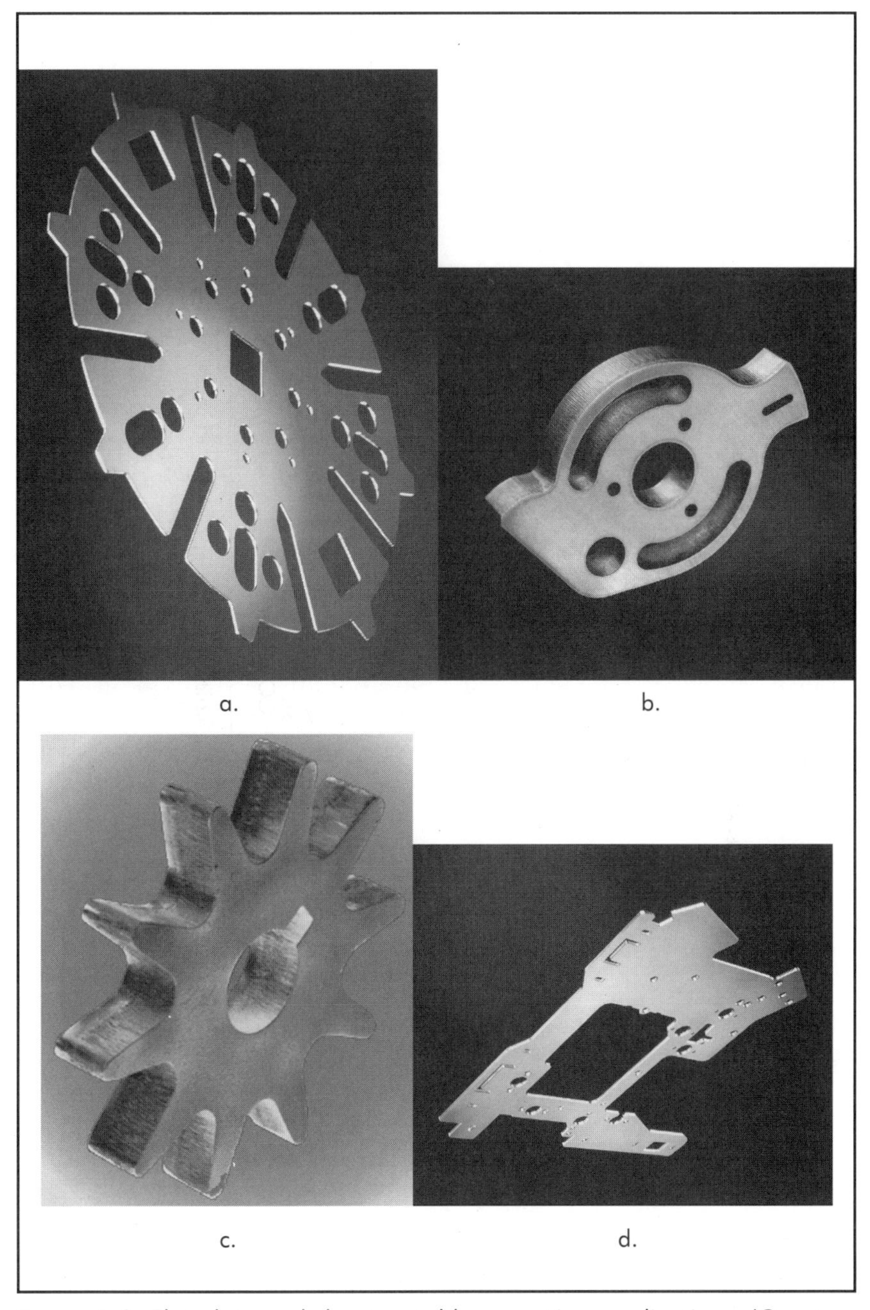

Figure 1-9. Flat plate and sheet-metal laser-cutting applications. (Courtesy Trumpf, Inc.)

before forming. The forming operation will deform the pierce and trim contours and create poor repeatability of the deformation (in this context, "pierce" means cutting a small radius hole on a panel, which is not to be confused with piercing that needs to occur before cutting can start on thick-gage materials). With these products, 3D piercing and trimming are performed after forming. At present, most of these cuts are made using expensive trimming dies in presses. The same operations can be produced using articulated robots or gantries and lasers. A successful combination in the automotive industry consists of articulated robots and neodymium: yttrium-aluminum garnet (Nd:YAG) lasers with fiberoptic-beam delivery. This combination is much less expensive than using a gantry motion system. The drawback comes from a robot's 3D positioning accuracy: it can be much worse than a gantry's motion accuracy, which does not lend itself to parts involving high-accuracy trimming, such as some transmission and suspension parts.

The system of choice for hydroformed parts is a combination of YAG lasers with fiberoptics and articulated robots. Besides fiberoptic-delivered YAG laser-beam cutting systems, a growing number of manufacturers offer and service new CO_2 laser-cutting systems for trimming and piercing tubular and roll-formed structures. For stamped sheet metal, an articulated robot with a YAG laser is a low-cost system combination with sufficient accuracy and precision for automotive-body trimming jobs.

LASER-CUTTING PROCESS

Cutting metals with lasers has become common practice throughout the industrial world. An understanding of its mechanism deserves careful attention to ensure that new improvements can be properly evaluated and implemented. The closest analogy is recognition that laser cutting, as it is predominantly implemented, remains a thermal process. Existing sciences and technologies recognize the merits of short-wavelength ultraviolet (UV) laser-beam ablation techniques that can cut material without imparting any heat into it. Ablation uses photon-induced chemical bond destruction to cut material. For example, excimer lasers emitting UV light at about 0.3 μm wavelength successfully cut and drill ceramics with no significant heat generation. Ablation is, however, no match to thermal cutting when compared in an industrial setting in which other considerations, such as cycle time, productivity, and profitability influence decision-making. From that regard, ablation techniques need further development.

Several publications describe the theoretical aspects of heat and mass transfer and present the governing equations for modelling the physics and chemical thermodynamics of laser cutting of metals. Therefore, it is not necessary to duplicate such in-depth effort in this book. Consult the literature for further reading on theoretical modelling (see the Bibliography at the end of this chapter).

Thermal-cutting processes involve a source of heat concentrated on a workpiece's surface. Heat is generally transferred locally to the workpiece by conduction, convection, or radiative-absorption mechanisms until the metal reaches a liquid or vapor state, which makes it easily removable with help from assist-gas pressure flow. In the case of a laser, the heat-transfer mechanism is radiative transfer. The photons of a laser-beam light are absorbed by the workpiece, and their energy is converted into heat with an efficiency that varies with the type of metal, wavelength of the laser beam, its polarization, and the temperature of the metal. When laser cutting with oxygen as the assist-gas, the oxygen reacts with most metals, such as steel (iron), in an exothermic-oxidation reaction that advantageously adds more heat to the cutting process.

Laser Output

Laser output's advantage is taken from the unique coherence and monochromaticity properties of laser beams—an incident laser beam is focused onto a small spot on a workpiece. The power density is raised above 10^6 W/cm^2 levels, at which most metals can be vaporized. Power densities are directly proportional to laser power. In comparison, the power density of sunlight reaches less than 0.1 W/cm^2 in the earth's atmosphere. *Figure 1-10* illustrates liquid metal and metallic vapor being flushed out through the bottom of the kerf by pressurized assist-gas flow.

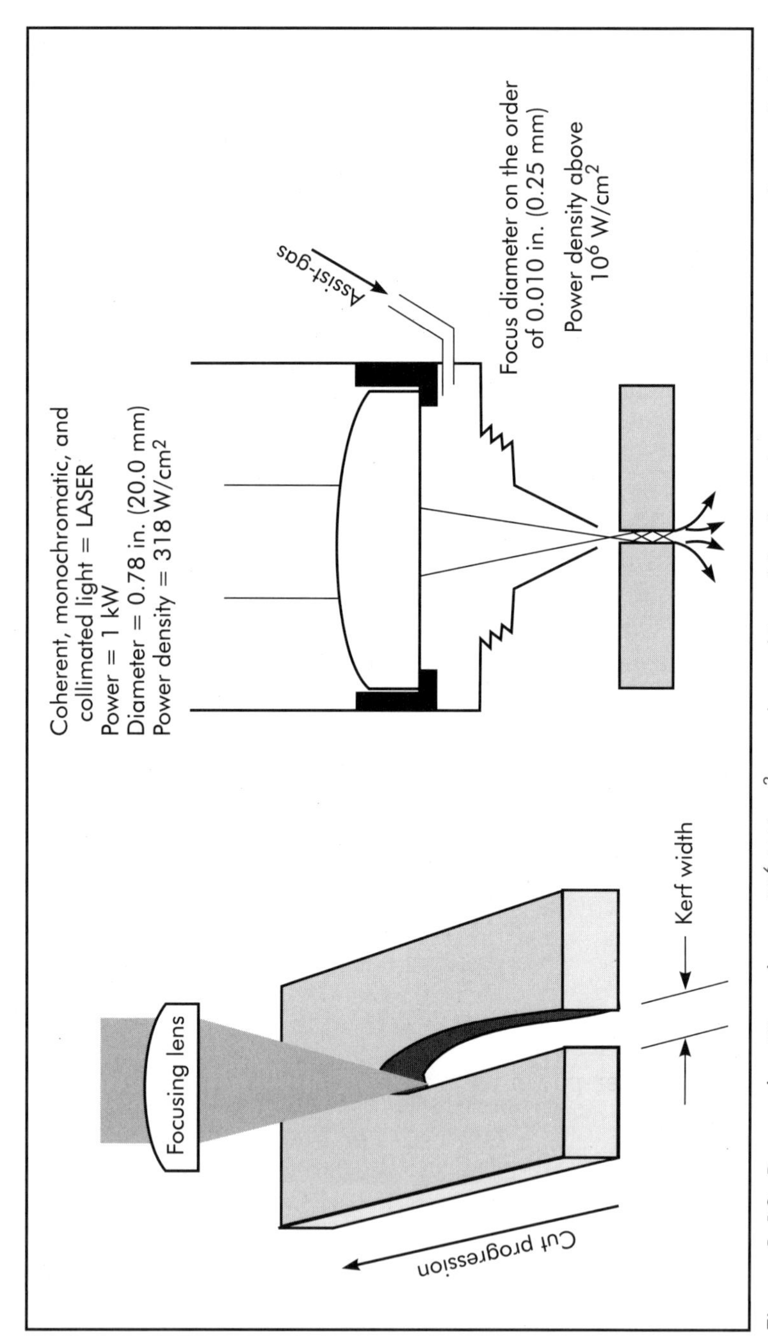

Figure 1-10. Power densities above 10^6 W/cm^2 can be achieved by focusing a coherent, monochromatic laser beam. Such power densities are enough to melt and even vaporize most metals. Molten metal and metallic vapor are flushed out through the bottom of the kerf by pressurized assist-gas flow.

Only part of the laser power applied to a workpiece is actually used for cutting. The rest is wasted by reflection off the workpiece surface or transmitted through the workpiece by successive partial reflections against the walls of the cut trough, also called the kerf. The remaining laser energy absorbed by the metal's surface and the kerf elevates the temperature around the point of incidence on the workpiece by a simple heat-conduction mechanism. In other words, the energy absorbed locally is partially used to melt and vaporize metal and partially lost by conduction in the workpiece and radiation. Radiation loss is evidenced by the visible plasma plume energy originating from a kerf during cutting as seen in *Figure 1-11*. The nozzle standoff distance (d) and focus position (e) are relative to the workpiece surface and set up independently. The nozzle diameter (D) is generally not adjustable on the fly. The set value of the nozzle standoff distance (d) is maintained constant by the Z-axis motion in a closed loop with a height-sensor system. The set value of the focus position (e) is adjusted manually before the start of the cut or on the fly with, for example, an additional axis servomotor motion for the nozzle assembly only or an adaptive-optics system.

At constant laser power, as metal thickness increases, the power absorbed locally to melt through the workpiece at a given feed rate becomes insufficient to cut through the metal. Therefore, a portion of the bottom of the workpiece is not in molten form and cannot be flushed away. Molten metal being flushed takes the path of least resistance through the upstream part of the kerf.

Periodical striations along a cut edge can be observed. These striations exhibit a cut section and a "break" section, which is analogous to the jargon used for the mechanical shearing process. *Figure 1-12* illustrates a cut-to-break ratio that increases when the feed-rate-to-laser-power ratio decreases. This explains the more pronounced slopes of striations in the break section observed in thick-metal cutting when the feed-rate-to-laser-power ratio increases past a threshold. For the same reason, when approaching a corner angle feature, most part programs slow the feed rate to obtain complete kerf cut through at that angle before changing direction. Another trick consists of programming a loop contour feature that not only eliminates the need to decelerate, but avoids burning metal, particularly when the corner angle is small.

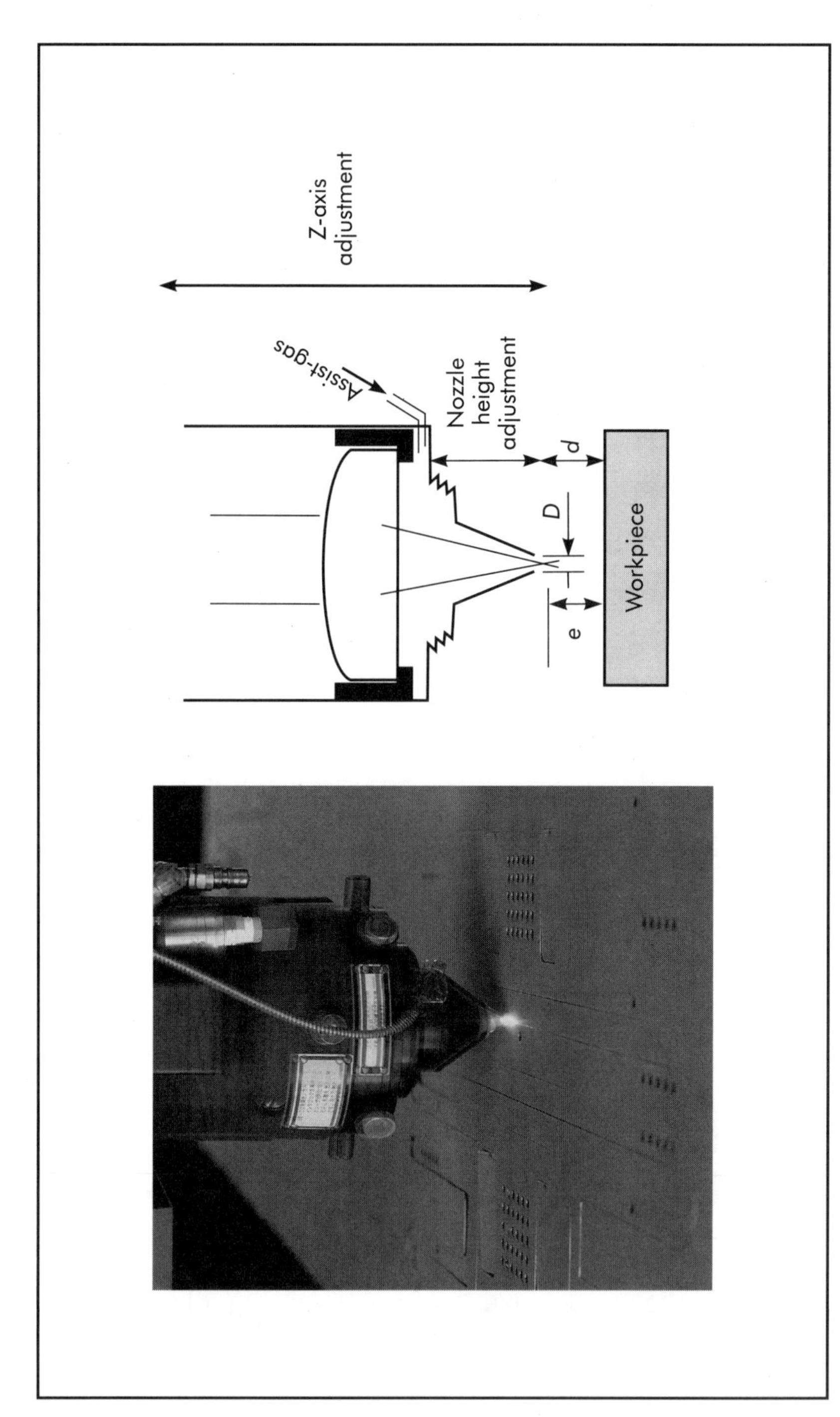

Figure 1-11. Nozzle height and Z-axis setups can be adjusted independently.

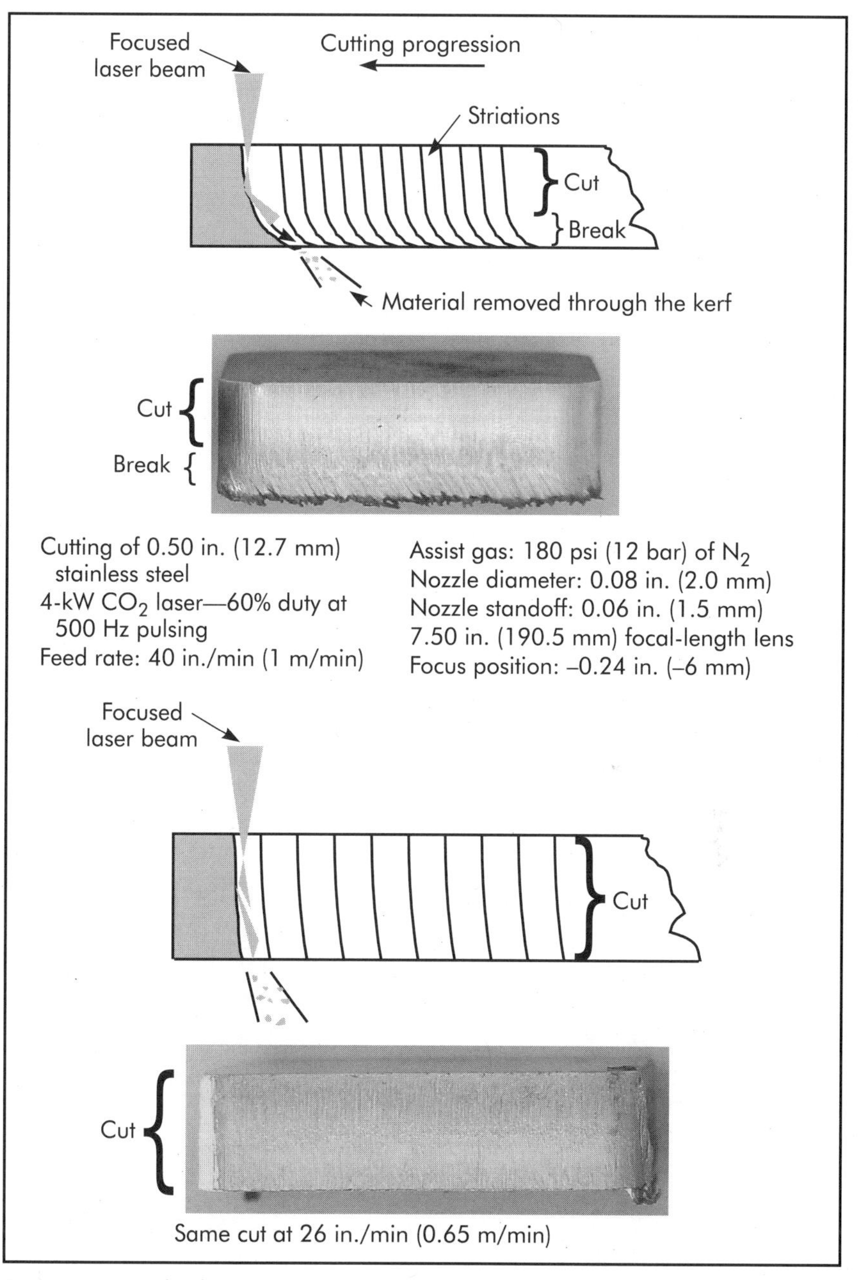

Figure 1-12. The laser melts and vaporizes the metal, creating a kerf. The walls of the kerf show striations exhibiting cut and break sections. The cut-to-break ratio increases when the feed-rate-to-laser-power ratio decreases.

Cutting Parameters

Cutting parameters can be put into the memory of a numerical controller manually by an operator or automatically by download from a remote personal computer (PC) with a proper interface to the machine. Key parameters, such as focal length, nozzle geometry, and diameter are generally part of a manual setup. Other parameters, such as feed rate, assist-gas type, pressure, nozzle standoff, focus position (shown in *Figure 1-11*), peak output laser power, laser frequency, and laser duty may be downloaded automatically or retrieved from a parameter library. Parameters can even be adjusted in the machine's numerical controller on the fly with special command codes during execution of a part program.

Typical laser-cutting feed rates are displayed in *Figure 1-13*. These feed rates are plotted only for reference: actual feed rate depends heavily on material type and surface conditions, methods, manpower training, and machine design, particularly the laser resonator and beam-delivery designs. Most importantly, feed rates depend heavily on the cut-edge-quality standards specified. At equal average YAG laser power, high energy-per-pulse output beams outperform low energy-per-pulse beams. Better-quality edges are obtained with high-peak, low-duty power systems. This enables faster cutting speeds up to a limit inherent to pulse regimes. At cutting feed rate V, pulse frequency f, and duty-ratio percentage D, it is desirable to have $V \times (100\% - D)/f$ smaller than about 0.004 in. (0.1 mm). Laser-cutting-machine builders generally supply a cutting parameters database adapted to their machine design, and based on types of materials, including recommended cutting feed rates at rated laser-power settings.

For thick-gage materials, either begin cutting from the outer periphery of the plate or proceed with piercing a hole through the workpiece from which to initiate a kerf formation. Key parameters for piercing are frequency, duty, peak power, duration, assist-gas pressure and type, nozzle standoff, and focus position. A traditional method of piercing consists of peck-piercing (in other words, at maximum peak power, duty and frequency are programmed to rise from a low level of close to 0 for each to upper levels set for each in the program). The rise in duty and frequency follows the progression of piercing through the thickness of metal.

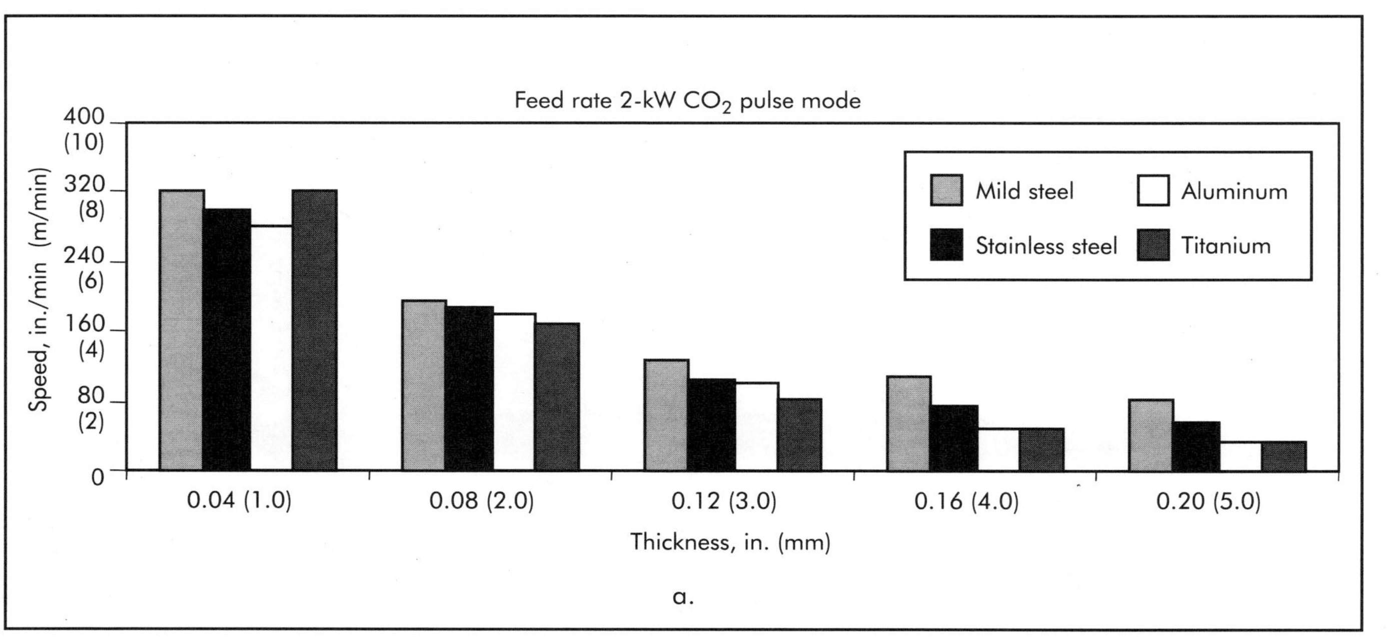

Figure 1-13. Typical cutting feed rates versus metal thicknesses in laser operations. (a) 2-kW, 2,000 Hz, 85% duty, assist-gas selection on mild steel with O_2, aluminum with air, stainless steel with N_2, and titanium with argon. A 5.0-in. (127-mm) focal-length lens was used. (b) 4-kW, CW, high-pressure N_2 assist-gas and 5.0-in. (127-mm) focal-length lens. (c) 4-kW, 700 Hz at 65% duty with an assist-gas selection on mild steel with O_2, aluminum with air, and stainless steel with N_2. A 7.50-in. (190.5-mm) focal-length lens was used. (d) YAG laser operation at different average power with an assist-gas selection on mild steel with O_2, aluminum with air, stainless steel with N_2, and titanium with argon. A 6.00-in. (152.4-mm) focal-length lens was used.

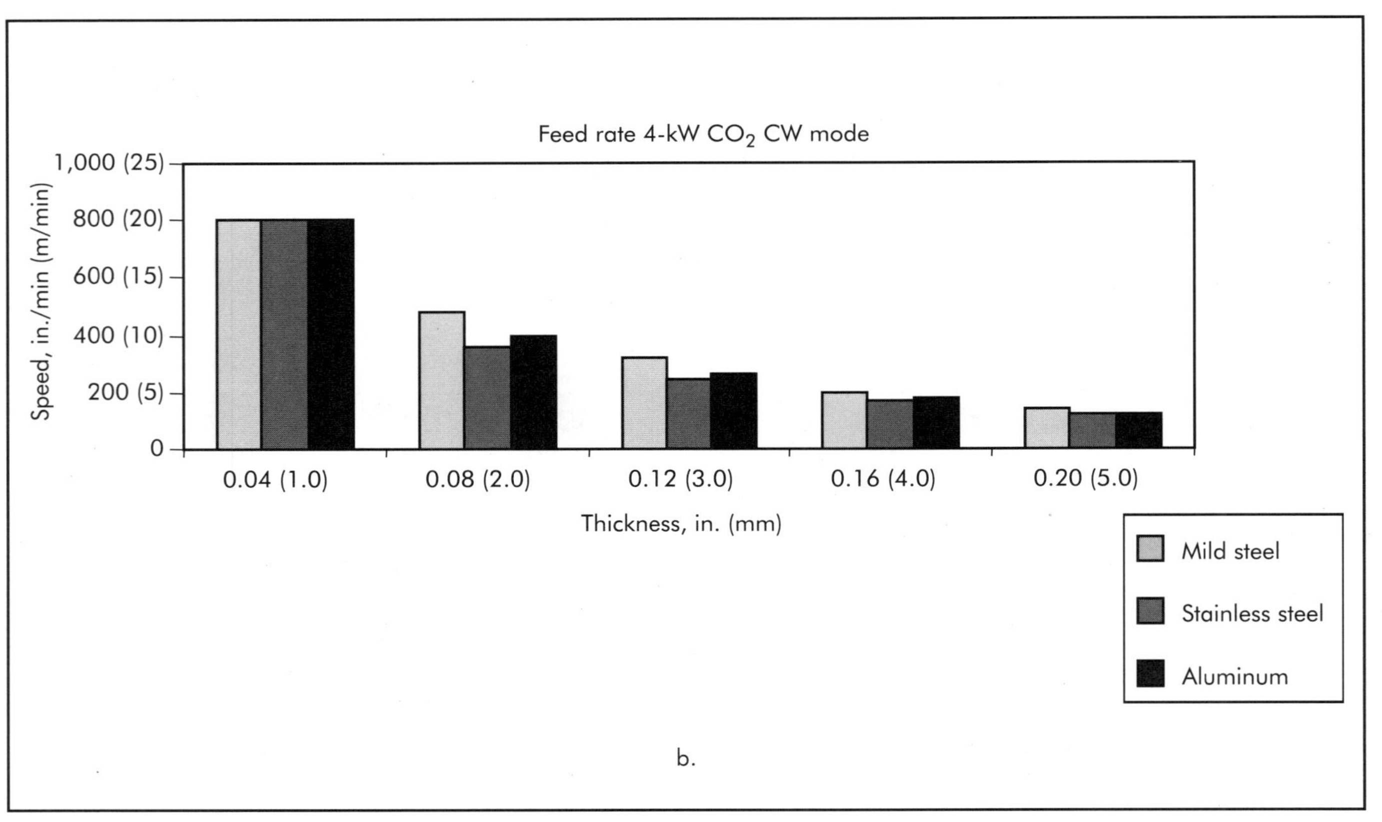

Figure 1-13. continued.

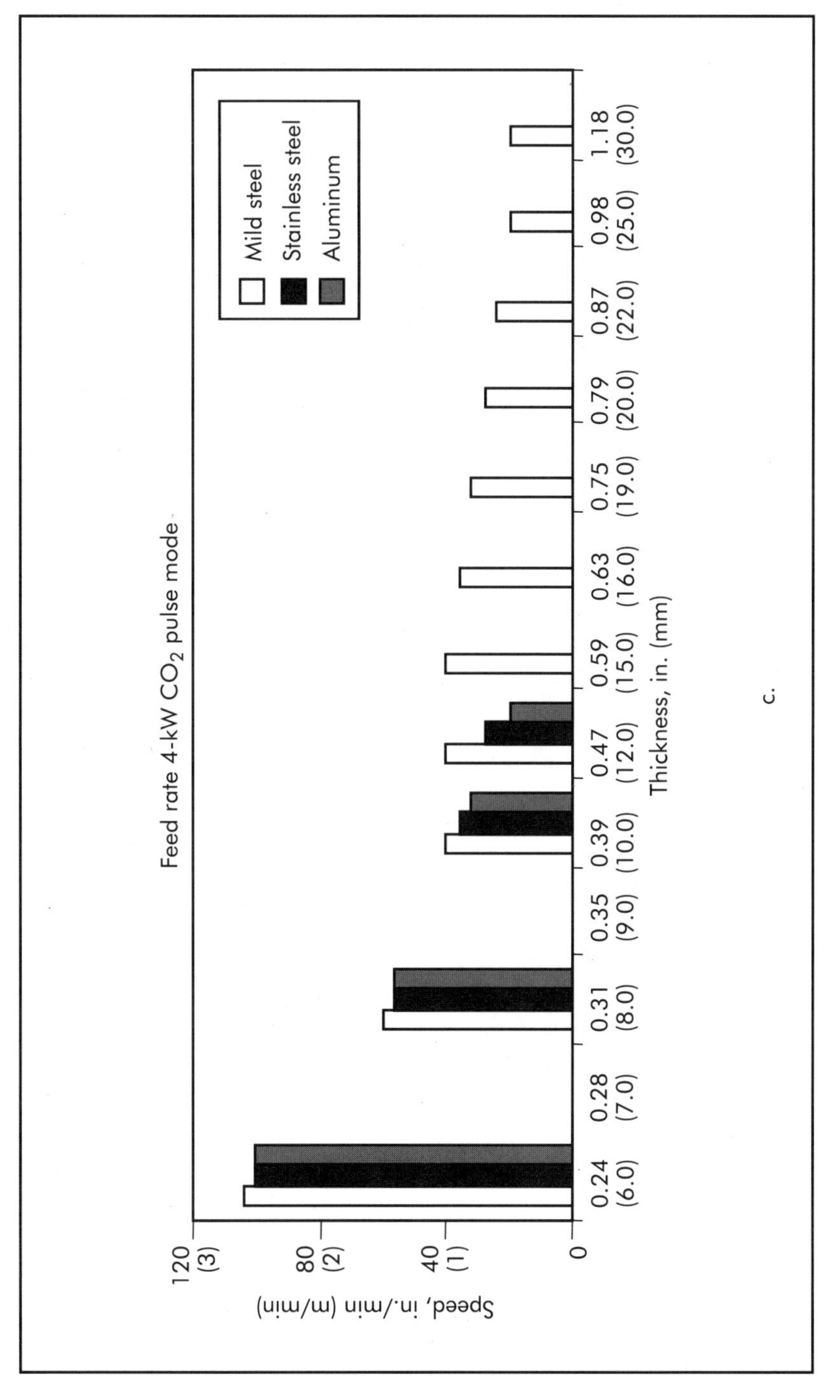

Figure 1-13. continued.

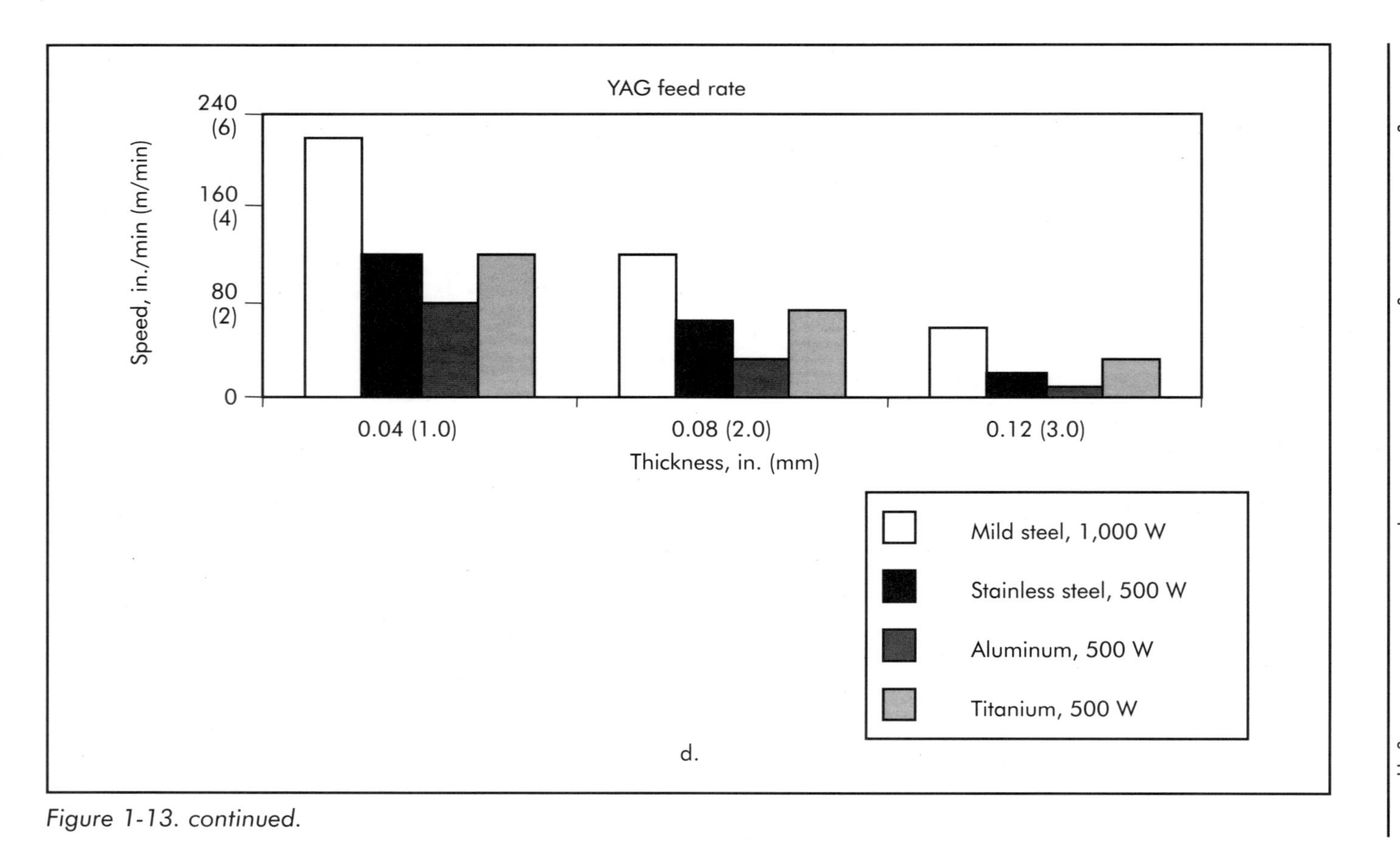

Figure 1-13. continued.

Peck piercing becomes time-consuming when repeated many times in the course of batch production. Rapid-piercing methods result in holes of much larger diameter. Holes of 0.25-in. (6.4-mm) diameter are not uncommon in 0.75-in. (19.1-mm) thick mild steel. They are cut by using maximum rated CW power on the workpiece along with a lateral high-pressure air knife to blow away ejecting metal spatters. Rapid-piercing methods can transform a 20-second peck-piercing time on 0.50-in. (12.7-mm) thick mild steel with a 2.5-kW CO_2 laser into a 1-second piercing time.

REFERENCE

American Society for Metals. 1985. *Metals Handbook*, Desk Edition. Materials Park, OH: American Society for Metals.

BIBLIOGRAPHY

Automotive News. 2000, June 10. Detroit, MI: Crain Communications, Inc.

Bicleanu, D., Brandt, M., Kaebernick, H. 1996. "An Analytical Model for Pulsed Laser Cutting of Metals." International Congress on Applications of Lasers and Electro-Optics (ICALEO). Volume 81C, pp. C68-C77. Orlando, FL: Laser Institute of America.

Ivarson, A. 1993. "On the Physics and Chemical Thermodynamics of Laser Cutting." Doctoral Thesis. Lulea, Sweden: Lulea University of Technology.

Modest, M. 1996. "Laser Machining of Ablating/Decomposing Materials Through Cutting and Drilling Models." International Congress on Applications of Lasers and Electro-Optics (ICALEO). Volume 81C, pp. C58-C67. Orlando, FL: Laser Institute of America.

O'Neill, W., Steen, W.M. 1994. "Review of Mathematical Models of Laser Cutting of Steels." *Lasers in Engineering*, Vol. 3., pp. 281-299.

Petring, D. 2001. "Basic Description of Laser Cutting." *LIA Handbook of Laser Material Processing*. John F. Ready and Dave Farson, eds., pp. 425. Orlando, FL: Laser Institute of America.

——. 1995. "Anwendungsorientierte Modellierung des Laserstrahlschneidens zur rechnergestutzten Prozeßoptimierung." Doctoral Thesis. Aachen, Germany: University of Aachen.

Market for Laser Cutting

"The best way to predict the future is to invent it."

—Alan Kay

The North American automotive industry consumes about 16 million tons of metal sheets and plates (nearly 95% steel and 4% aluminum) per year to build automobile bodies. In contrast, the total yearly production of aluminum sheet and plates in the U.S. is about 4 million tons (Aluminum Association, Inc. 2002). All sheets and plates need to be cut to shape before forming, trimmed to dimensional tolerance afterward, and then pierced in additional fabrication before assembly. The aerospace, appliance, and shipyard industries combined use millions of tons of metal annually, including specialty titanium and nickel-based alloys. The volume of required metal cutting is staggering.

Increasingly, metal cutting is being performed with industrial lasers (see *Figure 2-1*) for one major reason—laser cutting offers superior "value-adding" qualities when compared with most traditional thermal and non-thermal cutting processes. Value-added quality can be created from the elimination of costly and less flexible tooling, or higher part accuracy and definition that enable material savings through better nesting. New product-design ideas that were not possible or too costly with traditional cutting processes are now feasible. Cutting hydroformed tubes is one example

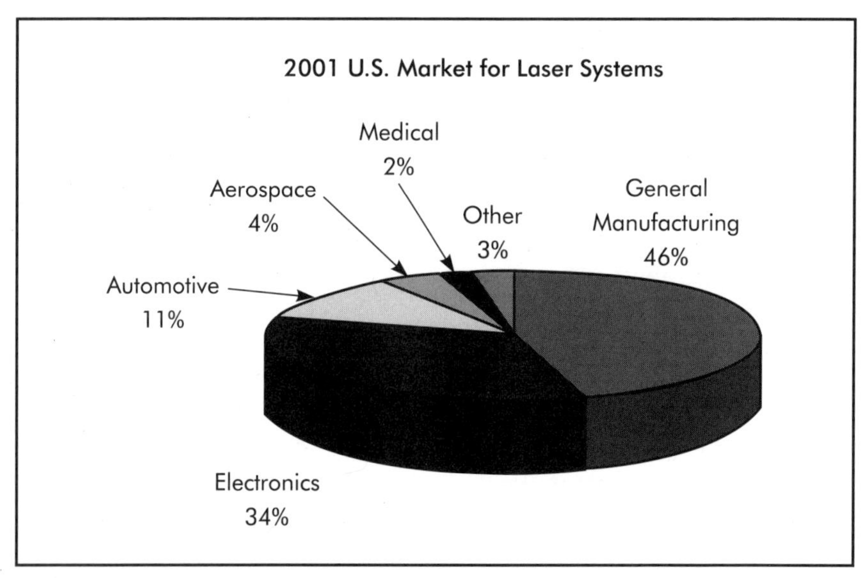

Figure 2-1. The electronics industry (including telecommunications) is the largest user of laser processes, and automotive uses are growing the fastest (Zimmermann 2002).

of an application that can be performed with a laser better than any other method.

Laser cutting eliminates costly, time-consuming, non-value-added finishing operations by yielding superior, ready-to-use edge quality. These and other advantages have brought new meaning to *laserfacturing*, the art of manufacturing with lasers.

COMPARISON OF METAL-CUTTING TECHNOLOGIES

Laser-cutting technology is the latest among metal-cutting processes for sheets and plates. A century ago, the Industrial Revolution brought Taylorization and mass production, which meant producing large lots of the same product at the same time. Pressure to lower piece-cost required solutions to problems that involved dedicated cutting tools operated on hydraulic and mechanical presses in only two ways: up and down. To this day, die blanking and punching are the overall dominant methods of metal cutting, with perfected engineering design of ram motions and ultra high-speed capability surpassing several hundred punches per minute.

In the 21st century, the total volume of production continues to grow for global consumption, but the quantity of part numbers is growing much faster. Thc life cycle of products shrinks under competitive pressure. The initial response emphasizes increasing the speed of presses. This solution has hit a roadblock, as faster press speeds also mean more lost production per downtime, particularly for frequent setups for smaller batch sizes to accommodate the just-in-time (JIT) production requirements of customers. Moreover, with dedicated cutting-tool requirements, little or no flexibility is left for product design and engineering adjustments within controlled tooling costs.

The existence of computer numerical control (CNC) and programmable logic control (PLC) machinery for plasma, waterjet, and laser cutting has grown to the appreciable market share they enjoy today. However, all three of these cutting technologies have a different range of applications, tolerances, advantages, and disadvantages. Several authors have attempted to describe these differences (Julian 2002; Guha 2000; Mombo Caristan 2000; Woodward 1999; Belforte and Levitt 1992). *Table 2-1* highlights the differences between these material-removal cutting technologies.

MARKET TRENDS

The laser-cutting industry thrives from a dynamic interaction between groups of end-users and machine-tool builders. One measure of this industry's activity is how many cutting machines with industrial lasers of 1 kW or more are being used. The Laser Systems Product Group (LSPG) of the Association for Manufacturing Technology (AMT) reported that in 2001, almost 900 laser systems worth about $501.8 million were shipped from U.S. companies, of which $145.8 million were exported (LSPG 2002). This demonstrates exceptional growth for this industry in only 20 years of existence. For reference, the entire U.S. machine-tool industry, including the laser systems industry, shipped about $4.5 billion worth of machinery in 2001. Further data from LSPG/AMT (Zimmermann 2002) reveals that quarterly growth of the

Table 2-1. Differences between laser, waterjet, and plasma cutting

	Laser	Waterjet	Plasma/Fine Plasma
Cutting process	High-power-density light absorption heats the material beyond its melting and vaporization points. Pressurized assist-gas flushes molten metal through the kerf.	High-pressure water beam, with or without abrasive files the material away.	Beam of ionized gas plasma heats the material beyond its melting point and flushes molten metal through the kerf.
Energy source	Laser beam	High-pressure water pump	Beam of hot plasma gas
Energy delivery system	Laser beam guided by mirrors for CO_2 lasers; fiber transmission for Nd:YAG lasers	Rigid high-pressure hoses transmit the energy.	Electrical arc between electrode and workpiece ionizes a beam of pressurized gas to extreme temperatures >26,540° F (>15,000 K).
3-D processing	No problem	Difficult and not recommended	Difficult
Metals processed	All metals	All metals	Only conductive metals can be processed.
Key process input	Optical properties of material's surface at 10.6 μm or 1.06 μm wavelengths	Material hardness is a key factor.	Electrical conductivity

Table 2-1. continued

	Laser	Waterjet	Plasma/Fine Plasma
Range of application	Cutting of flat and shaped metal sheets; steel plates up to 1.25 in. (31.8 mm). High-pressure assist-gas can cut as thin as 0.030 in. (0.76 mm).	Cutting of stone, ceramics, and up to 8.00-in. (203.2 mm) thick metals. Gages thinner than 0.125 in. (3.18 mm) are difficult to process.	Preferable for metal thicknesses between 0.125–2.000 in. (3.18–50.80 mm)
Major consumables	Focusing lens, intra- and extra-cavity mirrors, nozzle tips	Waterjet nozzle, focusing nozzle, and all high-pressure components, such as valves, hoses, and seals	All torch components (nozzles, electrodes)
Specialty gas	CO_2 laser: 0.7 ft^3/hr (20 L/hr); YAG laser: none	Water: 158.5 gal/hr (600 L/hr); Abrasive: 79.4 lb/hr (36 kg/hr)	
	Assist-gas through 0.06-in. (1.5-mm) nozzle	Water through 0.08-in. (2-mm) nozzle	Assist gas through 0.06-in. (1.5-mm) nozzle
Gas/water	145 psi (10 bar) N_2: 424 ft^3/hr (200 L/min); 22 psi (1.5 bar) O_2: 55 ft^3/hr (26 L/min)	Water: 15.9 gal/hr (60 L/hr); Abrasive: 79.4 lb/hr (36 kg/hr)	80 psi (5.5 bar) N_2 = 581 ft^3/hr (16,440 L/hr) 80 psi (5.5 bar) O_2 = 618 ft^3/hr (17,500 L/hr)
Kerf width relative to laser-cut kerf width	1:1	3:1	4:1

Table 2-1. continued

	Laser	Waterjet	Plasma/Fine Plasma
Cut-edge quality	Cut surface will show a striated structure.	Sand-blasting appearance	Cut surface will show a striated structure; bevel-cut edges.
Dross	Mild steel: none Stainless steel: small Aluminum: medium	none	Mild steel: none Stainless steel: small Aluminum: small
Metallurgical change	Deformation, tempering, and significant hardness changes may occur in the heat-affected zone	No thermal stress	Deformation, tempering, and significant hardness changes may occur in the heat-affected zone. Large width of heat-affected zone.
Eye safety	CO_2 laser: standard plant safety glasses; YAG laser: total enclosure preferred	Standard safety glasses and protection against contact with high-pressure waterjet are needed.	Standard safety glasses
Noise safety	Low dB noise level	Above 85 dB—ear protection required	Low dB noise level
Maintenance	Low cleanup	High cleanup	Low cleanup
Waste	Cutting waste is mainly in the form of dust requiring vacuum extraction and filtering.	Large quantities of cutting waste occur due to mixing water with abrasives.	Cutting waste is mainly in the form of dust requiring vacuum extraction and filtering.

laser systems industry mirrors U.S. machine-tool consumption (see *Figure 2-2*). In addition, 50% of all industrial laser systems shipped were equipped with CO_2-type lasers (LSPG 2002). It is estimated that high-power CO_2 laser systems of more than 2 kW represent about 60% of all CO_2 laser-system shipments. *Figure 2-3* illustrates that, although laser cutting represented 59% of all laser systems applications in 1996, it fell to 44% in 2001. It is estimated that for CO_2 laser systems alone, cutting accounts for more than 85% of all material-processing applications.

TECHNOLOGY TRENDS

The predominance of laser cutting over all other metal-cutting processes makes it a leading field for many technological advances in apparatus, processes, and consumables.

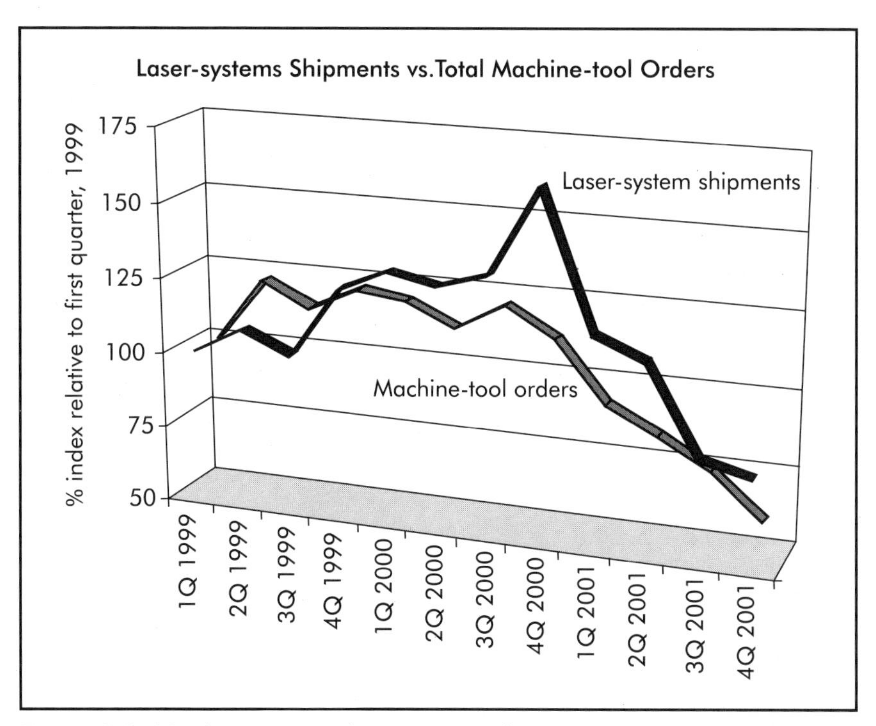

Figure 2-2. North American laser-system shipments versus total machine-tool orders (Zimmermann 2002).

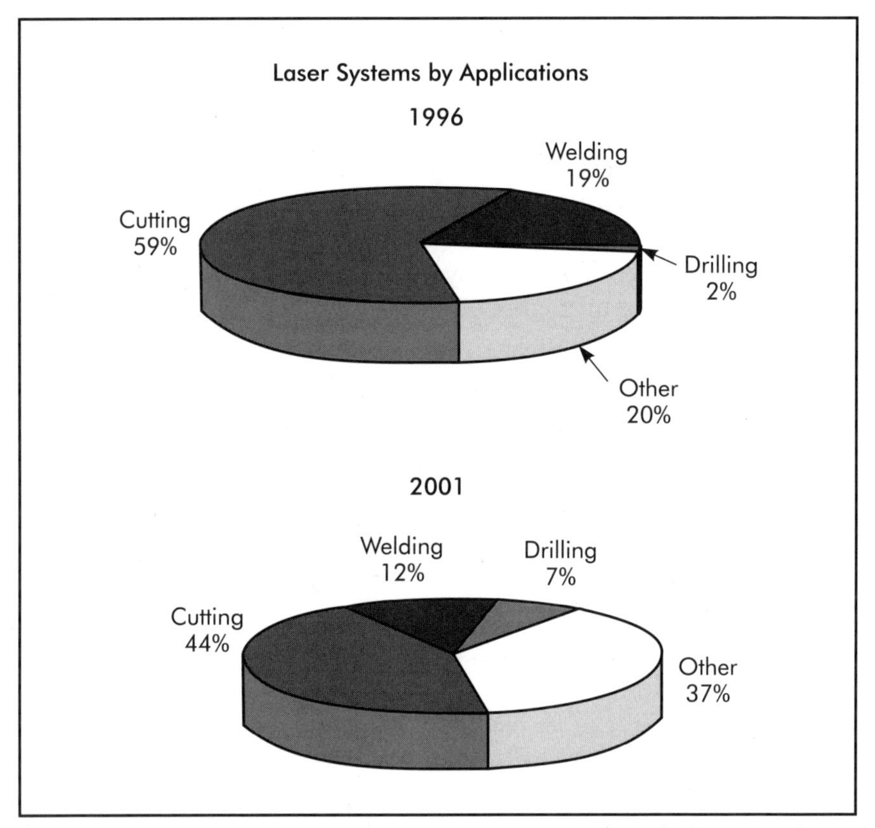

Figure 2-3. Laser cutting accounts for the vast majority of all material-processing applications (Zimmermann 2002).

Machine Motion Concepts

Several types of motion designs, with a variety of features for different applications, are commercially available and define a system.

- Flatbed laser-cutting machines with flying optics generally have two axes (*X* and *Y*) and a *Z* adjustment driven by a surface-follower sensor system (also called a tracing system). The workpiece remains stationary. Most modern machines have three full axes (*X*, *Y*, and *Z*) of motion. The flying optics configurations are characterized by long optical-path-length variations between the near and far fields on a work envelope. Because of the natural divergence of a laser beam, special beam-conditioning optics must be used to maintain control of beam-focusing characteristics over an entire work envelope.

- Flatbed laser-cutting machines with stationary optics accommodate a moving table or workpiece. Similar workpiece/table motion systems also can be found in laser/punch combination machines. The optical-path length is absolutely constant, guaranteeing uniform beam-focusing characteristics over an entire work envelope. The optics move only slightly in the *Z* axis for surface following or setup and maintenance.
- Flatbed laser-cutting machines with hybrid motion combine flying optics and a moving table/workpiece. The workpiece moves in the longitudinal *X* direction and optics move in the *Y* and *Z* directions. This is a compromise between the two configurations previously stated. Variations in optical-path lengths are limited to the *Y*-axis gantry travel. A variant has the entire laser resonator travel along the *X* axis by standing attached to the *Y*-axis gantry; the workpiece is stationary in such hybrid systems. Hybrid machines cannot handle high-acceleration, high-speed operations but are well suited for very large work envelopes. Some systems process work envelopes longer than 100 ft (30.5 m).
- A five-axis, 3D-laser-machining gantry cuts formed or stamped parts. This is almost a standard type of sheet-metal cutting for automotive prototype development. It can have a very wide work envelope covering the entire vehicle's size.
- Six-axis, 3D-laser-machining articulated robots are the fastest growing segment of the laser-cutting industry, mostly driven by the body fabrication needs of the automotive industry. A six-axis articulated robot is coupled with a yttrium-aluminum garnet (YAG) laser with fiberoptic-beam delivery. Its speed and accuracy are sufficient for most automotive prototype cutting applications. The low cost of such a system enables multiple-line duplication to add redundancy and capability, and output the required large volumes under JIT delivery constraints. Small, additional axes on focusing heads help adjust the focus-point position for 3D surface profiling and perform small-diameter-hole piercing. An articulated

robot has a smaller work envelope than the five-axis gantry referred to previously.

An optional rotary axis to handle tube cutting and optional stacking and de-stacking material-handling automation can be added to any of the above configurations.

For thin sheets with an emphasis on high cutting speed, flatbed flying optics are the preferred choice. For thick plates and large work envelopes with an emphasis on the best cut-edge quality, flatbed machines equipped with hybrid- or stationary-beam-delivery systems are preferred. Cut-edge quality is generally measured by the surface roughness of the edge and the amount and nature of dross.

Beam-delivery Systems

YAG laser systems are appreciated for their ability to use flexible fiberoptics-beam delivery. Fiberoptics guarantee a constant optical-path length. Two types are used—step- and gradient-index fibers. The latter enables the beam to focus better. For industrial metal-cutting use with multikilowatt YAG systems, commercially available fibers have a core width of 0.02–0.04 in. (0.6–1.0 mm) in diameter. Fiber diameters of less than 0.02 in. (0.6 mm) are making their way toward commercial availability.

Flexible fiberoptics for a CO_2 laser-beam wavelength of 10.6 μm are not commercially available. Developments in various 10.6 μm fiberoptics materials are underway and may lead to industrial products starting with low-power systems. Waveguide systems looked promising for a 10.6 μm wavelength, but never yielded industrial products for multikilowatt CO_2 laser systems. Instead, technology developments have accelerated over the past 15 years to yield rugged industrial beam-delivery systems that help maintain process stability over an entire work envelope (Haas 2002). Such systems still use basic mirrors and lenses in various clever optical and mechanical arrangements, such as the following:

- Collimators are formed by two mirrors or equivalent lenses based on the telescope principle. The output beam generally is magnified to a larger diameter, but with a reduced divergence. This enables less variation in the diameter of a beam on a focusing lens from one diagonal end of a work envelope to the next. The magnification can be carefully chosen to best optimize cutting performance.

- An absolute constant beam path can be achieved either with flexible/articulated beam-delivery systems, such as fiberoptics for YAG lasers or an articulated optics delivery arm for CO_2 lasers (*Figure 2-4*), or with stationary beam/moving workpiece systems. Hybrid systems are a compromise solution in which only the *Y*-axis motion produces a moderate variation in the optical-path length. Constant-beam-path length also can be achieved by adding a motion *U* axis for a mirror mechanism to divert a laser beam toward a continuously adjustable optical-path detour. The *U* axis can be powered independently, or judiciously share power with the *X* axis or transverse gantry *Y* axis. The length of the detour is a function of the *X-Y* position on the table, so variations in total optical-path length remain small or preferably null at any position of a work envelope at any time.
- Autofocus heads adjust the focal length of the optical path at every area of a work envelope. Adaptive mirror technology can enable the same feature by achieving on-the-fly radius curvature changes to a specially designed mirror placed upstream of a focusing lens.
- Auto standoff consists of numerical control software that manages a closed-loop control between a height-sensor signal and *Z*-axis motion to keep the focus position and nozzle standoff constant, despite material height variations on a worktable.
- Dynamic collimation consists of a collimator with either moving or adaptive optics. It was designed to adjust the collimation magnification as a function of position on a work envelope. The result is similar to that of a regular collimator combined with autofocus.
- Optimal use of a linearly polarized beam can be achieved by orienting the direction of polarization parallel to the direction of cutting. This requires at least one additional rotary axis system at the focusing head. Appropriate software will

maintain the direction of the linear polarization of a focused beam spot tangent to the cutting path.

- Similarly, an oblong focused beam spot (Scott et al. 1995) can be oriented such that its longitudinal axis remains parallel to the direction of cutting. This also requires an additional rotary axis system at the focusing head and appropriate software to maintain the longitudinal direction of the oblong focused beam spot in constant tangent relationship to the cutting path.

Bifocal technology advantageously uses beam-delivery systems that yield two different focal lengths. A portion of a laser beam ends up being focused at a different position than the remaining part of the laser beam (Nielsen 1998), thus potentially creating more than one power density optimum along the optical axis. Such technology enables faster cutting speeds and more efficient assist-gas consumption, particularly for high-pressure, nitrogen-assist laser cutting.

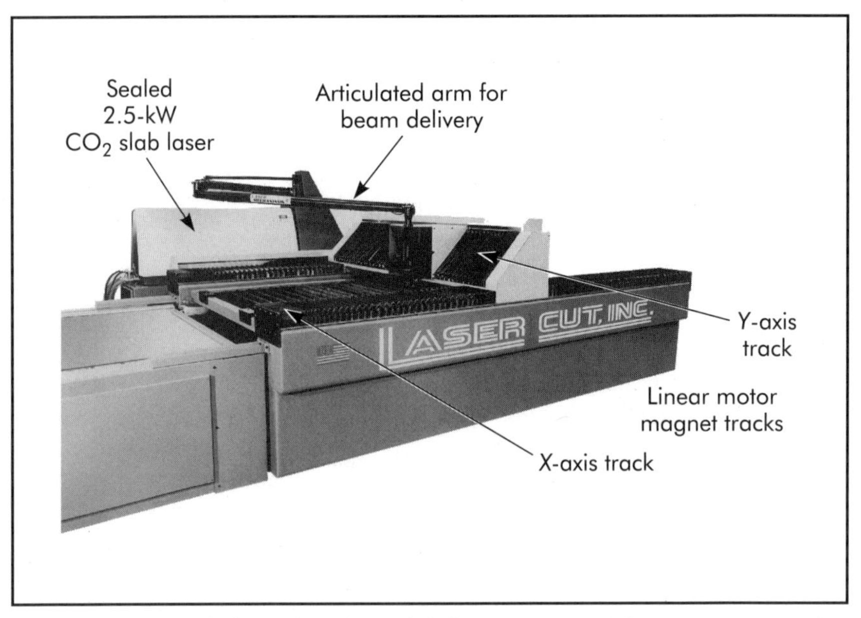

Figure 2-4. A sealed 2.5-kW CO_2 slab laser system. A linear-motor motion system yields high acceleration rates with high speed and accuracy. (Courtesy Laser Cut, Inc.)

Motion Systems

Motion systems are transitioning from traditional servomotors with a rotating shaft to linear-motor technology. Traditional servomotors transmit rotating torque into linear motion by clutching a ball screw. Linear motors use interaction between two magnetic-field vectors to induce force and linear motion. Since the coupling is made directly by magnetic-field interaction, no physical contact between moving parts takes place. It yields less friction and backlash, faster accelerations, and rapid traverse-motion capability. The result is higher definition and greater accuracy of intricate contours at high speed and acceleration, as well as less mechanical wear.

Laser Resonators

Laser resonators have experienced a tremendously high degree of evolution and improvement over the past 20 years. A visually noticeable change has resulted from their miniaturization to smaller footprints and less weight. The contemporary turnkey 4-kW CO_2 laser resonator in *Figure 2-5* occupies less than half the footprint

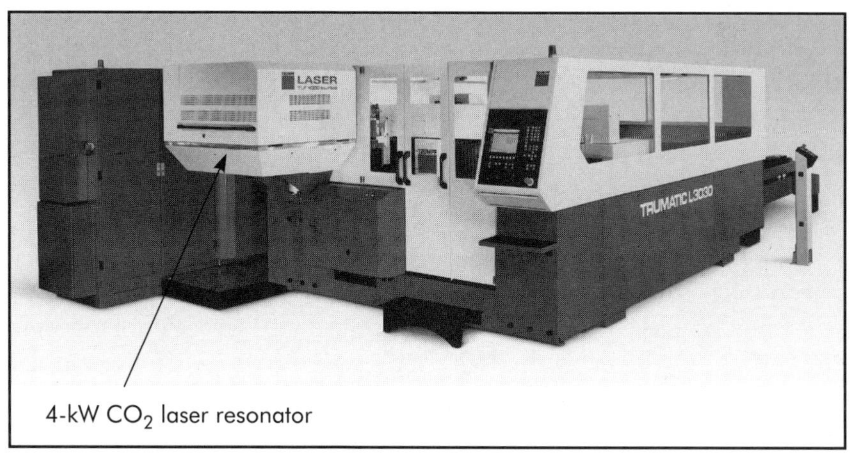

Figure 2-5. By 2000, this 4-kW CO_2 laser resonator in a square-box, folded cavity configuration occupied less than half the footprint of its predecessors 20 years earlier. (Courtesy Trumpf, Inc.)

of a 1-kW CO_2 laser of 20 years ago. The packaging of resonators plays an important role in achieving effective miniaturization. Strategic maintenance considerations, along with field reparability requirements, impose modularity in a resonator design. Accessories, such as water chillers, numerical controls, and power supplies, had to be miniaturized as well in this quest for progress.

At 10.6-μm wavelength, CO_2 lasers emit in the infrared (IR) spectrum of light with the best available overall wall-plug electricity producing power efficiency of about 10% for most industrial cutting lasers. Those with a stable resonator design try to forge a compromise between conflicting features in high output power, high beam-mode quality, and a small footprint. Higher beam-mode quality results in higher focusability of the laser beam to reach higher power-density levels at the focus spot for melting and vaporizing metals. For maximum overall efficiency, higher beam-output power can be enabled by allowing a larger beam diameter with lower mode quality to resonate in the laser cavity. However, if beam-mode quality is improved, it almost inevitably results in less output power and lower overall efficiency. New resonator designs with hybrid cavities are considered stable in one transverse plane and unstable in another. Such is the case with CO_2 slab lasers. This hybrid configuration enables extraction of a high-output-power beam with high-beam-mode quality (in other words, high focusability). This feature is a decisive advantage for high-speed laser cutting of thin sheet metal. It must be cautioned that, as explained in Appendix B, the stability or instability of a resonator characterizes its design and has nothing to do with the stability of its output beam. There are many industrial lasers, such as slab lasers, with unstable resonator designs but perfectly stable output-beam characteristics and performance.

Shorter wavelength light couples better with metals, as experienced with YAG lasers in metal processing. Most industrial YAG laser beams have a wavelength of 1.06 μm, 10 times shorter than that of a CO_2 laser. Industrial YAG lasers with sufficient pulse energy and power for metal cutting are pumped with flash-lamp systems, yielding dismal overall efficiency (below 4%) and second-rate mode quality. YAG lasers have considerable market growth, particularly in the automotive metal-fabrication market, where the flexibility of their fiberoptic-beam delivery makes them easy to integrate with low-cost and small-footprint articulated robots.

The technology and design for diode-pumped YAG lasers has been ready for some years. Their overall efficiency has increased to highs of 15%, with a noticeable increase in beam quality. By the end of the 20th century, several manufacturers offered commercially available, multikilowatt, diode-pumped YAG lasers. However, the scarcity of suppliers of diodes and the initially high price of such lasers has slowed their proliferation. Diode-pumped YAG lasers promise to replace flash-lamp-pumped YAG lasers within a few years, and even challenge CO_2 lasers in the sheet-metal-cutting industry, particularly for automobile fabrication. Safety considerations with the shorter 1.06 μm wavelength play a role in slowing the use of YAG lasers in small job shops.

The quest for shorter-wavelength lasers does not end with YAG lasers. Multikilowatt power, direct-diode lasers with a wavelength of 0.8 μm are already commercially available in extremely compact footprint packages (Zedicker et al. 2000). Their pumping efficiency can reach an impressive 60% in the laboratory environment. When factoring in the efficiency of necessary accessories (for example, a water chiller), they reach an overall efficiency of about 25%. However, this superior efficiency and compactness come at the price of poor beam quality. Currently, focusability is too poor for laser metal-cutting applications. *Table 2-2* compares the efficiency of various industrial laser systems.

Technological improvements to make direct-diode lasers possible candidates for metal laser cutting will probably emerge within a few years. In the meantime, direct-diode lasers are not yet ready to cut metals with edge quality comparable to that of CO_2 and YAG lasers.

Automation

CAD/CAM software products proliferate as machines' part-program codes become increasingly similar and closer to a universal standard. These softwares convert a part design into a machine part program, including laser-specific features such as common line programming, loop startup, output power, duty clamped by

Table 2-2. New direct-diode lasers and diode-pumped YAG lasers challenge established CO_2 lasers and flash-lamp-pumped YAG lasers

	Direct-diode Laser	CO_2 Laser	Flash-lamp-pumped YAG	Diode-pumped YAG
Wavelength	0.8 μm	10.6 μm	1.06 μm	1.06 μm
Average power	4 kW	4 kW	2 kW	2 kW
Net system efficiency (including water chiller)	25%	6%	1%	8%
Beam quality	Still too poor for cutting	High	Medium	Medium
Beam delivery	Fiberoptics	Mirrors	Fiberoptics	Fiberoptics
Footprint of system	8 ft^2 (0.7 m^2)	25 ft^2 (2.3 m^2)	40 ft^2 (3.7 m^2)	40 ft^2 (3.7 m^2)

Note: Laser system includes a laser resonator, its power supplies, and a necessary water-chiller device.

radius, and corner-angle processing. Together, software and material-handling automation yield flexible manufacturing cells, such as the one illustrated in *Figure 2-6*.

SPECIAL APPLICATIONS

When processing thin-gage metal in continuous-wave (CW) mode with a neutral gas, cutting speed can increase almost proportionally to laser power. The benefits of high-speed cutting of thin gages have translated into industrial applications, such as laser cutting displacing traditional mechanical shearing. The current trend toward more high-speed laser-cutting applications certainly will be sustained in the future.

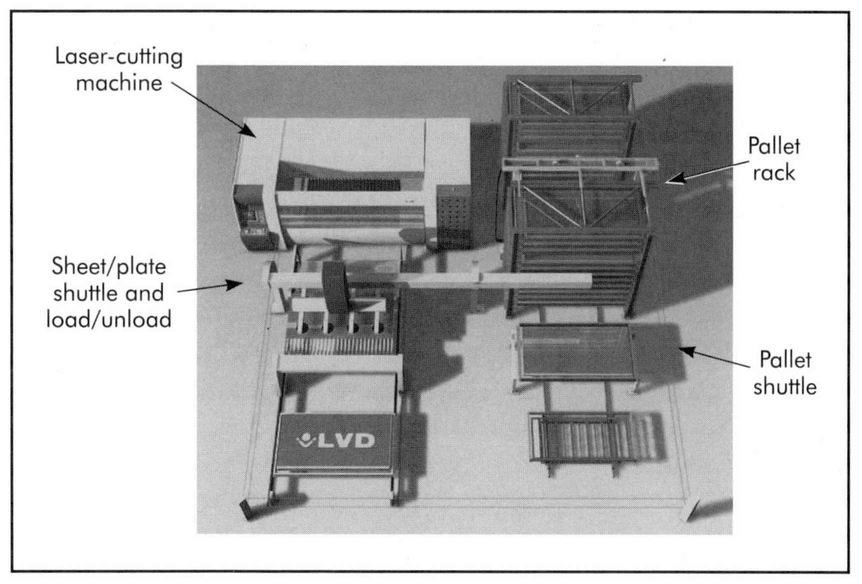

Figure 2-6. Complete flexible manufacturing cells include pallet racks with automatic shuttle and stacking and de-stacking systems to load sheets and plates into the cutting machine and unload finished parts. (Courtesy Strippit-LVD)

Laser Coil Slitting

Laser coil-slitting technology exemplifies the aforementioned trend. Laser coil-slitting machines are used in production in European steel mills. Ambitious, real-scale research and development (R&D) efforts for this application were first undertaken by the industrial R&D laboratories of the Fraunhofer Institute for Laser Technologies in Aachen, Germany in the 1990s. A slitting operation that used circular knives, which enabled high-speed cutting of metal coils into narrower strips, now can be performed by a noncontact laser-cutting apparatus, such as the one shown in *Figure 2-7*. The setting of knife tools is replaced by numerically controlled focusing-optics head positioning. This enables multiple strips to be slit as narrow as 2.4 in. (60 mm) from a single wide steel coil. Thin 0.009 in. (0.23 mm) electric steel coils have been slit at speeds in excess of 328 ft/min (100 m/min) at the Thyssen Steel production facility in Gelsenkirchen, Germany since the end of the 1990s (Schneider and Petring 2001). Despite relatively high laser-cutting speeds, a laser slitter is still slower than a conventional mechanical slitter. However, the consistent, excellent, burr-free laser-cut-edge quality, elimination of tooling and refurbishing, added flexibility for setting the width of each strip to the exact specified value within seconds, and reduced setup time are benefits that make a favorable case for laser slitting.

Laser Blanking

Laser blanking introduces a more flexible and tool-less process of producing automotive sheet-metal blanks for low- to medium-volume vehicle production. Laser blanking eliminates the need for blanking dies and presses. Benefits include the elimination of blanking die expenditures and a reduction of the corresponding maintenance, transportation, and storage operation costs. Other benefits are enhanced flexibility in production scheduling and increased capability to implement engineering changes with no new

Figure 2-7. Example of a coil-slitting operation. (Courtesy Fraunhofer Institute)

tool cost penalty. Better nesting opportunities result in the elimination of non-value-adding manufacturing steps, such as coil slitting and right-hand side (RHS) to left-hand side (LHS) pallet flipping, as well as a reduction of engineering scrap.

Applications

One recent successful application of laser blanking is for automotive stampings. With the steady increase of car and truck models evidenced in *Table 2-3*, the multiplicity and cost of tooling drags down the auto companies' net income. Although many models share the same underbody platform, the increase in traditional sheet-metal fabrication has resulted in a heavy tooling cost burden. Laser blanking eliminates this tremendous tooling burden for programs such as the all-aluminum body Jaguar® introduced in January 2003 at the Detroit Auto Show. Dozens of blanking dies have been totally eliminated from the manufacturing of this low-volume model vehicle. This change is indicative of a call to cut tooling costs and increase flexibility and agility to respond to growing demand, and adapt to the speed of transactions in an

Table 2-3. The number of different models of cars and trucks in circulation in North America increased 44% between 1995 and 2002 (Automotive News Magazine 2002)

Year	Models		
	Cars	Trucks	Total
1995	480	430	910
1996	464	484	948
1997	447	477	924
1998	423	573	996
1999	441	610	1,051
2000	461	660	1,121
2001	472	693	1,165
2002	545	769	1,314

increasingly build-to-order-driven automotive market (Mombo Caristan 2000).

Product and process development enhancements initiated and successfully produced by a team of engineers at FANUC Laser Laboratories resulted in a new set of technology enablers. This team built the first prototype laser-cutting machine equipped with a computer numerical control (CNC) and reduced instruction set code (RISC) combination processor to minimize processing time. Linear motors enabled higher accelerations, and new cutting lasers equipped with solid-state power-supply units allowed the controller to simultaneously control laser output and motion. The FANUC team also confirmed that to achieve high-speed laser cutting of thin sheets, oxygen assist-gas could not be used because it was combustion-limited and generated hard-chipping, metallic oxide scales on the edges of blanks. With nitrogen assist-gas, cutting speed became proportional to laser power, as illustrated in

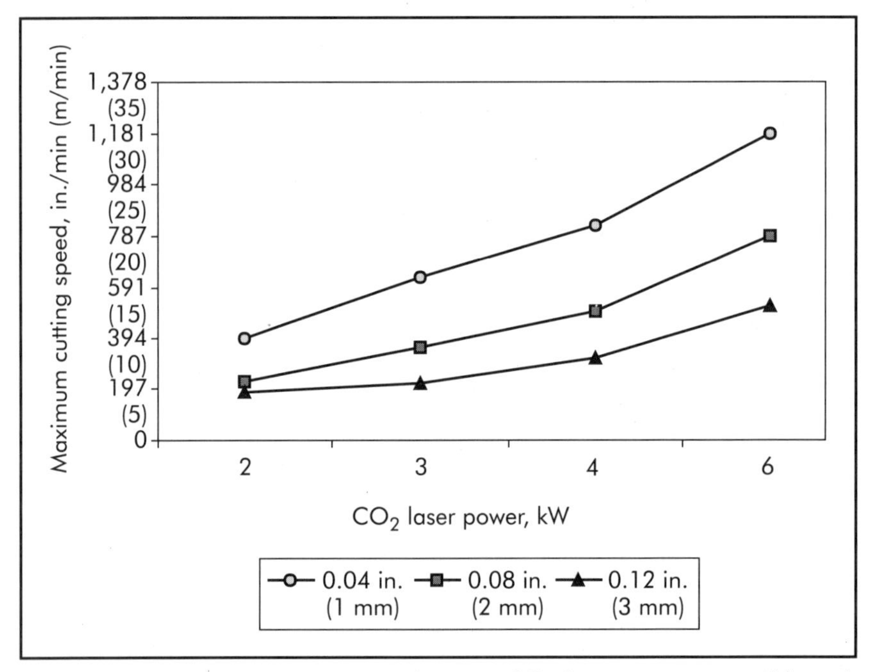

Figure 2-8. Maximum cutting speed versus CO_2 laser power on mild steel, with high-pressure nitrogen assist-gas and a 5-in. (125-mm) focusing lens. Cutting speed increases linearly with power.

Figure 2-8, and metal edges were kept clean and free of scales (Karube et al. 1996).

An early commercial system, illustrated in *Figure 2-9*, contained a 6-kW CO_2 laser and linear motors fully integrated within a CNC with RISC processor. Laser output and motion controls were commanded simultaneously within each CNC interpolation. Using 2g acceleration, 400 in./sec (10 m/sec) rapid traverse speed could be achieved with 0.002-in. (0.05-mm) precision. With 218-psi (15-bar) nitrogen-assist laser cutting, 0.04-in. (1.1-mm) thick mild steel could be cut at 1,200 in./min (32 m/min), whereas 0.04-in. (1.1-mm) thick aluminum could be cut at 1,500 in./min (37.5 m/min) with a 5-in. (127-mm) focal-length lens (Mombo Caristan et al. 1999). (Cutting speed decreases when material thickness increases.) A coil-fed, double laser-blanking system concept for high-volume production is illustrated in *Figure 2-10*.

Figure 2-11 compares coil-fed nesting progression in traditional press-and-die and laser-blanking processes. With laser blanking, non-value-adding coil-slitting operations can be eliminated by designing nesting patterns and engineering stacking automation to enable multiple parts to be blanked and stacked during each coil progression. In addition, right- and left-hand side panels can be produced simultaneously or consecutively with just the push of a button to select the proper corresponding CNC part program. This eliminates the non-value-adding pallet flip-over machine and operation. Generally, a slit coil costs more per pound of metal than a standard 72-in. (183-cm) wide coil. By nesting solely from wider coils, laser blanking enables a leaner and lower-cost manufacturing process.

Blank Design

Blank contours are still being designed with as many straight segments and corner angles as possible. This reduces the initial price and maintenance costs of blanking dies, despite the fact that features with curved contours and corner radii generally improve formability and deep-drawability. In particular, the development of splits and wrinkles during the forming of corner angles in sheet metal results in the need to use oversized blanks with increased binder stock to make the final part defect-free. Wrinkles and splits

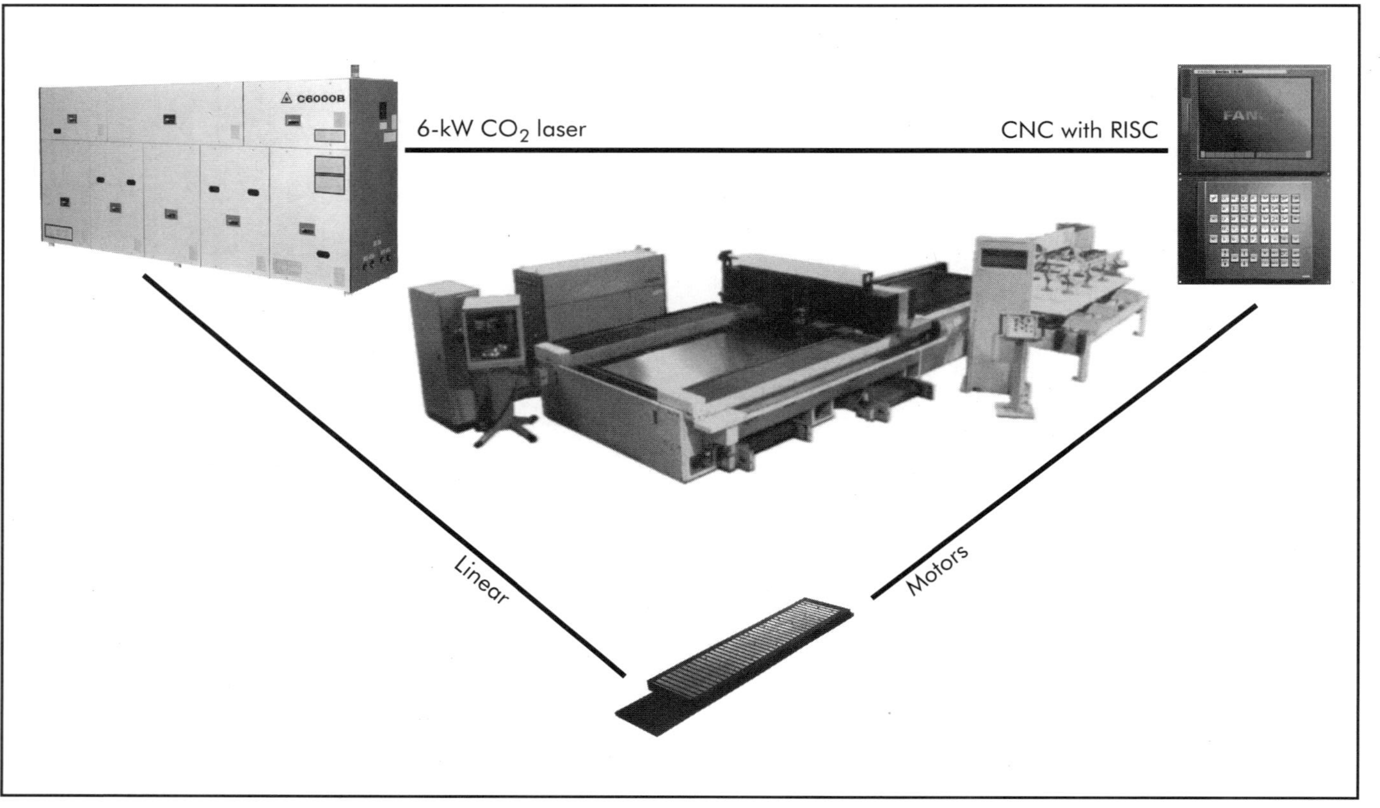

Figure 2-9. Example of an early commercial laser-blanking system (Mombo Caristan 2000).

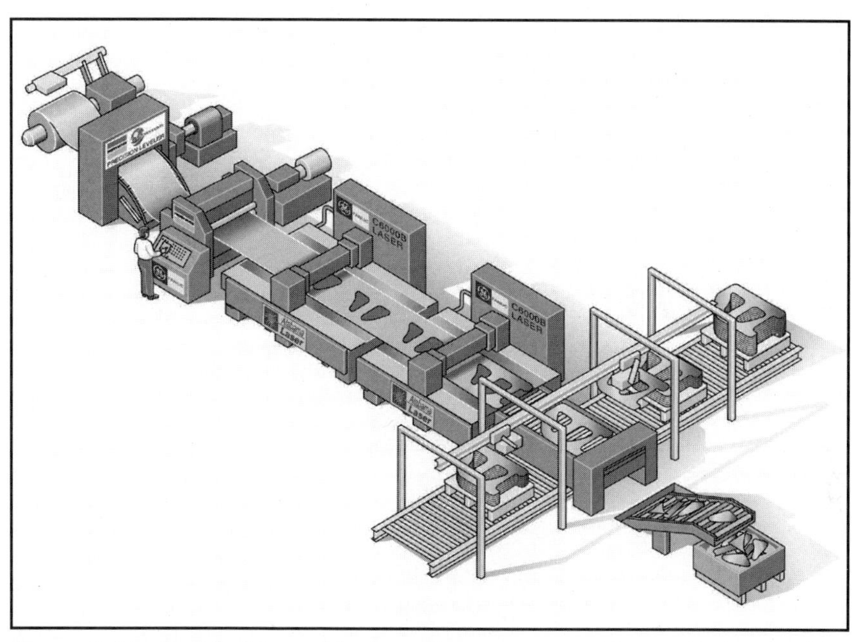

Figure 2-10. Coil-fed laser-blanking line concept, with two high-speed laser-cutting machines in tandem configuration. Each laser-cutting machine is equipped with a 6-kW CO_2 laser (Mombo Caristan 2000).

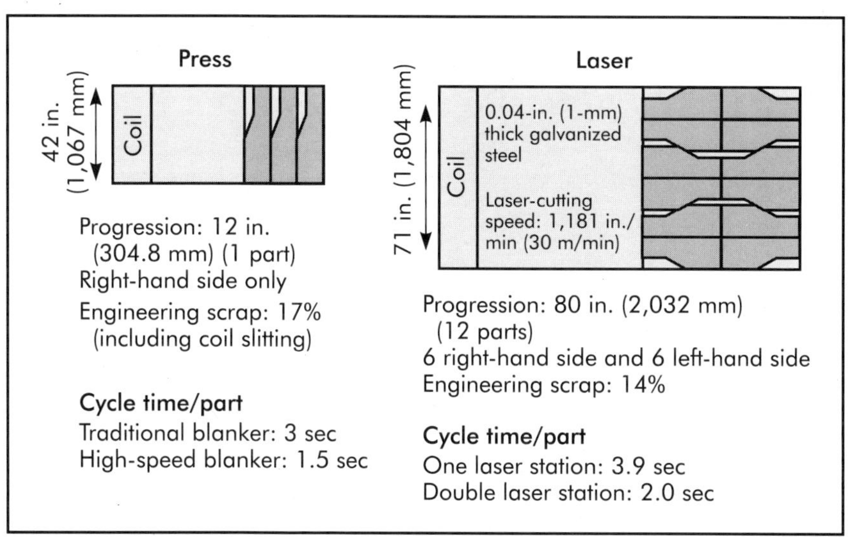

Figure 2-11. Example of part nesting in two types of coil-fed blanking lines.

often can be reduced or eliminated by strategically designing proper curvilinear features and replacing corner angles with corner radii, as illustrated in *Figure 2-12*. In some cases, laser cutting actually yields faster contour cutting speed with corner radii than corner angles, thus enabling a significant reduction in binder stock and dramatic cost savings.

Product Design Flexibility

Engineering changes are routinely ordered during the development phase of a part, and even after the production launch or during the life of the vehicle model. Each engineering change yields cost penalties in design, engineering, construction, transportation, and administrative cost. In addition, it is estimated that during the life of a blanking die, its initial cost is multiplied by three due to maintenance, transportation, and storage expenses. All these costs are eliminated or significantly reduced with tool-less laser

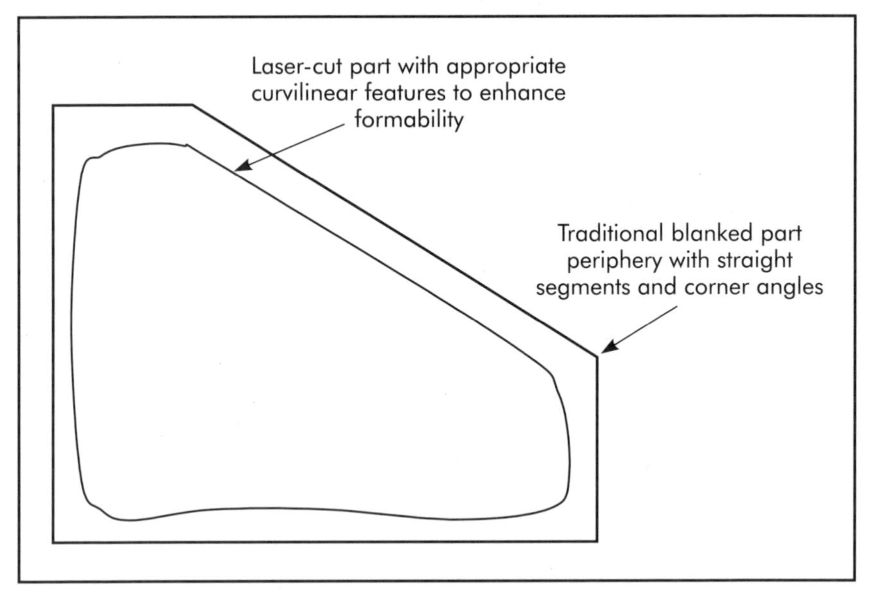

Figure 2-12. Blanking dies with corner angles and straight segments are cheaper and have lower maintenance costs than dies with curvilinear features.

blanking. Laser blanking creates flexibility for more frequent engineering changes to optimize the forming process and results in metal savings with less or no cost penalty.

REFERENCES

Aluminum Association, Inc. 2002, April. "Economics and Statistics," www.aluminum.org.

Belforte, D. and Levitt, M. 1992. *The Industrial Laser Handbook*. "Laser Versus Nonlaser Process Comparison." New York: Springer-Verlag.

Guha, J. 2000. "Water-jet Cutting Applications." Conference on Comparative Cutting. Dearborn, MI: Society of Manufacturing Engineers (SME).

Haas, G. 2002, June. "Sensors & Special Optics for Laser Cutting." Technical Forum Seminar. Advanced Thermal Processing of Metal Sheets & Plates: Cutting, Welding, & Inspection, Ohio State University, Columbus, OH. Dearborn, MI: Society of Manufacturing Engineers (SME).

Julian, A. 2002, June. "Comparative Economics of Thermal-cutting Technologies." Technical Forum Seminar. Advanced Thermal Processing of Metal Sheets & Plates: Cutting, Welding, & Inspection, Ohio State University, Columbus, OH. Dearborn, MI: Society of Manufacturing Engineers (SME).

Karube, N. et al. 1996. "Fast Contour Cutting Using Linear Motors." Proceedings of the International Congress on Applications of Lasers and Electro-Optics (ICALEO), Southfield, MI. Orlando, FL: Laser Institute of America.

Laser System Product Group (LSPG). 2002, March. News release. www.mfgtech.org. McLean, VA: Association for Manufacturing Technology (AMT).

Mombo Caristan, C. 2000, November. "High-speed Laser Cutting for Automotive Sheet-metal-blanking Production." Fabtech International Conference Reading, Cleveland, OH. Dearborn, MI: Society of Manufacturing Engineers (SME).

Nielsen, Steen E. 1998, September. "Dual-focus Laser Cutting." Proceedings of the European Conference on Laser Treatment of Materials (ECLAT), pp. 377-383. Hanover, Germany: Werkstoff-Informationsgesellschaft, GmbH.

Schneider, F. and Petring, D. 2001. "High Speed and Thick Sections: CO_2 Laser Cutting." *Lasers in Manufacturing, The Industrial Laser User*. Issue 25. December.

Scott, J.E., Latham, W.P., and Kar, A. 1995. "High-speed Material Processing of Thick Stainless Steel with a Chemical-oxygen-iodine Laser." Proceedings of the International Congress on Applications of Lasers and Electro-Optics (ICALEO), pp. 118-127. Orlando, FL: Laser Institute of America.

Woodward, K. 1999. "Thermal and Water-jet Cutting." *Metal Center News*. August.

Zedicker, M. S., Haake, J.M., and Cook, C.M. 2000. "Laser-diode Material-processing System." Proceedings of the International Congress on Applications of Lasers and Electro-Optics (ICALEO), pp. D1-D8. Orlando, FL: Laser Institute of America.

Zimmermann, B. 2002, June. "Laser Systems Industries, Technologies, & Applications Trends." Technical Forum Seminar. Advanced Thermal Processing of Metal Sheets & Plates: Cutting, Welding, & Inspection, Ohio State University, Columbus, OH. Dearborn, MI: Society of Manufacturing Engineers.

BIBLIOGRAPHY

Automotive News. 2002, June 10. Detroit, MI: Crain Communications, Inc.

Mombo Caristan, C., Penn, W., Mudiam, S., and Karube, N. 1999. "High-speed High-power Laser-blank Cutting and Welding." International Congress on Applications of Lasers and Electro-Optics (ICALEO), San Diego, CA. Orlando, FL: Laser Institute of America.

three

Materials

"Light is the first of painters. There is no object so foul that intense light will not make it beautiful."

—Ralph W. Emerson

INTRODUCTION

Metals are the subject of continuous research to enhance their ability to be processed with lasers, particularly for cutting and welding applications. Many steelmakers, such as Rautaruukki Raahe Steel in Europe, Bethlehem Steel and U.S. Steel in North America, and Chubu Steel in Japan, have developed grades of steel that yield superior laser cut-edge quality. One study compares the ability of various aluminum alloys, namely 6111, 5754, and 5182 series, to be laser cut (Penn 2000). The conclusion recommends cutting automotive-grade aluminum-alloy sheet metals with a laser instead of die-blanking them for volume production. Generally, laser cutting is forgiving of variations in metallurgical and mechanical properties. However, although metallurgy clearly affects levels of performance, it alone is far from being the determining factor for the productivity, quality, and profitability of a laser-cutting operation. The following sections describe other key material parameters and their impact on laser-cutting output.

METAL ALLOY TYPES

Laser cutting offers a variety of opportunities and challenges, whether the material is mild steel with deep drawability for appliance panels and automobile body sheets; high-strength steels for structural members; stainless steel for kitchen utensils; aluminum, titanium, and nickel alloys for the aerospace and energy industries; or copper alloys in the electronics industry.

Mild Steels

Steel is the principal metal that is cut with lasers due to the large volume of industrial applications and because it is one of the easiest to laser cut.

Mild steel consists predominantly of iron with some alloying elements in very small but controllable quantities. The main alloying elements of mild steel are carbon (C), manganese (Mn), silicon (Si), phosphorus (P), and sulfur (S). Most steels used in consumer goods are low-carbon of either commercial, drawing, or structural quality (0.05–0.40% carbon content). To ease forming, fabricating, and welding, the level of carbon is minimized, Mn is maintained at 0.25–0.50%, P is kept under 0.035%, and S under 0.04%. These steels are magnetic.

Whether in thin sheet or thick plate form, mild steels can be laser cut to yield acceptable to superior cut-edge quality when compared with conventional thermal-cutting technologies. Once a desired alloying composition is specified, its mill output variations remain well within laser-cutting process tolerance. Alloying composition variations are not a source of significant proportional differences in cut-edge quality or cutting speed. This indicates that a laser-cutting process is forgiving enough for use in a standard heavy-duty metal fabrication environment. Metals on the boundary of the aforementioned content ranges exhibit different laser-cutting performances.

- Structural-quality steel with a carbon content close to or above 0.40% is prone to micro-cracking on the cut edge, whereas drawing-quality steel with a carbon content below 0.15% renders practically crack-free edges. Micro-cracking can develop into splits and failure of the part due to fatigue while in use. Micro-cracking failure can be averted by heat-treating (annealing) the cut edge of high-carbon-content steels.

- At equivalent cut-edge quality, steels with low-carbon content enable cutting speeds up to 20% higher than steels on the high end range of this element.
- At equivalent cut-edge quality, the maximum thickness that can be laser cut is about 20% higher with low-carbon steel as opposed to structural-quality steel.
- Steels with levels of about 0.4% Si are preferred in electrical component applications, such as transformer frames, because of their increased electrical resistance and threshold for thermal oxidation. However, the laser-cutting speed of these steels is reduced by more than 20% and severe dross is generated in contrast to steels with Si content below 0.25%.
- Tool steels with Mn content, respectively S content on the high 0.5% end, respectively 0.04%, also disrupt laser cutting sufficiently to reduce cutting speed and worsen cut-edge quality. In particular, sticking dross at the bottom edge of the cut grows almost proportionally to the thickness of the material being cut.

Stainless Steels

Stainless steels, also referred to as chrome-nickel steels, have an alloying content 10–20 times higher than mild steel. Chrome (Cr) is the major alloying element, with about 18% content, followed by nickel (Ni) at about 8% for the most common types. These alloying elements increase weldability and reduce brittleness.

Although most stainless steels are nonmagnetic, a few types containing zero or little Ni are magnetic. This is to be considered when designing material-handling and scrap-removal equipment.

Stainless steel is highly resistant to corrosion due to the natural Cr_2O_3 film formation on its surface when exposed to free atmosphere. This Cr_2O_3 oxidation film shields the metal from further corrosion. It is also responsible for lesser O_2 combustion-assist contribution to thermal cutting in comparison to the

O_2 assist contributed in thermal cutting of mild steel. However, the presence of O_2 increases the formation of dross at the bottom of the kerf. To reduce dross, stainless steel is often laser cut with nitrogen (N_2) assist-gas. The pressure of N_2 assist-gas yields a large consumption of nitrogen and increases processing costs. At equal laser power and equivalent cut-edge quality, the maximum thickness that can be cut for stainless steels is less than half of that for mild steels.

Aluminum Alloys

Aluminum (Al) is second behind steels in terms of volume of industrial laser-cutting applications. However, the number of applications involving aluminum laser cutting is growing strongly in key sectors, such as the automotive industry, despite the fact that aluminum sheets are 70% higher in cost per ton than steel sheets at equivalent performance. In fact, 87% of the total aluminum content in an automobile consists of castings, extrusions, and forgings. The remaining 13% consists of sheets for hoods, trunk lids, liftgates, heat shields, trim seats, and foils for heat exchangers (Schultz 2000). Aluminum alloys in thin sheets for automotive body panels are predominantly 5xxx series (easier to weld) and 6xxx series (easier to form). Both can be laser cut with comparable cutting performance.

As with stainless steel, aluminum is quickly oxidized when exposed to free atmosphere, forming an Al_2O_3 auto-protective surface film that prevents further corrosion penetration. This thin Al_2O_3 film oxidation also prevents effective combustion-aided O_2-assist laser cutting along the kerf. Neutralization of the O_2 combustion process is a bigger factor when cutting thicker plates. Since O_2 assist-gas provides little advantage, aluminum is mostly laser cut with lower-cost air assist-gas. To reduce dross and cut-edge oxidation, aluminum is often cut with nitrogen assist-gas.

Aluminum is not magnetic; therefore, the design of material-handling and scrap-removal equipment should not use magnetic conveyors and end-effectors, except in a judicious arrangement involving additional magnetic metal plates.

Titanium and Nickel Alloys

The aerospace and energy industries represent some of the largest users of titanium (Ti) and Ni alloys. These metals exhibit high toughness and a high strength-to-weight ratio advantage over more common metals, including aluminum and steel. Nickel alloys, such as Monel® (66% Ni and 30% copper [Cu]), Inconel® 600 (76% Ni, 15% chromium [Cr], and 8% iron [Fe]), and Hastelloy® (57% Ni, 16% Cr, 15% molybdenum, and 6% Fe) are known for their high corrosion resistance under an acid chemical environment and high temperatures. These advantages counterbalance their significantly higher cost per pound. Such alloys are commonly used for aircraft engines and gas-turbine engine blades due to their high strength-to-weight ratios and ability to sustain high-temperature operations.

Titanium has been used as a structural metal since the early 1950s. Titanium alloy is an expensive metal mostly used in the aerospace industry and in high-temperature, high-pressure environments, such as in gas turbines where judicious and efficient air cooling enables it to sustain temperatures well beyond its melting threshold. Titanium is biologically compatible with human tissues and bones, which explains its use in medical prosthetic devices.

During oxygen-assist thermal cutting, titanium reacts with O_2 in a highly exothermic reaction. It also reacts with neutral gases, such as N_2, in an environment in which temperatures rise above 896° F (480° C). The highly reactive combustion of titanium can generate explosive flame plumes, so it does not lend itself to fine, intricate feature cutting. Generally, it is not recommended to process titanium with either nitrogen or oxygen assist-gas. During oxidation at high temperature, the migration of oxygen between room atmosphere and interstitial zones between the titanium atoms (closed-pack-hexagonal-crystal or body-centered-cubic structures above 1,625° F [885° C]) is facilitated and yields a brittle edge. Oxidation of titanium is characterized by an ink-blue edge appearance. It also results in a sharp increase in hardness in the heat-affected zone (HAZ), to the point of potentially developing small cracks along the cut edge. O_2 combustion-assist cutting results in dross hanging from the bottom of the kerf.

It is recommended to laser cut titanium with an inert assist-gas, such as argon (Ar). This enables finer cutting of intricate features since oxidation is minimized, if not eliminated. Dross formation is reduced or eliminated. Micro-cracking along the cut edge is eliminated as long as the kerf is shielded from oxidation at high temperature during and after interaction with a laser beam. A shiny, metallic gray appearance indicates an oxidation-free titanium cut edge. The HAZ exhibits a much less severe hardness increase than what is obtained with oxygen-assist thermal cutting.

Copper Alloys

Lasers can cut copper in pure form as well as in alloyed form, such as brass with one-third zinc (Zn) content or bronze with 10% tin (Sn) content. These form the three major groups of commercial copper alloys in use. Bronze material is usually formed from castings rather than sheet-metal or plate fabrication, so it is not often laser cut, but is mechanically cut and shaped. Copper and brass, however, often are fabricated from flat stock and can be laser cut.

The high electrical conductivity of copper, according to the laws of physics, goes hand in hand with high thermal conductivity. This makes it highly desirable in consumer electronics and industrial electrical systems. It also works well in applications requiring high heat-conductivity properties, such as heat exchangers. Copper alloys are generally nonmagnetic.

Similar to noble metals such as gold, copper alloys have strong resistance to corrosion under various industrial environments. Oxidation of copper by oxygen is moderately exothermic compared to steel or titanium. Oxygen-assist laser cutting of copper alloys enables a higher cutting speed than neutral or inert gas assist.

MECHANICAL AND PHYSICAL PROPERTIES

The mechanical properties of metals, such as yield and tensile strengths, hardness, ductility, and fatigue resistance, are not key influences on a laser-cutting process. Laser cutting is a thermal process with fast heating and cooling rates, so the mechanical properties of a HAZ are noticeably different than those of the base metal. *Figure 3-1* illustrates hardness variations from the cut edge through the HAZ to the base metal. For ferrous metals, hardness in the HAZ rises 50–100% depending on key process input variables, including metal alloys, laser wavelength, power, duty cycle, and assist-gas type. Ductility is lowered and fatigue resistance weakened, which may represent a defect for some applications, such as with structural components.

Mechanical die-cutting methods affect edges with mechanical property alterations comparable to that of laser cutting, as they apply cold working on a metal to achieve cutting. In some situations, such as in laser cutting or mechanical die cutting, these property changes are welcome. In most cases, they are localized

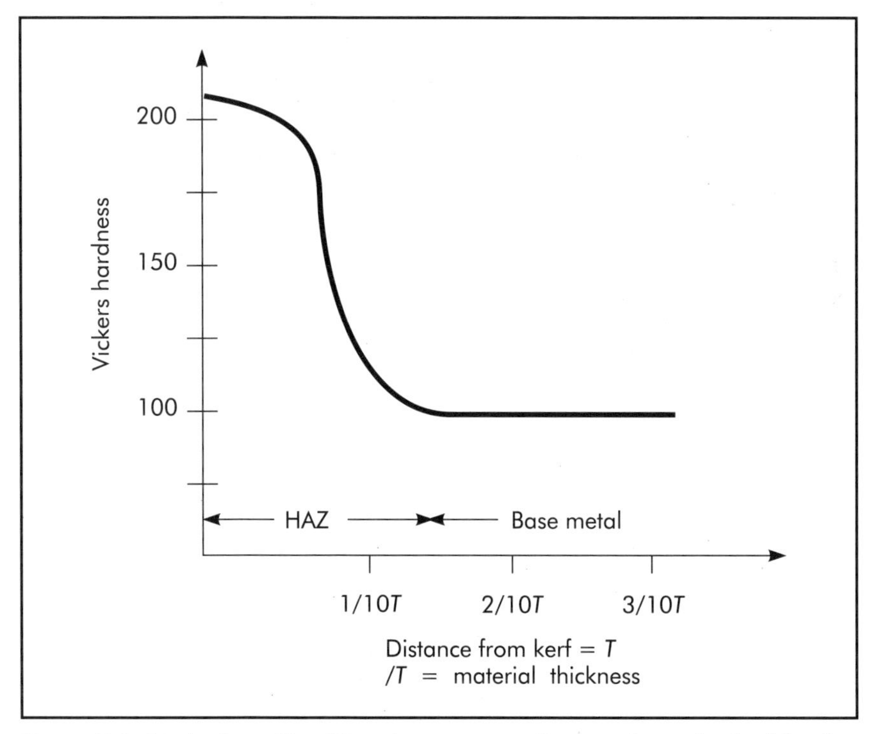

Figure 3-1. Typical profile of hardness versus distance from the kerf for ferrous metals.

in a heat-affected zone too narrow to be significant at the scale of a sheet-metal component. More likely, the width of a HAZ extends to less than half the material's thickness and is by definition at the periphery of the part, which usually gets either trimmed out or hemmed in before final assembly.

Hemming is a common forming operation that consists of folding the contour edge of a part onto itself, as shown in *Figure 3-2.* Hemming cut flanges is common practice in automobile body fabrication and assembly. It enhances aesthetics, removes hazardous sharp edges from contact with the consumer, and stops the edge from becoming a source for the start of corrosion and crack propagation.

Physical properties, such as thermal conductivity and material viscosity, have noticeable influences on the quality, productivity, profitability, and safety of a laser-cutting operation. *Tables 3-1* and *3-2* compare the physical properties of various metals. The energies in *Table 3-2* represent only a fraction of the laser-beam energy needed, since most of it is wasted by reflection on the surface, partial transmission through the kerf, heat conduction through the body of the workpiece, and cooling by convection with ambient atmosphere and radiation of the heated workpiece.

At equal cutting feed rate, heat loss wasted by conduction is noticeably higher in the aluminum 5xxx series compared with the aluminum 6xxx series. Stainless steel and Inconel exhibit low thermal-conductivity losses. Laser cutting is inherently less efficient with higher heat-conduction losses. This becomes evident when processing thick plates at a slower feed rate. A lot of laser energy is wasted by conduction heating of the main body of a workpiece away

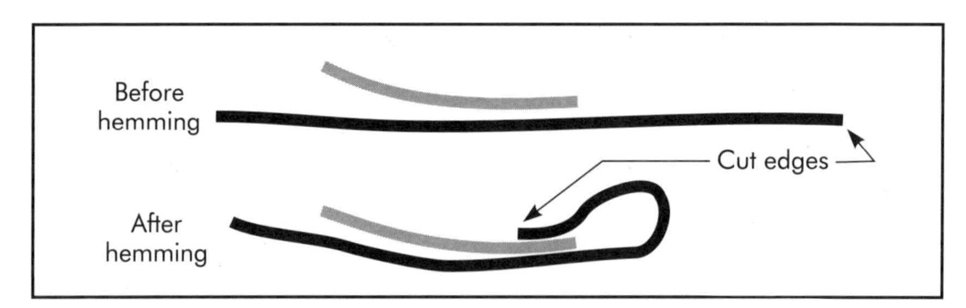

Figure 3-2. Hemming reduces fatigue failure and corrosion propagating from a panel's edge periphery.

Table 3-1. Physical properties of some metals (American Society for Metals 1985; American Welding Society 1996)

Material	Thermal Conductivity at Room Temperature, Btu/h ft-° F (W/m-K)	Viscosity at Melting Temperature 10^{-2} poise	Melting Temperature, ° F (K)
Iron	91.7 (53)	2.200	2,798 (1,810)
Low-carbon steel	51.9 (30)	6.100	2,798 (1,810)
Stainless steel	29.4 (17)		2,896 (1,864)
Aluminum 6009, 6010 T4	259.7–289.1 (150–167)	4.500	1,112 (873)
Aluminum 6101, 7075 T6	377.4 (218)	4.500	1,112 (873)
Aluminum 5052, 5662	238.9 (138)	4.500	1,112 (873)
Aluminum 5456, 5083	202.5 (117)	4.500	1,112 (873)
Oxygen-free copper	640.5 (370)	3.360	1,981 (1,356)
Brass	209.5 (121)	3.420	1,688 (1,193)
Inconel®	29.4 (17)		2,741 (1,778)
Titanium	190.4 (110)		3,038 (1,943)
Chromium	45.0 (26)	0.684	3,407 (2,148)
Nickel	162.7 (94)		2,647 (1,726)
Zinc	199.1 (115)	3.930	786 (692)

Table 3-2. Comparison of thermal properties and heat energies required to either melt or vaporize a *volume of metal

Property	Steel	Aluminum	Titanium
Density, ρ, lb/ft^3 (kg/m^3)	491 (7,858)	169 (2,700)	282 (4,510)
Fusion temperature, T_f (° F [K])	2,786 (1,803)	1,220 (933)	3,034 (1,941)
Vaporization temperature, T_v (° F [K])	5,432 (3,273)	3,734 (2,330)	5,900 (3,533)
Latent heat of fusion, L_f, Btu/lbm (J/kg)	64 (2.67 10^5)	95 (3.97 10^5)	104 (4.35 10^5)
Latent heat of vaporization, L_v, Btu/lbm (J/kg)	1,505 (6.3 10^6)	2,723 (11.4 10^6)	1,194 (5.0 10^6)
Specific heat for solid metal, C_p, Btu/(lb × °F) (J/[kg × K])	0.11 (460)	0.23 (961)	0.12 (519)
Specific heat for molten metal, C_p, Btu/(lb × °F) (J/[kg × K])	0.15 (627)	0.26 (1,087)	0.16 (650)
Heat energy to melt kerf volume ($w \times l \times t$), Btu (J)	0.002 (1.88)	0.0006 (0.68)	0.001 (1.45)
Heat energy to vaporize kerf volume, ($w \times l \times t$), Btu (J)	0.004 (4.34)	0.002 (2.15)	0.003 (2.74)

* Volume = ($w \times l \times t$)

where:

kerf zone width, w = 0.010 in. (0.25 mm)
length, l = 0.4 in. (1 mm)
thickness, t = 0.4 in. (1 mm)

from the cut line. A metal heated by conduction can burn human skin if it is touched immediately after a cut is completed. In some cases, the combination of a heated metal part with lubrication oil used to protect metal from corrosion can result in a fire hazard.

The viscosity of a metal also plays a role in quality and productivity. In general, metals have low viscosity at melting temperature. Viscosity decreases even further as the temperature increases. For example, the viscosity of aluminum estimated at 4.5 centipoise (cP) at melting temperature drops to less than 2 cP at 1,328° F (993 Kelvin [K]) (Makarov et al. 2002; American Society for Metals 1985; Hatch 1984). Low viscosity becomes a major contributor to dross build-up, particularly if the melting temperature of the material is relatively low, as with aluminum.

Oxidation

When processing a metal thermally, its chemical reactivity with gases in the surrounding atmosphere generally increases with temperature. Most metals react exothermically with oxygen present in the air. To avoid oxidation, laser cutting can be performed with non-reactive assist-gas, including inert gases such as argon. To a lesser degree, but with significantly lower cost, a neutral gas, such as nitrogen, can be used. Oxidation also can enhance cutting performance. However, it has consequences for the edge finish and properties.

Mild Steel

When cutting thick plates of mild steel, oxygen-assist gas is used to enhance cutting performance by taking advantage of the exothermic reaction between iron and oxygen, which occurs at 2,240° F (1,500 K), before metal melting starts:

$$Fe + 1/2\ O_2 \rightarrow FeO + 260\ \text{kJ/mol} \tag{3-1}$$

where:

Fe = iron
O_2 = oxygen
FeO = iron oxide

The heat power generated by exothermic reaction ultimately depends on material thickness, O_2 assist-gas flow rate, and feed rate. However, with typical settings and for order-of-magnitude reference, this exothermic reaction can be equivalent to a laser power of 500 W added to a laser-material interaction zone the size of the spot of a focused laser beam (in other words, about 0.01 in. [0.3 mm] in diameter). This heat-input advantage enables an increase in cutting speed of up to 30% when compared with cutting the same plate with neutral and inert assist-gas. When cutting with 1,000 W of laser power, such chemical energy represents an additional 50% of the processing energy input into the workpiece. Cutting with 2,000 W, respectively 4,000 W at the same focus-spot diameter, drops the ratio down to just 25%, respectively 12%. Alternatively, if the focus-spot diameter on a workpiece is reduced, the resultant power density for laser-heat input increases quadratically. This correspondingly reduces the relative contribution of oxygen gas-assisted exothermic reaction to cutting performance. When cutting with a neodymium: yttrium-aluminum garnet (Nd: YAG) laser, compared to a CO_2 laser of identical output power, the focus spot of a Nd:YAG can be equal or smaller, and its absorption of laser radiation by a metal is several folds higher. The Nd:YAG laser-cutting advantage using oxygen assist-gas becomes more modest than with oxygen-assisted CO_2 laser cutting.

Most mild steels contain 99.5% Fe. The remaining 0.5% consists of different chemical compounds, including carbon, manganese, phosphorus, sulfur, and silicon. An analysis of metal particles ejected through the kerf of a mild steel laser-cut edge with O_2 assist reveals almost equal proportions of Fe and FeO, with a negligible amount of Fe_2O_3 and Fe_3O_4. Fe_2O_3 forms a thin outer layer, below which a layer of Fe_3O_4 is formed that is about seven times thicker than the Fe_2O_3 outer layer (Fontana 1986). Underneath this Fe_3O_4 layer is a third layer composed of FeO, which is five times thicker than the layer of Fe_3O_4. Oxide FeO has a tendency to aggregate in scales that stick slightly to the core iron of the base steel metal on the cut. These FeO scales, coated with Fe_2O_3 and Fe_3O_4, are harder than mild steel, although they easily flake away and disintegrate into sand-size particles under mechanical shocks. The scales, such as those shown in *Figure 3-3*, are undesirable in stamping-press operations where they have a tendency to survive blank-washing stations and accumulate on and wear the surfaces of forming dies. They even affect part formability by altering a surface's tribology characteristics locally and deteriorating the appearance of class I surface specifications. Oxide scales sometimes contaminate downstream painting operations as well.

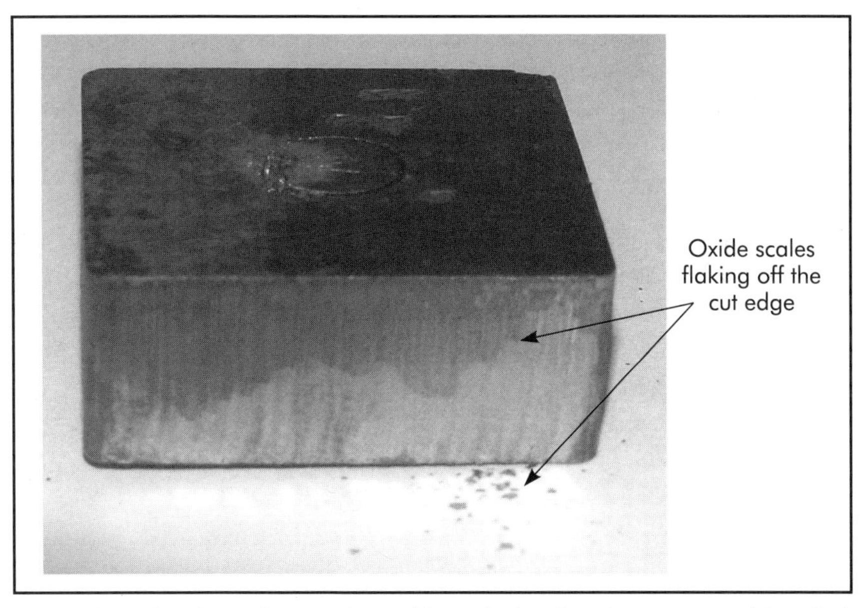

Figure 3-3. Oxide scales on this mild-steel plate's edge appear shiny dark blue. They easily flake off from the cut edge.

Stainless Steel

Whereas mild steel is more than 98% iron, stainless steel is made from the alloying of iron with a significant proportion of chromium and nickel. Some call stainless steel "chrome-nickel steel." Proportions of chromium (Cr) alone can be between 11–20%. When exposed to oxygen, a stainless-steel surface generates a highly protective film of chromium oxide (Cr_2O_3) diluted with FeO. For example:

$$2\ Cr + 3/2\ O_2 \rightarrow Cr_2O_3 + heat \qquad (3\text{-}2)$$

where:

Cr = chromium
O_2 = oxygen
Cr_2O_3 = chromium oxide

Film containing Cr_2O_3 effectively prevents further oxidation to penetrate deeper in the stainless-steel alloy surface and limits exothermic oxidation of iron and chromium in the molten metal during cutting. Thus, the use of oxygen as an assist-gas does not generate a significant exothermic heat advantage but generates FeO corrosion scales, a disadvantage. Cr_2O_3 has a higher melting temperature than iron. The protective film of Cr_2O_3 solidifies around droplets of molten metal during cutting and sticks to the bottom edge of the kerf, creating dross. Nickel oxidation creates a black film that coats the cut edge and will generate porosity when welded. For the previous reasons, neutral nitrogen assist-gas is predominantly used for laser cutting of stainless steel, particularly for a reduction of dross.

Aluminum

Contrary to popular belief, aluminum does rust. Corrosion of aluminum occurs systematically and rapidly at ambient temperature due to its surface exposure to oxygen in the atmosphere (Powell 1998). It forms an Al_2O_3 film too thin to be visible, but which is effective at protecting against deeper corrosion, thus the belief that no visible corrosion occurs. The same Al_2O_3 is produced at high temperatures during laser cutting if the hot kerf is left unprotected from surrounding oxygen.

$$2\ Al + 3/2\ O_2 \rightarrow Al_2O_3 + \text{heat} \quad (3\text{-}3)$$

where:

Al = aluminum
O_2 = oxygen
Al_2O_3 = aluminum oxide

Al_2O_3 has a melting-point temperature of 3,680° F (2,300 K), compared with only 1,250° F (950 K) for Al. During laser cutting with air assist-gas containing about 20% oxygen, Al_2O_3 solidifies around molten aluminum. It yields a rougher edge-finish appearance than a steel-cut edge, particularly at the bottom where it aggregates by sticking in the form of dross. However, the protective film also prevents further oxidation and therefore further exothermic heat generation. Consequently, the use of oxygen in an assist-gas does not generate enough energy to influence the cutting process, such as with mild steel, so it is not used as it is more expensive than shop air. Nitrogen is more expensive than shop air; however, it might be used for thick-plate cutting to reduce oxidation, which would minimize dross.

Titanium and Nickel

Laser cutting of Ti and Ni alloys can benefit greatly from chemical energy generated during exothermic oxidation:

$$Ti + O_2 \rightarrow TiO_2 + 900\ kJ/mol \qquad (3\text{-}4)$$

$$Ni + 1/2\ O_2 \rightarrow NiO + 240\ kJ/mol \qquad (3\text{-}5)$$

where:

Ti = titanium
O_2 = oxygen
TiO_2 = titanium oxide
Ni = nickel
NiO = nickel oxide

Titanium, which has a little more than half of the density of steel, has the exothermic reaction of *Equation 3-4*, which translates into significant heat power added to the laser-material interaction zone. Similar to Al_2O_3 on aluminum surfaces, titanium oxide forms a thin protective film on titanium, which effectively prevents further and deeper oxidation penetration. This explains the preferential use of titanium in corrosive environments, such as with seawater or other sodium chloride contact. However, TiO_2 is brittle and this thin film becomes thick enough (when generated under intense heat) to house fatigue cracks that can later propagate into the core metal when in use, leading to early fatigue failure of the component. Since the oxidation of titanium is violent, excessive burning can make cutting contours difficult to control, particularly small radii and corner angle features. For these reasons, most applications require titanium to be laser cut with a high-pressure, non-reacting gas such as argon (Maher and Machan 1999). Even nitrogen reacts with hot molten titanium and is avoided as an assist-gas. Hydrogen gas absorption under high temperature also has a negative impact on the brittleness of titanium, as the metal develops corrosion crevices. *Corrosion crevices* are stress initiation sites that lead to faster cracking failure under fatigue (Fontana 1986). It is not recommended to laser cut titanium under excessive humidity, mist, or an otherwise wet environment. Titanium in contact with corroding metals, such as steel, makes it more prone to absorb hydrogen gas, thus increasing brittleness and crevice corrosion. It may even develop severe pitting due to iron particles embedded on the surface.

Copper Alloys

Pure copper can be laser cut in sheet form using oxygen assist-gas. The oxidation that results can be summarized in the following main exothermic reaction:

$$Cu + 1/2\ O_2 \rightarrow CuO + 150\ \text{kJ/mol} \quad (3\text{-}6)$$

where:

Cu = copper
O_2 = oxygen
CuO = copper oxide

An additional metal oxidation takes place with brass, it being a copper alloy with zinc (70% Cu + 30% Zn):

$$Zn + 1/2\ O_2 \rightarrow ZnO + 350\ \text{kJ/mol} \quad (3\text{-}7)$$

where:

Zn = zinc
O_2 = oxygen
ZnO = zinc oxide

In both cases, oxygen assist-gas adds heat to the workpiece. The oxide layers created containing CuO and ZnO enhance absorption of infrared (IR) wavelength on the kerf walls, more for longer wavelength CO_2 lasers than shorter wavelength YAG lasers. Resultant cutting speeds are significantly higher with O_2 assist-gas than neutral assist-gas, although this advantage is not as strong as with mild steel.

LUBRICATION

It is common in the metal fabrication industry to receive metal sheets and plates coated with a thin film of lube oil. This oil is intended to protect the sheet or plate surface from corrosion during storage. Oil film also can serve as a formability enhancer by decreasing friction between metal and forming die surfaces. A laser-cutting process is rarely affected by oil because the latter evaporates rapidly around the kerf zone before the metal starts to melt.

Lubrication can have a devastating impact on productivity if material-handling and positioning equipment is not designed to handle slippery parts. Oil can make sheet metals stick to one another, making it difficult to avoid destacking several sheets instead of only one at a time, disrupting production flow. It can force a slowdown of sheet and plate handling to avoid acceleration and sharp change in direction, resulting in a loss of grip and a crash. Oil can be a safety hazard because it is flammable and can irritate skin. It should be disposed of according to Occupational Health and Safety Administration (OSHA) regulations. If unevenly applied, oil-less areas are susceptible to developing spot stains on metal surfaces, which can result in scrap if the painted part cannot pass surface-appearance quality specifications.

COATING

Zinc-based coatings are frequently used on steels to improve their corrosion resistance by taking advantage of the cathodic sacrificial action of zinc when in contact with steel. Most exposed sheet steels for automobiles are galvanized with a zinc-based coating. Some steels may be coated with aluminum. Organic films may be used on some parts to protect their appearance from scratches and stains until final assembly and paint.

In most cases, coatings have a melting and even vaporization temperature well below that of a base metal. Zinc has a boiling temperature of 1,160° F (900 K), whereas steel melts at about 2,780° F (1,800 K). Because of this, zinc coating is theoretically expected to have a minimal impact on laser-cutting performance. In practice, however, zinc vapors enhance the plasma-shielding effect and reduce the efficiency of the laser-cutting process, forcing a slower cutting speed. In addition (particularly if a metal is coated on both sides), dross generation negatively impacts the quality of a cut edge. Dross can be minimized by significantly reducing cutting speed when processing heavily coated metals. For typical order-of-magnitude purposes, 20% difference in production cutting speed can be experienced between bare steel of less than 0.08 in. (2 mm) thickness, and the same with a coating weight heavier than 0.2 oz/ft^2 (80 $grams/m^2$).

No meaningful differences in the cutting process result from using one galvanizing process over another (in other words, hot-dip galvanizing, electro-galvanizing, or galvannealing). However, the surface texture of a coating can make a difference. An extra-smooth surface finish is preferred to a spangled surface finish recognizable to the eye by a large, multi-faceted grain structure on the coating surface.

A coating's burned vapor and oxides can be toxic and must be filtered, collected, and disposed of according to applicable safety and occupational recommendations to protect operators and the environment.

It is important to realize that all metals rust, and at differing paces. Aluminum is so extremely slow at rusting that it is labeled as good as corrosion-free. Galvanized steel is better protected against corrosion than bare steel, but can still rust. White rust stains are common on galvanized sheets exposed for several hours to high summer humidity, particularly on the top and bottom sheets of a pallet stack.

Galvanized steel can be phosphatized to improve corrosion protection, paint adherence, and surface appearance after painting. The added phosphate treatment has not been reported to significantly impede a laser-cutting process.

STACKABILITY

Metal sheets and plates can be stacked on top of each other and de-stacked just as easily using either vacuum suction cups or magnetic end-effectors on the arm of a gantry or robot. Aluminum, however, presents a challenge for the cut edge with burrs or dross, regardless of which cutting process is used. Dross, stacked under the weight of other sheets and in the presence of moisture, can become cold-welded to the sheet metal below it, making it difficult to de-stack. Fortunately, when it comes to thin sheet metal, laser cutting of aluminum performs extremely well, resulting in much less dross than with conventional die-cutting methods, which create burrs.

Mild steel presents advantages in magnetic properties compared with stainless steel and aluminum. These properties can be taken advantage of when using a strong fanning magnet on a pallet table to spread individual thin sheets apart for de-stacking.

STORAGE

The vast majority of storage facilities are not air-conditioned, leaving metals under attack from the elements. Oil mist, gasoline pollution, dust, and humidity affect the surface of materials, potentially causing a great impact on a laser-processing operation. Oil lubrication of material surfaces helps protect against rust. The integrity of all sheets and plates on a pallet can be ensured by wrapping the pallet with paper for storage and transportation.

OPTICAL PROPERTIES

Most metal surfaces reflect infrared light at levels of 80% and above at room temperature. The remaining 20% or less is absorbed by the metal and, for the most part, converted into heat that initiates melting as a key part of the laser-cutting process. Besides a few exceptions, such as aluminum oxide, reflectivity generally increases with the laser wavelength as shown in *Figure 3-4*. For example, common mill-grade steel-plate surfaces at room temperature and normal incidence reflect less than 50% of a YAG laser

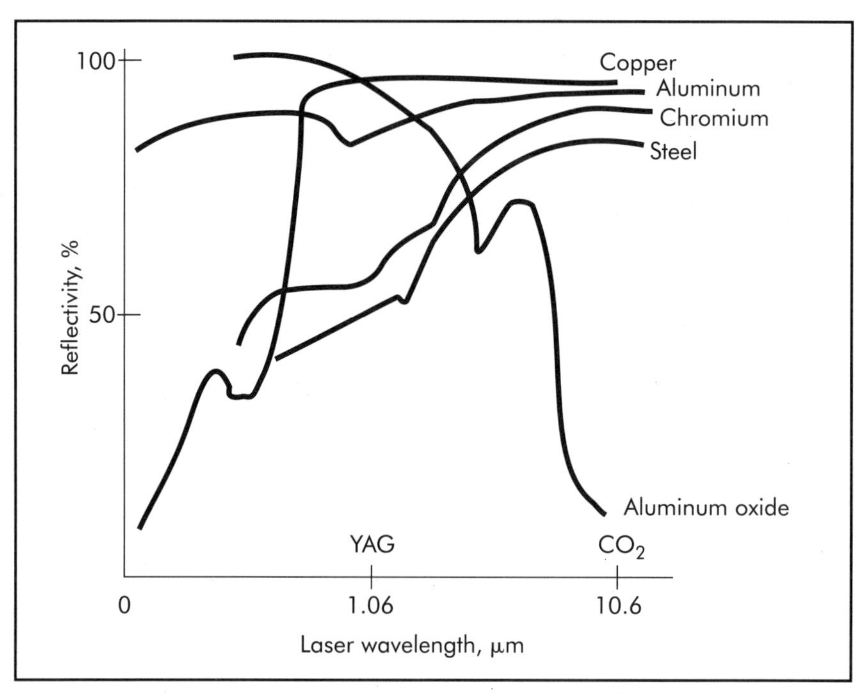

Figure 3-4. The surface reflectivity of metals at normal incidence and room temperature of 80° F (300 K) varies with light-beam wavelength (Ohse 1990).

light with a wavelength of 1.06 μm, whereas they reflect more than 85% of incoming CO_2 laser light with a wavelength of 10.6 μm.

The reflectivity of a metal can be highly altered by either its natural or an artificial coating on its surface. Aluminum oxide (Al_2O_3), for example, systematically and naturally coats aluminum sheets as a self-protection against further corrosion. It is highly reflective to YAG laser wavelength. However, as indicated in *Figure 3-4*, it absorbs and transmits CO_2 laser wavelength more efficiently than core aluminum. During laser processing, the thin Al_2O_3 film is quickly evaporated and the reflectivity of aluminum becomes the predominant factor.

Reflectivity also is a function of surface finish. An optically smooth surface is one for which the root mean square (rms) roughness is much smaller than the incident light's wavelength (Modest 2001; Luxon 1992). Typically, a polished steel surface with a roughness of less than 39.4 μin. (1 μm) can reflect 90% of CO_2

laser light, with less than 5% of this reflection being nonspecular. A sandblasted surface with a roughness of 787.4 μin. (20 μm) or more for the same steel would reflect only 35% of the CO_2 laser light, from which about 15% would be due to nonspecular reflections. The proportion of nonspecular reflections would increase on a given rough surface when the wavelength of incident light decreases. In other words, a Nd:YAG laser light with a 1.06 μm wavelength may generate a larger proportion of nonspecular reflections than a CO_2 laser light with a wavelength 10 times larger. Reflectivity generally decreases with temperature (Modest 2001; VDI Gesellschaft Produktiontechnik 1990). *Equation 3-8* reconciles the different incoming and outgoing radiative energies on the workpiece illustrated in *Figure 3-5.*

$$I = R + A + T \tag{3-8}$$

where:

I = intensity of the incoming beam
R = reflected intensity that includes direct reflection at the same angles, θ, as the incident beam and nonspecular reflection rays that can take any direction (isotropic reflections)
A = portion of beam energy absorbed by the material's surface and kerf in the material (part of A is useful energy responsible for cutting the workpiece, while the rest is wasted, mostly by conduction to heat areas of the workpiece that do not need to be processed)
T = part of the incoming beam energy transmitted through a kerf without being absorbed by the workpiece

The reflectivity of a metal's surface varies negligibly with the angle of incidence when the latter is within about 15° of normal. Most laser cutting is operated at or near normal incidence on the workpiece. *Figure 3-6* shows that when an angle of incidence, θ, is smaller than about 15°, the reflectivity of a surface remains the same for s-polarized and p-polarized components of light. However, the reflectivity for the p-polarization component of the laser light degrades significantly when the angle of incidence increases beyond 15° and reaches a minimum before increasing sharply toward 100% reflectivity at grazing incidence. This can have a serious impact if a linearly polarized laser beam impinges on several

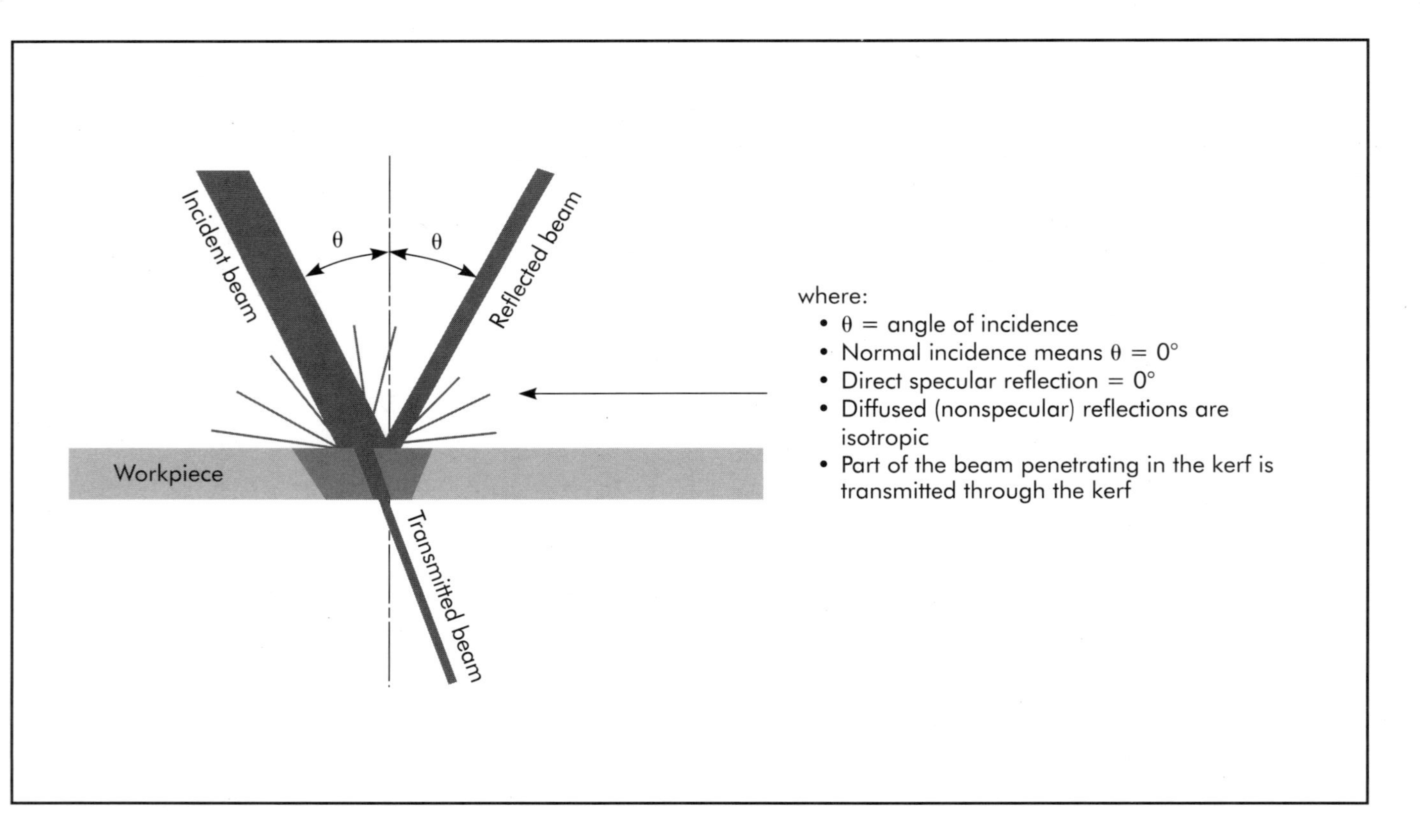

Figure 3-5. Once a kerf is formed, more than 80% of incoming laser-beam energy is absorbed through the kerf thanks to multiple reflections on the oxidized walls of the kerf as well as plasma absorption.

beam-bender mirrors at 45° incidence along the beam-delivery system. Most laser-cutting systems operate with a circularly polarized beam in which the polarization rotates continuously, on average reaching uniform s- and p-polarization and in-between states. Some operations that cut only rectilinear features or have an additional rotation axis to orient the polarization of the focused beam adequately along the part contour can take advantage of p-polarization reflectivity characteristics.

Metal reflectivity decreases when temperature rises, to the benefit of absorption. In one example of a steel surface under normal incidence of a CO_2 laser light, reflectivity decreases 5–10% between room and melting temperatures. Once the hot metal changes from solid to liquid, the steel's surface reflectivity experiences another sharp drop of about 40%. At that point, about 55% of

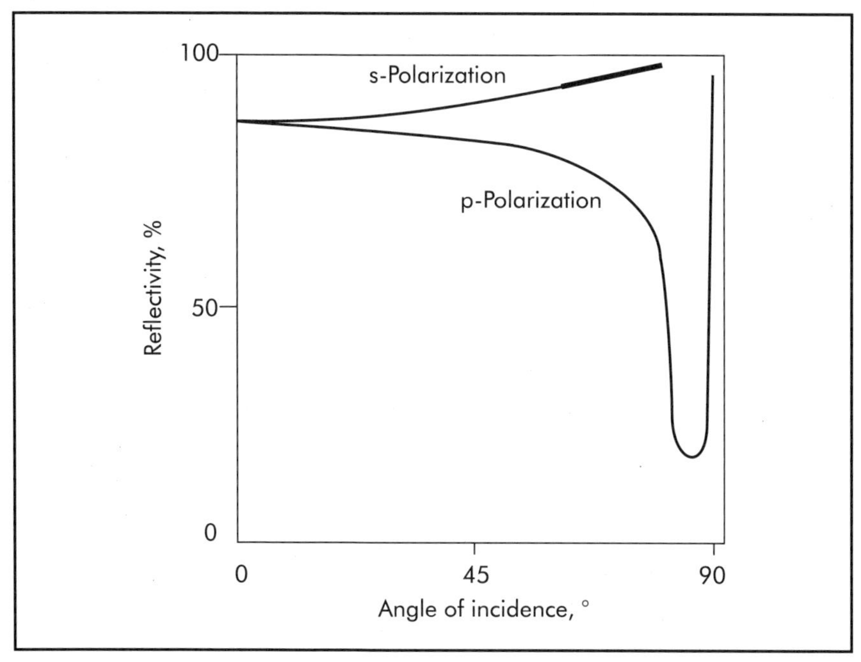

Figure 3-6. Typical profile of reflectivity versus angle of incidence for CO_2 laser beams of s- and p-polarization on steel at room temperature. The profile is almost unchanged and shifted up or down when the wavelength of the laser radiation and metal is changed. It is also unchanged but slightly shifted down toward lower reflectivity when the temperature increases.

incident laser energy is absorbed. For a multikilowatt laser delivering at least 500,000 W/cm^2 of focused beam-power density on a workpiece, it is estimated that the time from room temperature to vaporization lasts just a few tenths of a millisecond. Once a focused beam has penetrated a kerf, laser-beam rays are trapped inside it, reflecting and bouncing against the liquefied walls of the kerf trough until absorbed inside the kerf or partially transmitted out through the bottom of the kerf.

SURFACE CONDITIONS

Facilities that operate continuous casting machines or perform ingot casting produce steels in heavy slabs as thick as 1 ft (30.5 cm). These slabs are then plastically reduced while at about 1,340° F (1,000 K), then processed through a hot-roll mill into thinner section slabs or coils. During this process, hot metal is exposed to air and humidity, and water is sprayed to cool the slabs and remove oxide scales before transportation and storage. Oxidation of the surface occurs faster at high temperatures and results in thick, metal-oxide scales that adhere to the surface due to the action of thickness-reducing pressure rolls. Some mill scales remain despite attempts to remove them by blasting high-pressure cooling water on the metal surface immediately downstream of the last set of reducing pressure rolls.

Laser cutting with oxygen assist-gas yields faster cutting speeds because oxidation of the metal, activated by the laser energy, causes a highly exothermic reaction. This boosts laser-cutting efficiency and productivity. The presence of mill scales already oxidized on the metal surface works against the oxygen-assisted laser-cutting process. If inert gas is used as an assist, metal oxides still might hinder the cutting process by forcing a slowdown of cutting feed rate to reduce dross formation and edge gouging. Scales are much harder than the base metal, and have higher melting points. The difference in physical properties may force a need to adjust cutting parameters to yield satisfactory dross-free edge quality. For these reasons, the presence of mill scales and corrosion on metal surfaces is generally undesirable for laser cutting.

Mill scales on steel can be further removed by pickling in an acid bath, such as sulfuric acid (H_2SO_4) liquid solution, which is efficient at removing them and other surface contaminants. Once pickled, a metal can be oiled to prevent new oxidation from taking place. Pickled and oiled sheets and plates yield a higher laser-cutting feed rate, a more stable and repeatable cutting process, and better edge quality.

Another method to eliminate mill scales is to shot-blast a metal surface with ceramic dust particles. The hard ceramic particles must be brushed away from the surface afterward, otherwise they will replace mill scales as surface contaminants. The ceramic particles will work against the laser-cutting process because their physical properties are significantly different from the base metal. Mill scales are unfriendly to almost all forming and fabricating processes, from cutting and forming to welding and painting.

Plates or coil obtained from a hot-roll mill remain relatively thick. To further reduce their thickness to below 0.250 in. (6.35 mm), cold rolling is applied to hot-rolled coils. The cold-rolling process at room temperature results in thinner but stronger metal. If the strength of the metal needs to be reduced, annealing stations bring it down to workable and formable domains after brooding it for a few days at high temperature but below the melting point. At this stage, mill scales have been totally removed and the metal is ready to be cut from coil form into sheets. These coils are unwound and almost systematically blanked in rectangular, trapezoidal, or configured contour blanks before further fabrication or assembly. During a de-coiling process, some tensions in a metal are generated while others are released. This results in several categories of surface condition defects on blanked sheets, which impact laser-cutting performance.

Coil Set, Waviness, and Camber

While pulling a coil using a de-coiler, tensions in the metal are not uniformly distributed across the coil's width. This internal stress results in surface condition defects categorized as waviness and camber. *Camber*, also called *lateral bow*, is measured by a deviation of the concave side edge from a straight edge (*Figure 3-7*).

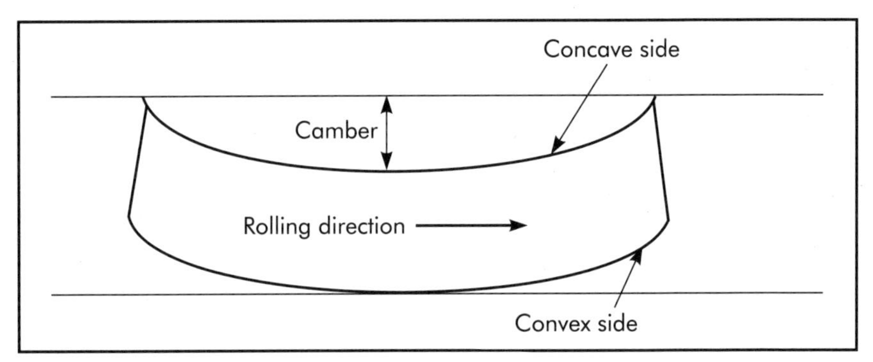

Figure 3-7. Top view of coil camber. The concave side of the sheet is shorter than the convex side.

The rolling direction usually has little impact on laser-cutting performance, but a customer may specify its orientation with respect to the contour geometry to be cut as it may impact subsequent operations, such as deep drawing.

The coil sheet shown in *Figure 3-8* exhibits another surface condition defect, known as *coil set*, which results from the plastic deformation of a metal retaining the "memory" of its coil radius. Processing a coil through a low-cost straightener or an upper-end tension leveler can rectify most defects. A *tension leveler* is composed of a large number of rolls (typically between nine and 21), which impose tension several times up to the plastic defor-

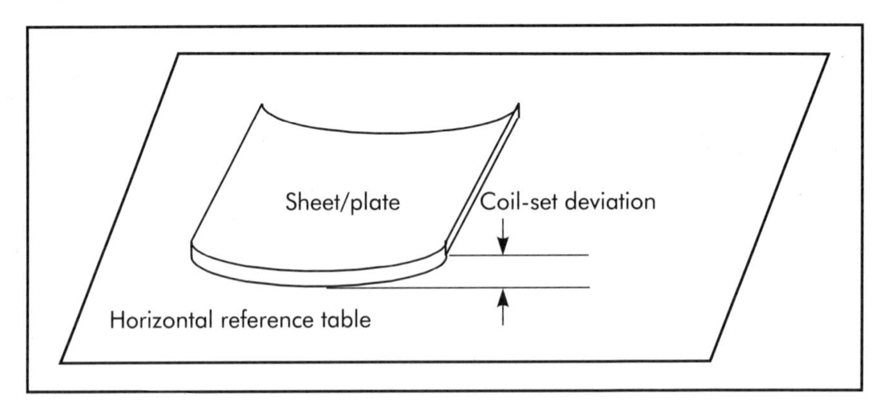

Figure 3-8. View of coil-set deviation on a sheet cut from a coil lying on a horizontal reference table.

mation level to "iron" a sheet of metal and eliminate internal tension stresses that cause waviness patterns and coil set.

Coil set and waviness result in out-of-control variations in the height of a sheet or plate across the work envelope of a laser-cutting machine. A laser-cutting head must be capable of following these reliefs at feed-rate speed to maintain uniform key process input parameters, such as assist-gas nozzle standoff and focus position. Failure to do so will result in variations in cutting quality and potential defects requiring troubleshooting downtime to fix.

A material-handling system's capability, whether manual or automated, also is impaired by waviness, camber, and coil set as crowding mechanism, suction cups, end-effectors, and position detection devices are designed with certain tolerance expectations of a sheet's geometry. Furthermore, undesirable variations in cut edges are a consequence of the sheet flatness and contour being out of tolerance. In particular, camber is often responsible for a large portion of variations in contour accuracy during traditional blanking operations.

REFERENCES

American Society for Metals. 1985. *Metals Handbook*. Desk Edition. Materials Park, OH: American Society for Metals.

American Welding Society. 1996. *Welding Handbook: Materials and Applications*. Miami, FL: American Welding Society.

Fontana, M. 1986. *Corrosion Engineering,* Third Edition. New York: McGraw-Hill.

Hatch, J.E., ed. 1984. *Aluminum: Properties and Physical Metallurgy*. Materials Park, OH: American Society for Metals.

Luxon, J.T. and Parker, D.E. 1992. *Industrial Lasers and Their Applications*. Englewood Cliffs, NJ: Prentice Hall.

Maher, W. and Machan, J. 1999. "Pulsed Laser Cutting of Titanium." November. International Congress on Applications of Lasers and Electro-optics (ICALEO), San Diego, CA. Orlando, FL: Laser Institute of America.

Makarov, S., Ludwig, R., Resnik, J., and Apelian, D. 2002. "The Effect of a Short Pulse of Current on Small Particles in a Conducting Fluid." Web communication, MA 01609-2280-2002. Worcester, MA: Metal Processing Institute, Worcester Polytechnic Institute.

Modest, M.F. 2001. "Reflectivity and Absorptivity of Opaque Surfaces." *LIA Handbook of Laser Material Processing*. Ready, J. and Farson, D., eds., pp. 175-182. Orlando, FL: Laser Institute of America.

Ohse, R. W. 1990. "Laser Application in Material Science and Technology: Materials Processing, Surface Modification, and High-temperature Property Measurement." *The Industrial Laser Annual Handbook*. Belforte, D. and Levitt, M., eds. Tulsa, OK: Pennwell Books.

Penn, W., Clark, E., and Quinn, E. 2000. "High-speed Laser Blanking of Aluminum." Proceedings of the International Congress on Applications of Lasers and Electro-optics (ICALEO), pp. B1-B7, Dearborn, MI. Orlando, FL: Laser Institute of America.

Powell, J. 1998. *CO_2 Laser Cutting*. New York: Springer Verlag.

Schultz, R.A. 2000. "Aluminum for Light Vehicle Bodies in North America: An Objective Look at the Next Ten Years." University of Michigan Management Briefing Seminars, August. Traverse City, MI: University of Michigan.

VDI Gesellschaft Produktiontechnik (ADB). 1990. "Materialbearbeitung mit dem Laserstrahl im Gerate-und Maschinenbau-Leitfaden fur den Anwender." Dusseldorf, Germany: Springer VDI Verlag.

Machines

"Computers are useless. They can only give you answers."

—Pablo Picasso

Laser-cutting machines represent the successful marriage of laser-engineering physics and optics engineering with traditional motion and numerical control engineering. One of the earliest industrial machines was created in the late 1970s as a combination of both a laser and a traditional punch-cutting machine. They operated simultaneously with a common numerical control and shared a common motion system and base frame.

This chapter discusses equipment features that can make a difference to output characteristics, such as environment, safety, quality, productivity, and profitability. When considering output characteristics, it is evident that compromises must be made to finalize machine design within an allocated time, stay within budget, keep the manufacturing cost competitive, and ensure reliability, stability, repeatability, serviceability, and performance for a finite range of applications. Machine builders and end-users must keep abreast of technology improvements that will become the sustaining force behind future applications and performances.

The overall specifications for laser-cutting machines are becoming more comparable from builder to builder. Impacts and obligations on the end-user within the actual manufacturing environment should be considered by the machine designers. Laser-cutting machines can be described as an integration of several modules: a laser resonator, an assist-gas and laser-gas delivery system, beam-delivery system, water chiller for the laser and beam-delivery system, air filter and motion systems and controls, and possibly sheet-metal handling and processing automation.

LASER RESONATORS

An industrial laser resonator generates an invisible light beam that seems to magically cut metals. It is costly to replace, so maintainability and accessibility for service and repair remain a necessity. CO_2 and neodymium: yttrium-aluminum garnet (Nd:YAG) lasers comprise close to 100% of laser resonators used for industrial metal cutting. Typical CO_2 and YAG industrial laser specifications include the characteristics listed in *Tables 4-1* and *4-2*. Some laser manufacturers provide useful downtime and mean-time-between-failure (MTBF) data for each laser component. All efforts should be made to obtain quantitative information. A few important considerations listed in the aforementioned tables should be addressed by the equipment buyer.

CO_2 Lasers

Excitation Technology

Two main excitation technologies, known as radio frequency (RF) and direct current (DC), electrical discharge are available. RF excitation is achieved by creating a high-frequency electromagnetic (EM) field through a chamber containing a laser gas under a semi-vacuum typically of a few hundred torr pressure. As illustrated in *Figure 4-1*, electrodes lie outside the gas chamber, thus avoiding additional sources of contamination inside the chamber. They apply a relatively uniform EM field across the intra-cavity beam diameter, which creates a stable output beam. Low voltage can be used with RF systems, thus reducing the risk of electrocution when maintaining and troubleshooting a laser. RF excitation is known to yield higher overall efficiency at equal beam-quality output than

Table 4-1. CO_2 10.6-μm wavelength laser specifications checklist

Specifications	Considerations
Excitation technology	Radio frequency (RF) or direct current (DC)
Gas circulation technology	Axial flow or transverse flow or no flow
Rated average output power	Repeatability, stability, monitoring, and control
Peak power	Repeatability, stability, monitoring, and control
Duty range	Repeatability, stability, monitoring, and control
Frequency range	Repeatability, stability, monitoring, and control
Beam's cross-section dimensions	Near-field and far-field data in two transverse directions
Waist dimensions and positions	Positions (in two transverse directions) relative to the output-coupler mirror
Beam divergence	Specify full or half angle
Beam quality	M^2 measurement or beam-diameter propagation plot
Pointing stability	Stability
Number of intra-cavity optics	Mean time between cleaning and between failure for each
Number of extra-cavity optics	Mean time between cleaning and between failure for each
Polarization	Circular or linear at 45° or 90°
Overall efficiency	Repeatability, stability, monitoring, and control
Gas consumption	Yearly consumption at rated power and during idling at 0 output power
Gas mixture requirement	Control of impurity of each gas component
Water-cooling flow requirement	Flow rate, inlet temperature range and stability, inlet pressure range

Table 4-1. (continued)

Specifications	Considerations
Water-cooling type requirement	pH range, deionized water channel, antifreeze tolerance, cleaning method
Water-cooling capability requirement	In BTU/sec (kW)
Electrical power consumption	kVA consumption at rated power and during idling at 0 output power
Environmental tolerances	Ambient temperature, humidity, atmospheric pressure, and ground vibration
Turnkey dimensions, weight, footprint	Include all power supplies and electrical cabinets as well as laser head

DC excitation. Industrial, RF-excited, multikilowatt CO_2 lasers for metal-cutting applications achieve overall efficiency of about 10% at the rated average output power.

Alternatively, DC excitation must apply several kV of high-voltage direct current between electrodes often in direct contact with a hot laser gas inside the discharge chamber. The uniformity of the discharge zone and, consequently, the stability of output and overall efficiency depend largely on the geometry of the electrodes and their spacing. However, it is easier and less costly to achieve high peak-power output with DC rather than RF excitation. The equipment to create DC excitation is generally less costly to purchase and repair.

Gas Circulation

In most CO_2 lasers, the laser gas is in motion, circulating inside a semi-vacuum chamber due to the action of a turbine blower. To limit the power requirement of the blower, the volume of the chamber is sometimes reduced to glassware tubes. Part of the

Table 4-2. Nd:YAG 1.06-μm wavelength laser specifications checklist

Specifications	Considerations
Excitation technology	Flash lamp or diode pumped
Rated average output power	Repeatability, stability, monitoring, and control—specify at output coupler (OC) or workpiece
Peak power	Repeatability, stability, monitoring, and control
Pulse duration range	Repeatability, stability, monitoring, and control
Energy per pulse	Repeatability, stability, monitoring, and control
Frequency range	Repeatability, stability, monitoring, and control
Beam's cross-section dimensions	Near-field and far-field data in two transverse directions
Waist diameter and position	Dimensions in two transverse directions and positions relative to the output coupler
Beam divergence	Specify full or half angle and in two directions transverse to the propagation direction
Beam quality	Diameter × divergence (specify whether full- or half-angle divergence)
Pointing stability	Stability
Number of intra-cavity optics	Mean time between cleaning and between failure for each
Number of extra-cavity optics	Mean time between cleaning and between failure for each
Polarization	Circular or linear at 45° or 90°
Overall efficiency	Repeatability, stability, monitoring, and control
Air-tightness requirement of enclosure	Yearly consumption of compressed dry air or dry nitrogen
Water-cooling capability requirement	In BTU/sec (kW)

Table 4-2. (continued)

Specifications	Considerations
Water-cooling flow requirement	Flow rate, inlet temperature range and stability, inlet pressure range
Water-cooling type requirement	pH range, deionized water channel, antifreeze tolerance, cleaning method
Electrical power consumption	kVA consumption at rated power and during idling at 0 output power
Environmental tolerances	Ambient temperature, humidity, atmospheric pressure, and ground vibration
Turnkey dimensions, weight, footprint	Include all power supplies and electrical cabinets as well as laser head

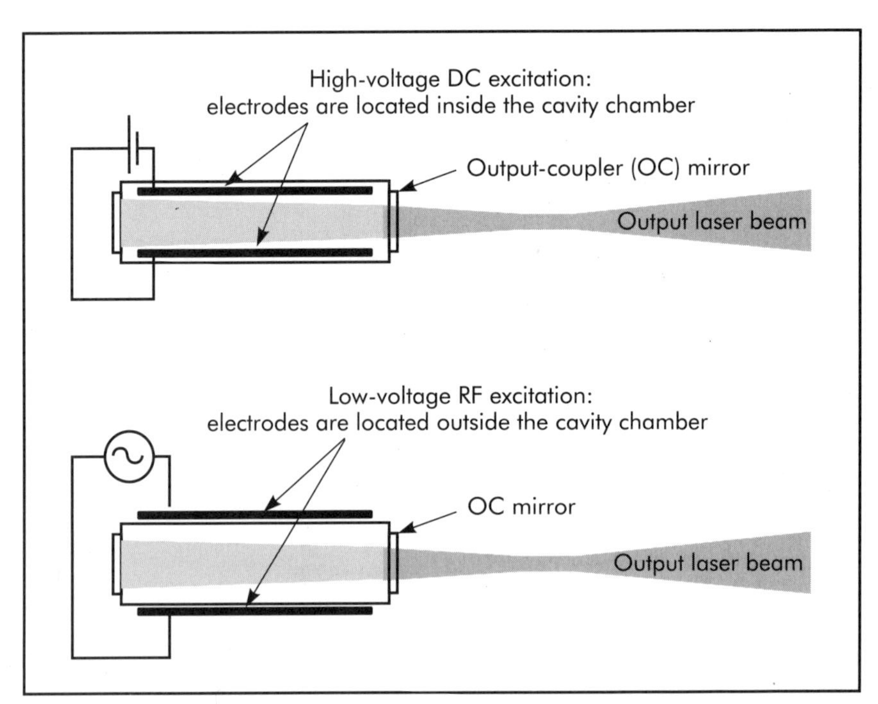

Figure 4-1. RF versus DC discharge excitation of a CO_2 laser.

recirculation gas is exhausted, while an equal volume of fresh gas is brought in the chamber, thus ensuring a stationary static pressure.

It is necessary to distinguish between two types of gas circulation designs: axial- and transverse-flow systems. In fast axial-flow lasers, the gas inside the cavity chamber travels at high speed in a direction coaxial with the laser-beam axis, as shown in *Figure 4-2*. Transverse-flow systems circulate the laser gas in a direction generally perpendicular to the laser-beam axis. Axial-flow systems yield better beam-output power and mode stability than transverse-flow systems. Transverse-flow systems have a more voluminous laser-gas chamber, enabling very high average-output-power systems but requiring more powerful gas blowers. However, they generally consume laser gas at a lesser rate than axial-flow systems. Sealed CO_2 lasers, including slab CO_2 lasers, have a resonator cavity in which the laser gas is stagnant and replaced in bulk only after extended operation or during maintenance downtime. Elimination of the turbine blower for gas recirculation is a major advantage that eliminates downtime and service costs associated with turbine operation.

Beam-output Characteristics

It is important to understand the monitoring and control capabilities of each resonator in both continuous-wave (CW) and pulse mode. Actual average output power is monitored with a power meter installed in the laser resonator. In most cases, it measures residual power (less than 1% of intra-cavity power) seeping through the rear mirror of the cavity. This measurement is calibrated to determine the actual average output power transmitted through the output-coupler (OC) mirror. It is a simple and common procedure to use an external power probe to verify the calibration of the internal laser-power meter. Pulses of energy have waveforms that are not perfectly rectangular, and power measurement takes a few seconds, which is typical of pyroelectric power-measurement devices. Therefore, they cannot accurately read actual peak power, but rather the power averaged over a few seconds of measurement time.

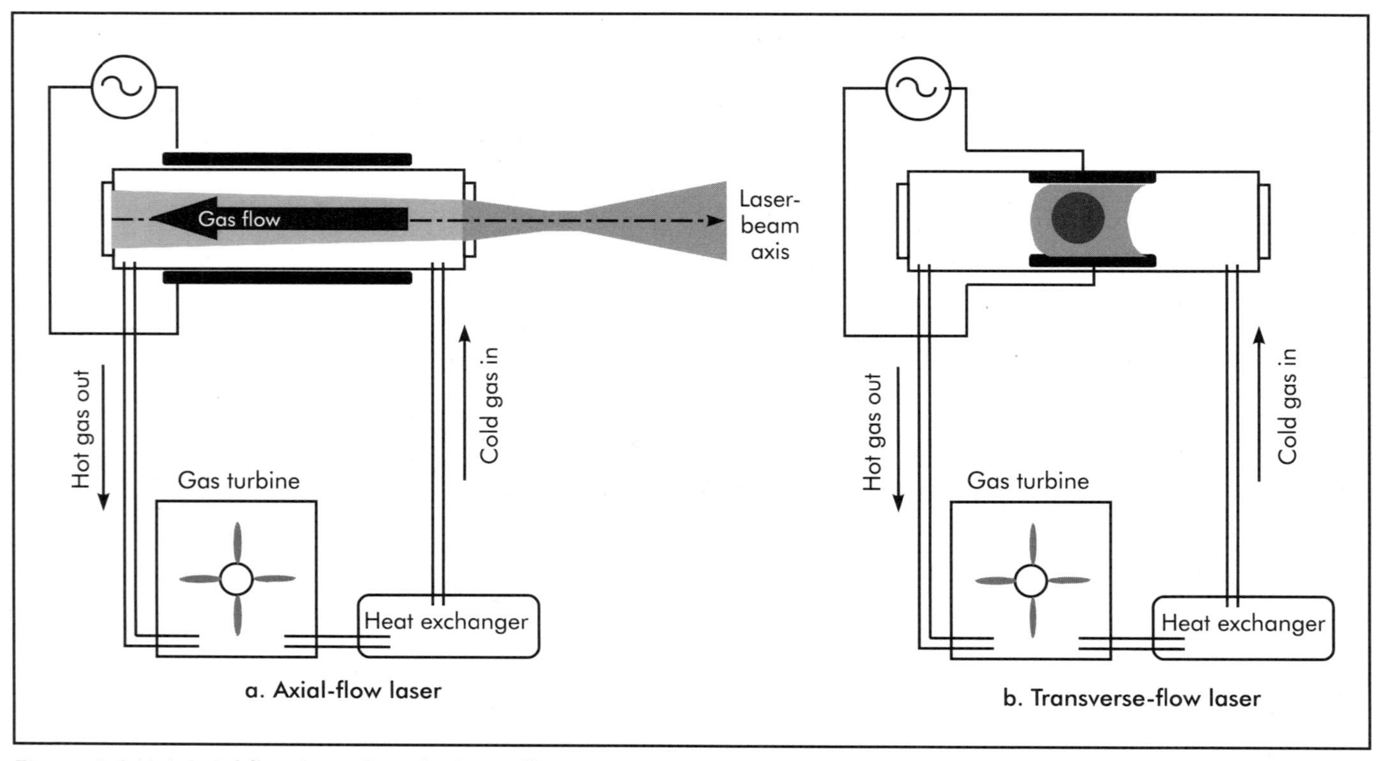

Figure 4-2. (a) Axial flow laser for which gas flows in the direction of the laser-beam axis. (b) A transverse-flow laser has the laser gas flowing in a direction transverse to the laser-beam axis. The laser-beam axis is perpendicular to the plane of this page.

Commanded power results from commanded voltage and current applied by the excitation discharge mechanism on electrodes. Actual peak output power and waveform corresponding to a specific commanded input voltage and current depend on the impedance of the resonator cavity. Impedance varies with the maintenance conditions of the resonator cavity. Key maintenance conditions include the level of impurity in the laser-gas mixture; pressure and flow rate of the laser-gas mixture; cleanliness of cavity mirrors, gas conduits, and discharge electrodes; efficiency of the cavity element's cooling; and drift in cavity-optics alignment. Laser manufacturers should prescribe monitoring, alarms, and control systems that ensure reliability and repeatability of peak laser-power-output characteristics throughout intervals between preventive maintenance.

Figure 4-3 illustrates the common occurrence of pulse differences in output power versus time when the same power, duty, and frequency inputs are commanded immediately before and after preventive maintenance on the resonator cavity. Although both profiles might yield the same average power, any differences, alone or in combination with other sources of performance variation, translate into noticeably different cutting capabilities. Modern industrial lasers are designed to maintain drifts at a minimum

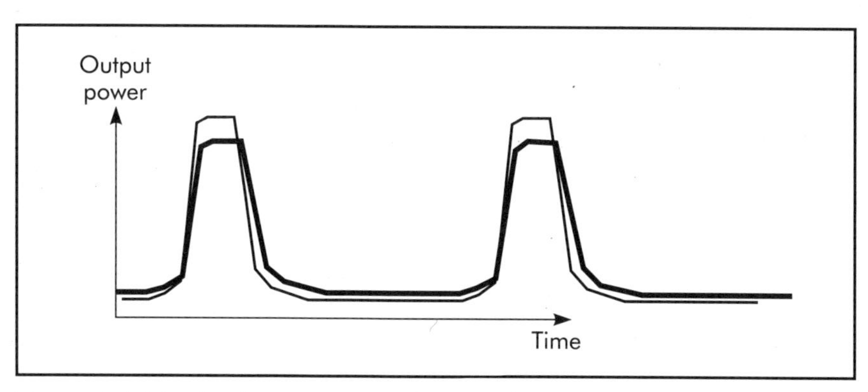

Figure 4-3. The thin line represents the actual output-pulse wave-power profile immediately after preventive maintenance, and the bold line immediately before. Drift in cavity impedance yields possible differences in measured average powers, actual peak powers, and response time of the cavity to a command signal. Resulting cutting performance can be different, despite identical commanded power.

level throughout the period between preventive maintenance or equipped with internal probes and numerical controls programmed to compensate by adjusting commanded peak power, duty, and frequency to reduce output variations.

Beam Divergence

Laser beams are mono-directional with exceptional pointing stability (this is explained in more detail in Appendices A and B). Sooner or later, however, their cross-section dimensions will increase progressively as they propagate away from the laser source. For benchmarking, confirm whether full- or half-angle divergence data is provided by the laser manufacturer. Beam divergence, typically on the order of one or two milliradians for most industrial lasers, can be altered by extra-cavity (external) optics arrangements, starting with the outside curvature of the OC mirror in stable resonators.

Beam Quality

Divergence is inherent to any beam extracted from an optical cavity and generally correlates with M^2, a quantitative measurement of beam quality, which is also referred to as K or k in the literature:

$$M^2 = K = 1/k \tag{4-1}$$

Some manufacturers instead supply near- and far-field measurement plots of the beam dimension's propagation or corresponding acrylic mode burns. The latter is easier to reproduce. Although beam divergence can be altered by external optics, M^2 numbers are defined only by intra-cavity design and cannot be altered by external optics. M^2 measurement is relatively high cost, since it requires downtime and expensive measurement systems.

Most laser-cutting machines must operate with an axis-symmetric beam cross-section at every location of the beam delivery system. *Axis-symmetry* implies a circular cross-section, a beam divergence, and energy distribution with radial symmetry. The user must be aware that, although most industrial laser-cutting applications prefer axis-symmetric beam properties, poor resonator design flawed in the assembly of a laser and inadequate cavity tuning may yield a laser beam with non-axis-symmetric divergence and a non-axis-symmetric M^2 number. However, intentional design characteristics of some industrial lasers also may yield an output laser beam with differences in divergence and M^2 number between two orthogonal transverse planes of beam propagation. Beam-shaping optics are used to transform the output laser beam into a usable axis-symmetric beam cross-section at the workpiece when necessary.

Cavity Optics Configurations

Figure 4-4 illustrates cavity-design configurations, each with different optics, as well as output-beam characteristics. Preventive maintenance costs and downtime will increase proportionally with the number of intra- and extra-cavity optics. MTBF data, mean-time-between-cleaning data, and downtime-to-clean-and-replace data for the optics help in the final evaluation of a machine's performance.

Polarization

Most laser-cutting machines must operate with an axis-symmetric polarized laser beam, which can be simulated with circular polarization. Multi-kilowatt lasers tend to produce linearly polarized light beams. Circular-polarizing units for industrial systems generally contain a phase-retarder mirror that changes a polarization from linear to circular when the incident polarization direction forms a 45° angle with the plane of incidence on the phase-retarder mirror. Failure to accurately maintain this 45°-angle relationship results in elliptical polarization rather than circular. With elliptical polarization, variations in cutting performance increase with the eccentricity of the polarization ellipse. Some manufacturers integrate a phase-retarder mirror inside the laser cavity. Depending on the design, intra-cavity mirrors must endure contact with high-temperature gas and sustain peak power

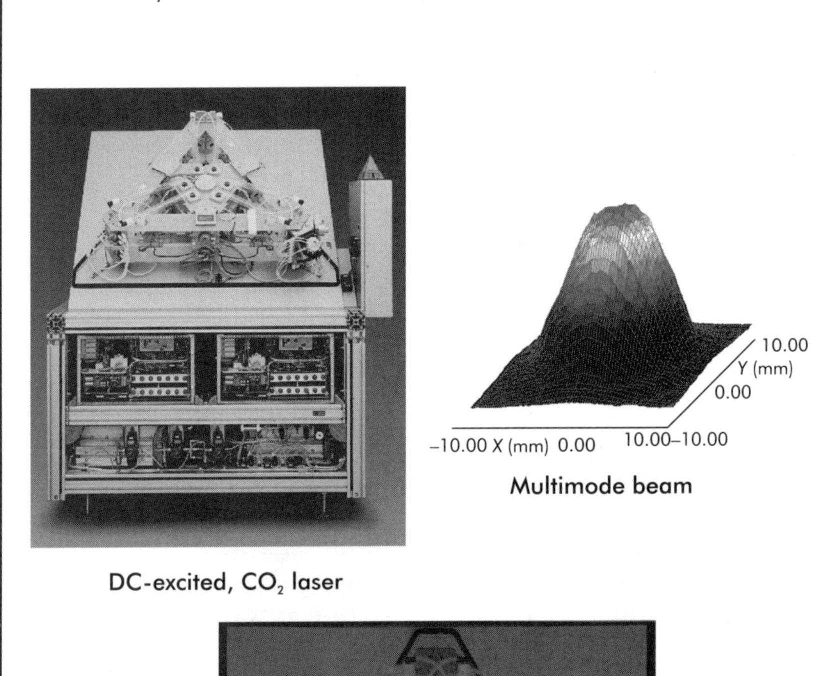

Figure 4-4. Various CO_2 laser-cavity configurations and technologies yield different beam modes to serve optimum applications and circumstances. The number of intra-cavity folding mirrors and glassware generally increases with power. Cavities are folded for footprint compactness. (Courtesy Rofin-Sinar, Inc.)

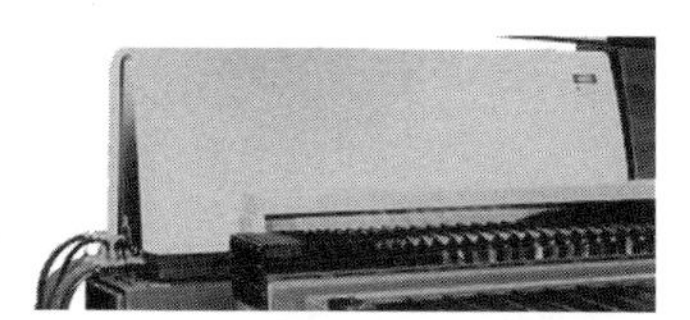

RF-excited, sealed CO_2 laser

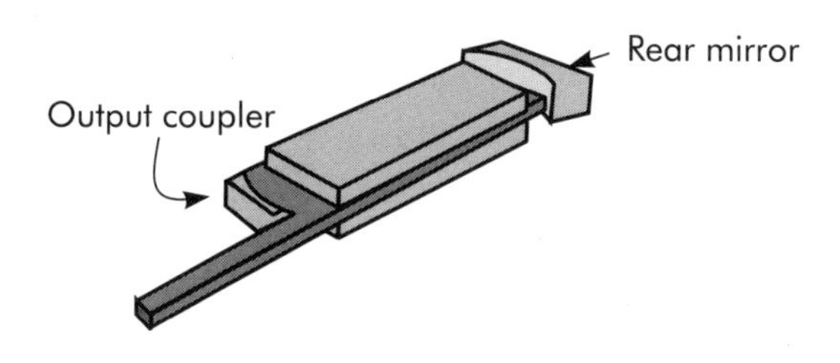

Slab cavity configuration
Hybrid stable/unstable cavity design

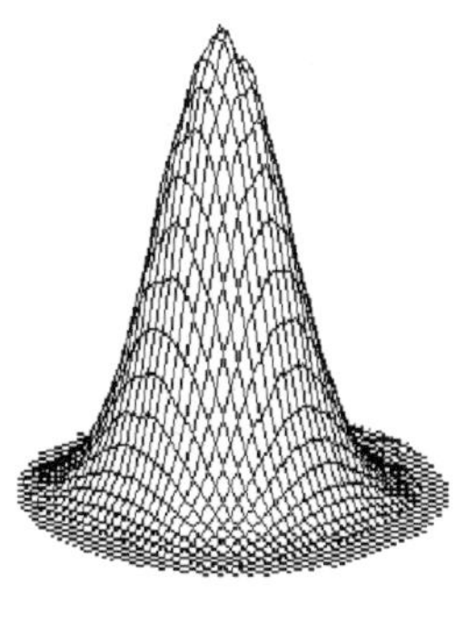

Transverse electro-magnetic (TEM_{00}) beam

Figure 4-4. continued.

at least double the output beam's peak power. With increasingly high-output-power laser-resonator models, it becomes preferable to install phase-retarder optics outside the resonator's cavity for longer life.

Overall Efficiency

As shown in *Table 2-1*, wall-plug kVA to average output power kW reaches about 10% efficiency for standalone turnkey industrial CO_2 lasers running at rated power, versus 5% or less for YAG lasers. When the water chiller is included, the overall efficiency of the system decreases by 50% or more. Generally, laser efficiency increases when the M^2 number increases (in other words, when beam quality worsens).

YAG Lasers

YAG lasers use a solid-state Nd:YAG crystal-active medium to generate a laser beam. Although the same physics principles as in CO_2 lasers apply, the technology, engineering, and design specifications differ drastically from the ones for CO_2 lasers.

Excitation Technology

Flash lamps are still the predominant method of pumping excitation for industrial YAG lasers of 500 W and above. Flash lamps are sophisticated light bulbs that emit black-body radiation with high intensity at the 810 nm wavelength, which is absorbed by the Nd:YAG crystal. For pulsed YAG lasers, flash lamps are generally filled with xenon or halogen gas. For CW YAG lasers, incandescent flash lamps are often filled with krypton and sometimes iridium or mercury vapors. Flash lamps are consumables with MTBF varying over an extraordinarily wide span and yielding an overall laser efficiency lower than 5%. To improve the reliability and efficiency of YAG lasers, the laser industry is replacing flash lamps with diodes, such as gallium-aluminum-arsenide (Ga-Al-As) diodes, which emit a 808-nm wavelength, monochromatic, and coherent beam of infrared light. Pumping diodes yield an overall efficiency triple to quadruple that of flash lamps, an MTBF at least 10 times higher, and a narrower variation in the span of time around the MTBF, making a schedule for preventive maintenance much more predictable.

Beam Quality

A YAG laser-beam quality measurement is generally expressed in mm-mrad units. This measurement can be directly related to an M^2 value by the following relationship:

$$D\theta = \frac{4\lambda}{\pi} M^2 \qquad (4\text{-}2)$$

where:

D = diameter at the waist location, mm
θ = full angle of divergence, radian
λ = wavelength of laser radiation = $1.06\ 10^{-3}$ mm for YAG lasers

For example, a multikilowatt industrial YAG laser with beam quality of 50 mm-mrad corresponds to an M^2 value of about 37. This may be at least 10 times higher than the M^2 value of typical industrial CO_2 lasers, but is counterbalanced for focusability by a wavelength 10 times smaller than that of CO_2 lasers.

LASER AND MOTION CONTROL

Laser-cutting machines can be operated, troubleshot, and serviced via various controls, including computer numerical control (CNC), programmable logic control (PLC), and personal computers. Computers must be adapted to an industrial environment for ruggedness and reliability, yet at the same time be flexible and open enough for integration and connectivity within a network of factory cells. They enable automation of maintenance, service, and logistic and supervisory control functions aimed at yielding enhanced productivity. Control of the laser resonator and peripheral equipment can be integrated with the motion control or interfaced with it through input/output modules. Speed of the communication between the laser control and motion control with the machine's numerical control (NC) becomes an issue when laser-processing speeds exceed more than approximately 80 in./min (203 cm/min).

WATER COOLING SYSTEMS

A water chiller is an essential peripheral component that ensures stability during operation. Its main function is to maintain the different components of the laser resonator and beam-delivery system at their nominal temperatures for optimum efficiency and performance. Like heat pumps, water chillers generally have a mediocre efficiency. The theoretically highest possible efficiency of a water chiller or of any heat pump is called its *Carnot efficiency* and is found by:

$$C_e = (T_h - T_c)/T_h \qquad (4\text{-}3)$$

where:

C_e = Carnot efficiency
T_h = temperature of the hot source expressed in Kelvin (the laser medium's mount or glassware can reach as much as 152° F [340 K] for very-high-power CO_2 lasers)
T_c = temperature of the cold source expressed in Kelvin (the coolant fluid of the chiller is typically about 63° F ±10° F [290 K ±10 K])

So,

$$C_e = 1 - 290/340 = 15\%$$

Cooling capacity (1 BTU/hr = 2.93 10^{-4} kW), flow rate (1 ft^3/hr = 0.47 L/min of water), and static pressure (14.7 psi = 1 bar) specifications vary from one machine model to another. For reference, a 2-kW CO_2 laser may require 80,000 BTU/hr (23 kW) cooling capacity with 50 ft^3/hr (23.6 L/min) water-flow rate at 75° F (297 K) and absolute static pressure of 30 psi (2.1 bar). Within the same laser family, cooling capacity and flow-rate specifications are generally proportional to the rated average-output power. However, a 1-kW Nd:YAG laser resonator typically requires more than twice the cooling capacity of a 1-kW CO_2 laser and, at equal cooling water temperature, and about twice the flow. By design, laser-resonator cooling circuits, such as external beam-delivery optics, servos, power supplies, etc., are separate from the rest of a laser-cutting machine. However, for simplification and cost reduction, they often share the same cooling-water source and pump. The water-chiller pump must be sized to provide a sufficient, simultaneous flow rate to all circuits. Since this generally results in oversizing the kilowatt capability of the chiller's pump, chiller manufacturers always provide pressure-relief bypass circuits with a variable valve to protect downstream equipment from excessive flow pressure.

Piping

Water-delivery piping has an inherent resistance to flow, which is proportional to its length and inversely proportional to its inner cross-section. Consequently, a larger inner-piping diameter is preferred. Typical installations have an inner-piping diameter between the chiller and laser of at least 0.50 in. (12.7 mm). Smaller-diameter tubes and longer lengths of tubing require more upstream water pressure than larger-diameter tubes and shorter lengths. Equally important for water-tubing design, the use of corner-angle elbows should be reduced, as they constitute much higher flow resistance than straight sections, or even corner radii. Plastics, such as hard polyvinyl chloride (PVC) and flexible polyethylene, have a thermal conductivity 400 times smaller than copper and about 20 times smaller than stainless steel. They are the preferred materials for water-delivery piping and hoses. Corrosion makes PVC water tanks preferable to stainless-steel tanks. The larger the tank, the easier it is to control water temperature to within a generally recommended ±2° F (±1° C). The shorter the water piping, the better assurance that the temperature stability at the resonator inlet matches that of the chiller outlet.

Water Quality

The majority of laser chillers recirculate cooling water within a closed loop between the resonator and chiller. The specifications on the water's quality require that it be of distilled quality with less than 50 parts per million (ppm) of alkaline ($CaCO_3$). To avoid clogging the water circuit due to particulate accumulation, laser manufacturers generally recommend that a 0.002 in. (50 μm) mesh or less water filter be installed upstream of the resonator. This filter considerably reduces the water-flow rate. A water-flow sensor can be used for added protection. As a simple switch, it triggers an alarm once a minimum flow-rate threshold is detected. As a more sophisticated gage, it indicates trends in flow rate.

Water Treatment

Chemical cleaners containing mainly hydrogen peroxide (H_3O) can be added at a rate of about 10% to the chiller water to maintain clean inner-piping surfaces, preventing the accumulation of adsorbed contaminants. Cleaners also may need to have anti-corrosion properties per the recommendation of the laser manufacturer.

Biocide compounds approved by both the chiller and laser manufacturer can be diluted in the chiller water to prevent bacteria growth inside the piping and resonator. Bleach is usually not appropriate and rather dangerous for laser resonators, as it attacks some of the material used for flexible piping, electrodes, and other components. It is not recommended in high voltage and current environments. However, it efficiently kills bacteria and fungi growth and can be used to flush and purge the chiller and water-piping distribution system as long as the resonator is not part of the loop. Before reconnecting the resonator to the bleached water-distribution circuit, fresh, clean water must be circulated to flush the bleach away from the chiller and water-piping distribution system. The design of the cooling-water distribution system should enable the flushing, purging, and isolation of certain circuits and provide adequately located shut-off valves.

For systems operating in a cold-weather environment, a glycol compound diluted at a rate of about 30% acts as an antifreeze and protects the laser, chiller, and water-distribution system from clogging with ice or even more destructive pipe cracking due to freezing.

Dual Water-cooling Circuits

Deionized water is generally required for cooling the optics and electrodes of the resonator cavity and power-supply modules where high voltage or high-frequency discharge occurs. As an added precaution, industrial lasers often have two separate water-cooling circuits—one for cavity optics, electrodes, and power supplies, and a second for other laser components, such as a turbine blower, heat exchangers, beam absorber, shutter mirror, and vacuum pump. The water-cooling circuit for the cavity and power supplies then can be isolated, thanks to a secondary water-to-water heat exchanger. One side contains regular chiller water and the other deionized water for the cavity and power supplies. The addition of the secondary water-cooling circuits calls for an additional set of control mechanisms to guarantee the stability of the outlet water temperature to within ±2° F (±1° C).

BEAM-DELIVERY SYSTEMS

The delivery of a laser beam from the resonator to the workpiece requires key features that insure safety and limit power losses while maintaining optimum focusability. A series of reflective and transmissive optics collect, guide, condition, and focus the laser beam into a usable high-heat source. In some cases, a flexible fiberoptic can be advantageously used in lieu of several mirrors for beam-guiding purposes.

Fiberoptic Cable for YAG Lasers

For YAG lasers used in metal-cutting applications, a beam-delivery system is simplified with the use of a flexible fiberoptic cable. All fibers have a center core generally made of fused quartz (silica) surrounded by a cladding (Hecht 1999). The core has a higher refractive index than the cladding to enable total reflection at the wavelength of laser-beam radiation, thus confining the propagation of laser rays to within the core, as shown in *Figure 4-5*. If the angle of incidence, θ_i, is larger than the critical angle given by Snell's law, which is:

$$\theta_c = \text{arc sin } (n_2/n_1) \quad (4\text{-}4)$$

then the refracted ray disappears and close to 100% of the incident ray is reflected back into the core. The complement angle defined by $\theta_{accept} = \pi/2 - \theta_c$ is called the acceptance angle, within which all rays incident at the entrance of the fiber with entrance angle $\theta_e < \theta_{accept}$ will remain confined and guided through the fiber until its other end. The specifications for this fiber include its:

- diameter—generally between 0.020–0.040 in. (0.60–1.00 mm) for high-power industrial lasers;
- core type—the difference between the graded refractive index and step refractive index is illustrated in *Figure 4-6*, and
- minimum allowed bending radius (*Figure 4-7*).

Fused quartz is mostly transparent to 1.06-μm wavelength light. The typical absorption rate of about 1.6 dB/mi (1 dB/km) is due mainly to impurities in the quartz core like OH radicals and metal atoms, such as iron and copper. This absorption rate would consume 99% of 1.06-μm laser energy after 31.1 mi (50 km) of fiber

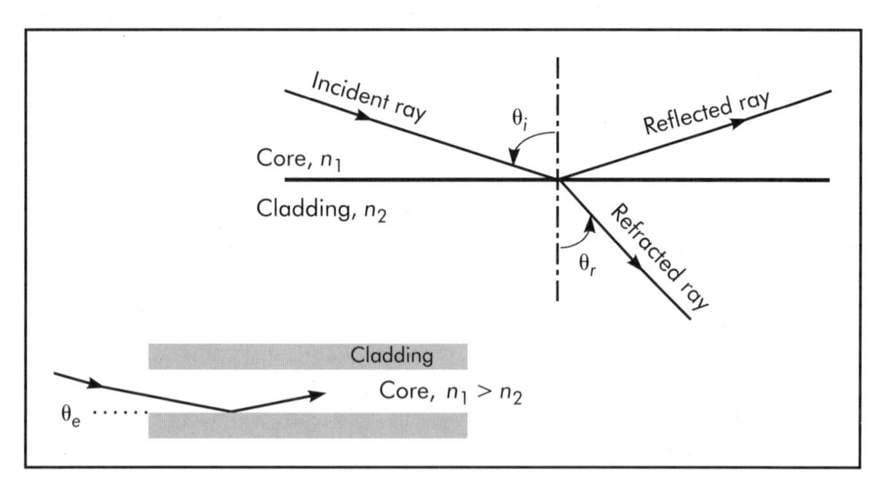

Figure 4-5. An incident ray at the interface between core and cladding will be partly reflected back into the core and partly refracted and absorbed into the cladding. Within appropriate known conditions, close to 100% of the incident ray is reflected.

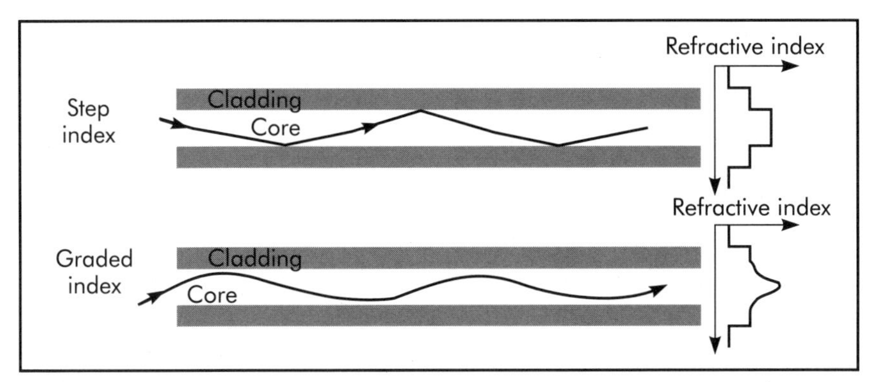

Figure 4-6. A step index fiber's core has a uniform refractive index. A graded index core has a refractive index higher at its center than its periphery. Most fiberoptics have a circular cross-section. A graded index core enables better beam focusability at the end of the fiber.

cable length. Since most installations have fiber delivery shorter than 109.4 yd (100 m), absorption loss of energy is relatively negligible at below 0.5% along its entire length. Energy losses by reflection on the cross-section surface at the entrance and exit of the fiber are more predominant and can amount to 4% of the laser power. More energy losses can be accounted for through each transmissive optic used in the cutting head. Energy losses through the fiberoptic-beam-delivery system can total 10–15% of the laser power (Bakken 2001). Transformed into heat, they may require the fiberoptic-beam-delivery system to be cooled for high-power lasers. Besides their high flexibility and low alignment and maintenance downtime advantages, fiberoptics ensure a constant optical-path length (the length of the fiber) over the entire work envelope. At the end of the fiberoptic, a cutting head mainly consists of collimating and focusing lenses and coaxial assist-gas delivery, as shown in *Figure 4-7*. The cutting head may also house an auto-focus height sensor to track surface-relief changes (*Figure 4-8*) and ensure that cutting parameters, such as nozzle standoff and focus position, remain constant.

Fiber breakage can occur due to:

- fatigue wear;
- curvature accidentally brought well below the minimum tolerance of the bending radius (about 7.9 in. [200 mm] for 0.6

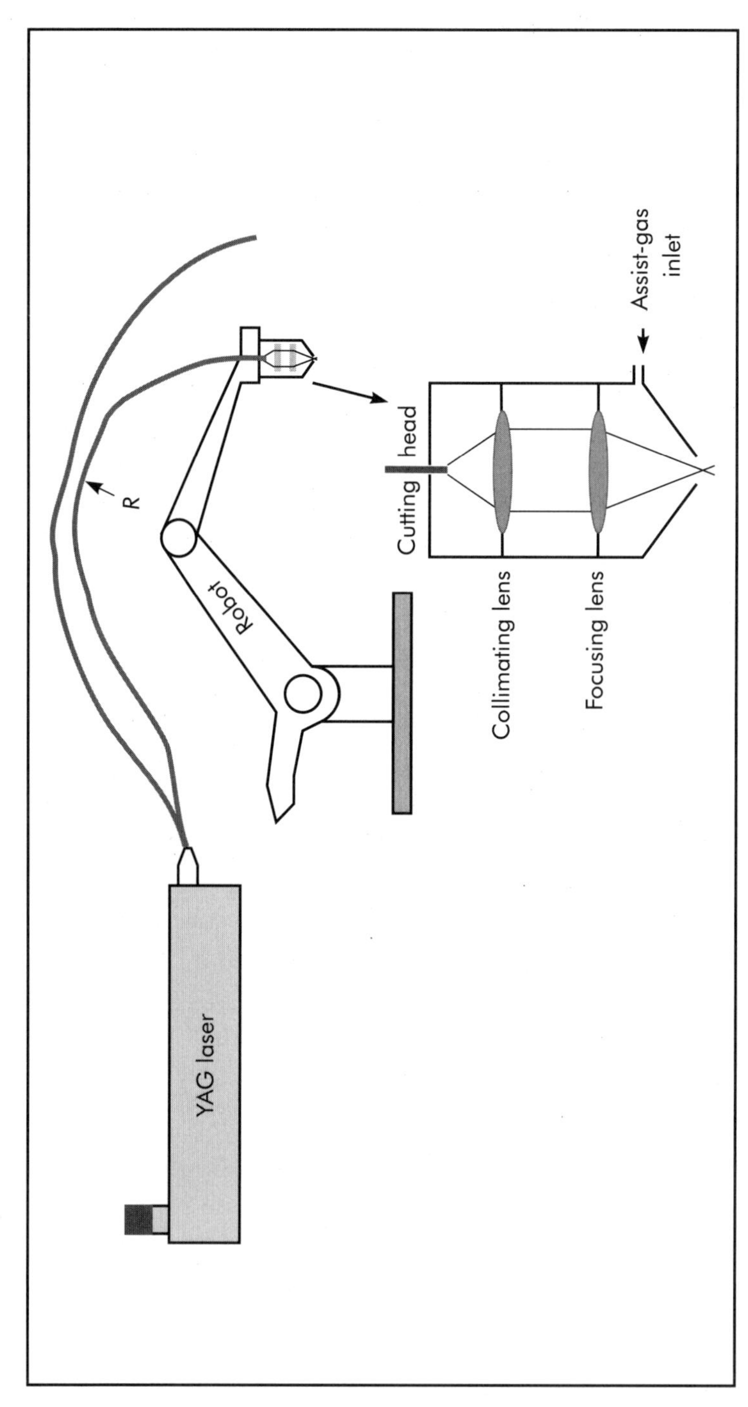

Figure 4-7. This cutting head houses collimating and focusing lenses. The fiber might break prematurely under fatigue bending if the bending radius, R, is allowed under a specified minimum value. A YAG laser beam can be dispatched simultaneously into several fiberoptics, each carrying an assigned percentage of the output laser-beam power. Two fibers are shown here.

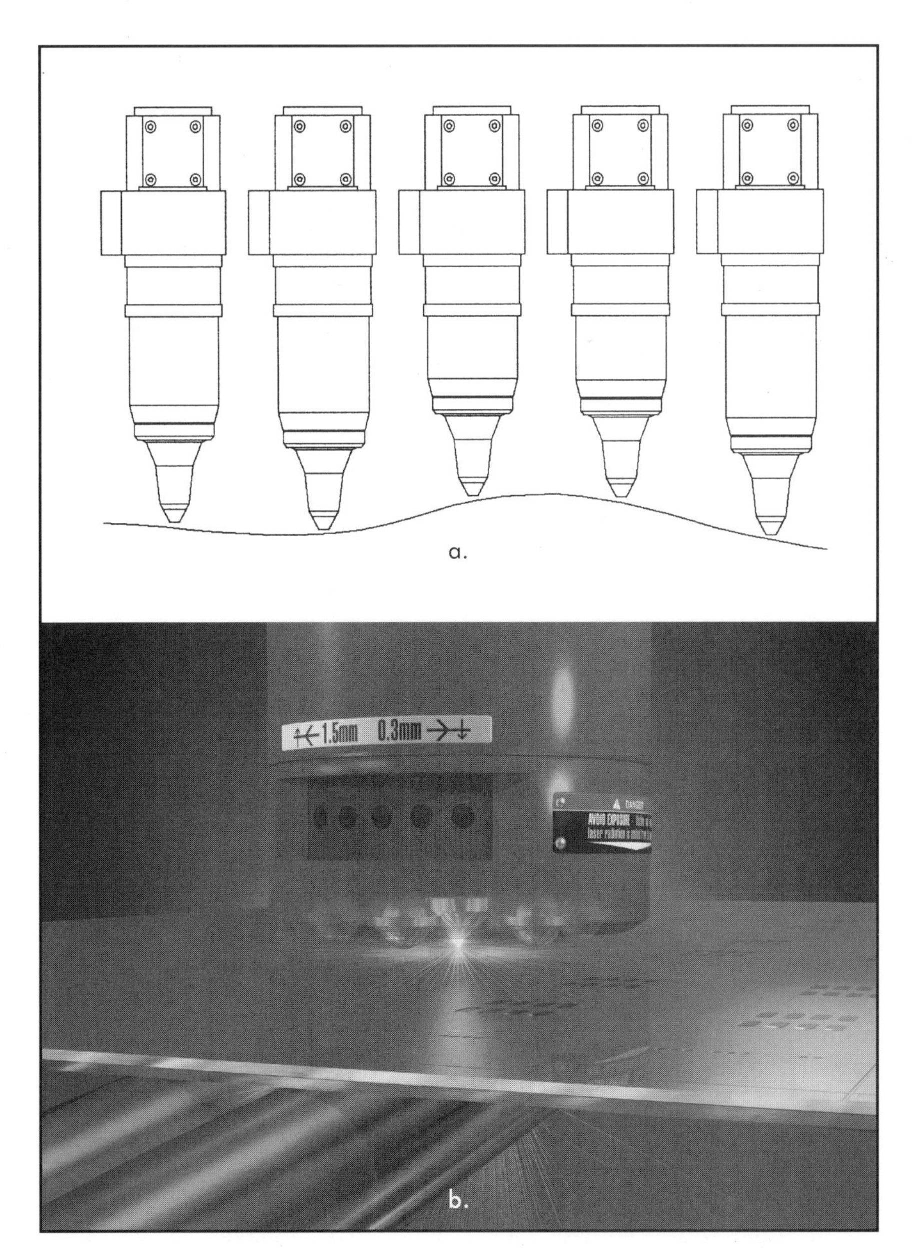

Figure 4-8. (a) A noncontact, capacitive height sensor enables surface tracking to maintain focus position and nozzle standoff constant across the workpiece relief. (Courtesy GSI Lumonics) *(b) In some applications, ball bearings with mechanical contact technology maintain constant nozzle standoff with the workpiece.* (Courtesy Amada, Inc.)

μm fiber; this minimum bending radius specification increases when the fiber diameter decreases), and
- accidental laser-beam reflection burning the fiber through its flexible encasing.

Such breakage allows hazardous, high-power laser energy to exit. Most fiberoptic-delivery systems for high-powered lasers have sensors that detect breakage. Such sensors can serve as safety switches to shut down operations.

Laser rays that reflect along the fiber result in a different total optical-path length in the fiber, and therefore varying phase shifts. Consequently, by the exit end of the fiber, the coherence of the laser beam is significantly altered, yielding a lower intensity at the focus spot on the workpiece. (For more information, refer to Appendix A.) Sometimes, this lower intensity can be equivalent to multiplication of the M^2 number of the beam by two or more. This explains why fiberoptic delivery for YAG processing applications requiring excellent focusability, such as fine cutting, microdrilling, and marking, is avoided. Standard mirror-and-lens beam-delivery systems are used instead.

Articulated Arms for CO_2 Lasers

For CO_2 lasers, effective, flexible-fiber delivery is not yet available at the 10.6 μm wavelength. A viable alternative to fiberoptics is an articulated arm with mirrors positioned at each pivot center, as seen in *Figure 4-9*. With articulated arms, the optical-path length is constant and maintenance downtime and alignment are minimized, although not as low as with optical fibers. Articulated arms have higher inertia and less maneuverability than fiberoptics.

Gantry Beam Delivery for CO_2 Lasers

For most higher-power CO_2 lasers with relatively large beam diameters (typically over 0.6 in. [15 mm]), conventional gantry beam-delivery systems seem preferred by the laser-cutting industry for their endurance of high-speed and high-power metal cutting. Gantry beam-delivery systems are mainly composed of fixed

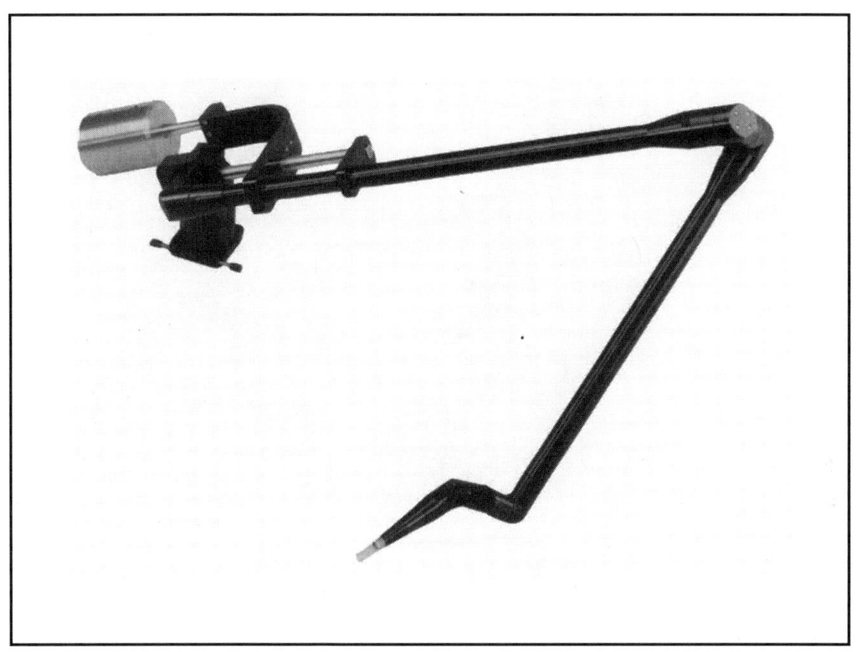

Figure 4-9. Articulated arms serve as a hollow wave guide for CO_2 laser beams. Mirrors at each pivot point deflect the laser beam for delivery to a cutting head. This arm can be mounted either on an articulated robot or a gantry system. (Courtesy Haas Laser Technologies, Inc.)

and flexible bellow tubes. Tubing protects the optical path and its optics from atmospheric contamination (dust, particles, fumes, humidity, etc.). Flexible bellow enclosures are used in lieu of fixed tubes for their variable lengths. They come in various forms, such as spring telescopic tubes, or the common telescopic bellow type shown in *Figure 4-10*. The aperture along the inside of the beam-delivery system should exceed three to four times the laser-beam diameter to limit the effect of diffraction interference during propagation of the beam in the enclosure. Larger apertures for the beam-delivery system also reduce atmospheric pressure gradients inside the system during motion of the gantry, thus decreasing beam dispersion. Mirrors, lenses, and windows must be used to condition, guide, and focus the beam from the laser output mirror onto the workpiece. These optics are made of various materials appropriate for 10.6 μm wavelength reflections and transmission.

Figure 4-10. Bellows can compress and extend while maintaining a dust-tight enclosure along the optical-beam path. They also provide light-tight enclosure of the optical path for safety. (Courtesy Alabama Laser)

Optics

Transmissive optics for multikilowatt CO_2 laser beams are made from zinc selenide (ZnSe) with a refractive index of 2.4 at 10.6 μm wavelength or gallium arsenide (GaAs) with a refractive index of 3.1. Zinc selenide is the material of choice for focusing lenses and output-coupler (OC) mirrors. Gallium arsenide is preferred for OC mirrors in very-high output power lasers because its thermal conductivity, almost three times greater than that of zinc selenide, enables more effective cooling. Another material, potassium chloride (Kcl) with a refractive index of 1.5, has an exceptionally low absorption coefficient at 10.6 μm wavelength—almost four times lower than zinc selenide. However, it is also more costly and its *hygroscopic property* (propensity to absorb moisture) limits its life.

Reflective optics for multikilowatt CO_2 lasers are generally made from copper surfaces with a diamond-turned finish, giving them a reflectivity of 98.5% at 10.6 μm. Adding a silver coating to the same copper-base mirror yields a reflectivity above 99.5%. An additional dielectric-type protective coating over the silver coating enhances the surface hardness of the mirror and reduces reflectivity to 99%. Molybdenum (Mo) is an alternative mirror coating with a lower reflectivity of 98% and a higher surface hardness, making it highly resistant to scratches and spatters. Molybdenum mirrors can be cleaned and reused many times, whereas copper mirrors must be replaced if spoiled by tough stains and spatters. Silicon (Si—reflectivity of 99.5%) mirrors are used for intra-cavity folding mirrors and beam-delivery-system mirrors. Silver and dielectric coatings also can be added to enhance their endurance to the elements.

For CO_2 laser-beam gantry delivery systems, it may become necessary to include special beam-shaping optics to optimize cutting performance for various applications. For example, flying optics systems must compensate for the natural divergence of a laser beam that would otherwise yield a different cutting capability in the near field (NF) versus the far field (FF). NF corresponds to the shortest and FF the longest optical-path length on the work envelope. On a flat bed they coincide with two of the diagonal ends of a worktable. The most common compensation device is a collimator. It is generally composed of a first mirror of focal length, f_1, and a second mirror of focal length, f_2. A collimator has a combining effect to expand a beam diameter by a magnification factor of f_2/f_1 and decrease its divergence by a factor of f_1/f_2.

Figure 4-11 illustrates a Galilean-type collimator with a first divergent mirror, which is more suited for high-power laser beams. In *Figure 4-11*, the first mirror is convex with radius of curvature R_1. The second mirror is concave with a radius of curvature, R_2. The collimator magnifies a beam diameter and reduces its divergence angle, thus reducing beam differences between the NF and FF as illustrated by mode burns. In contrast to a Galilean type, a Keplerian-type collimator has a convergent first mirror, yielding a high-power-density focus point between the two mirrors. For very-high-power lasers, this focus point must be in a contaminant-free atmosphere, otherwise severe beam absorption and dispersion may occur. The reduction in divergence due to the collimator reduces differences in beam characteristics between near and far field. The increase in beam diameter allows a smaller focus spot at the workpiece and, unfortunately, a shorter depth of focus. Focal lengths f_1 and f_2 should be selected based on a

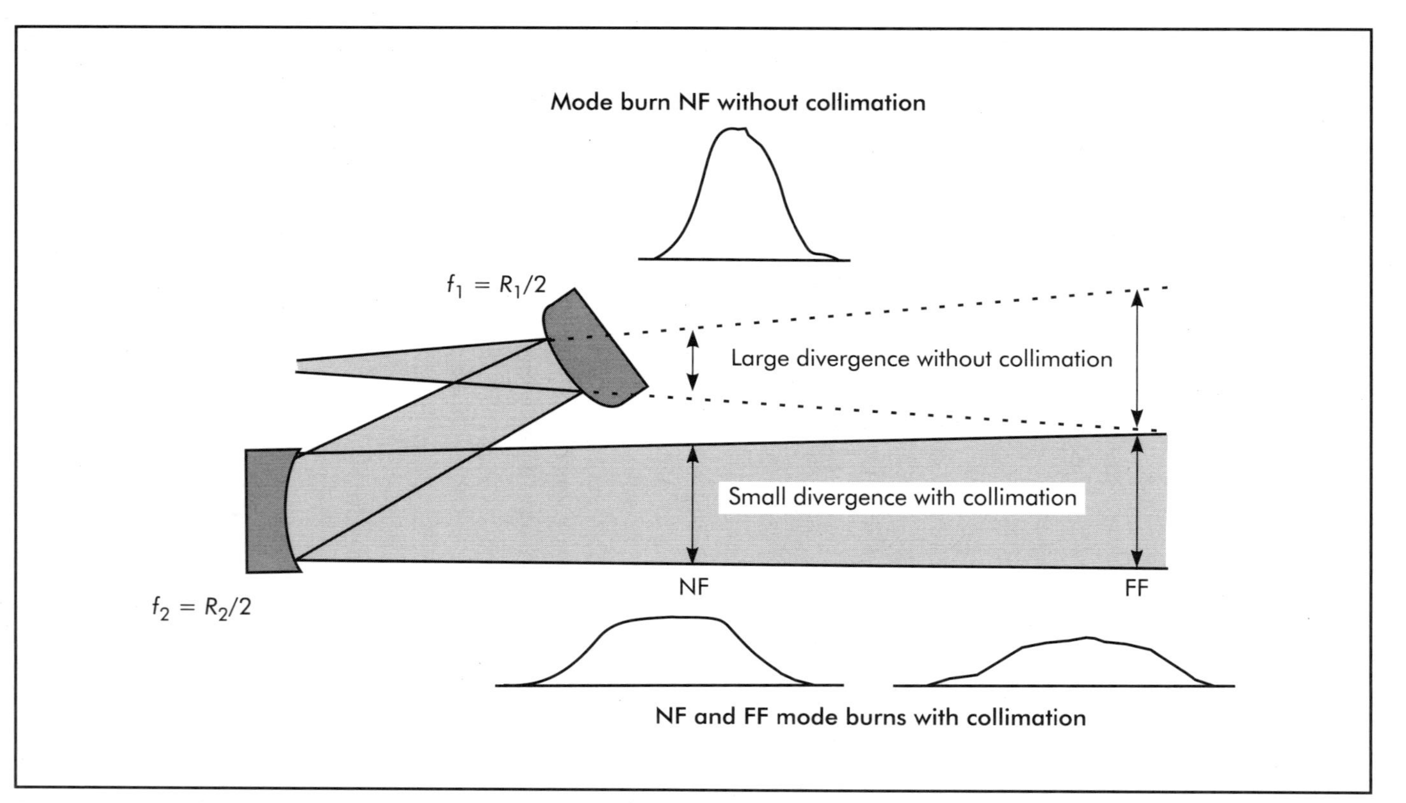

Figure 4-11. Galilean collimators are the most commonly used in industrial applications. They reduce beam divergence, thus reducing beam characteristic differences between the near and far fields.

resonator's output-beam characteristics for a compromise, yielding the best cutting performance for a specifically sought-after finite range of applications.

Systems featuring adaptive optics, shown in *Figure 4-12* (Haas 2002), and constant beam paths (*Figure 4-13*) can be adjusted during cutting to optimize the optical features of the beam-delivery system. Adaptive optics, initially developed for astronomy telescopes, are mirrors with a flexible and variable surface profile (Hoffmann and Neubauer 1995). A mirror's surface profile is changed under the pressure of piezzo-electric ceramic cells or, in some cases, fluid pressure. An analog voltage submitted by a machine's controls drives the piezzo cells' action; it can be tabulated as a function of a needed focal length or an *X*, *Y*, *Z* position on the work envelope. For concave and convex spherical mirrors, it leads to an adjustable radius of curvature and consequently adaptable focal length. This focal-length adjustment compensates for beam divergence between near and far focus, and even more powerfully adjusts beam characteristics on the fly for optimum cutting performance at every position on the work envelope and

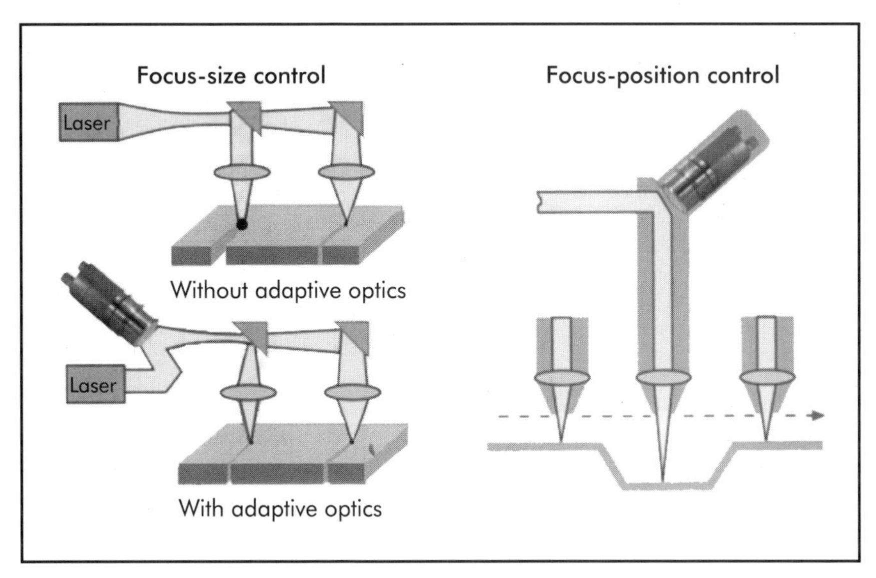

Figure 4-12. With adaptive optics, beam divergence can be compensated for to reduce focus-spot dimension and depth-of-focus variations at the workpiece. (Courtesy Haas Laser Technologies, Inc.)

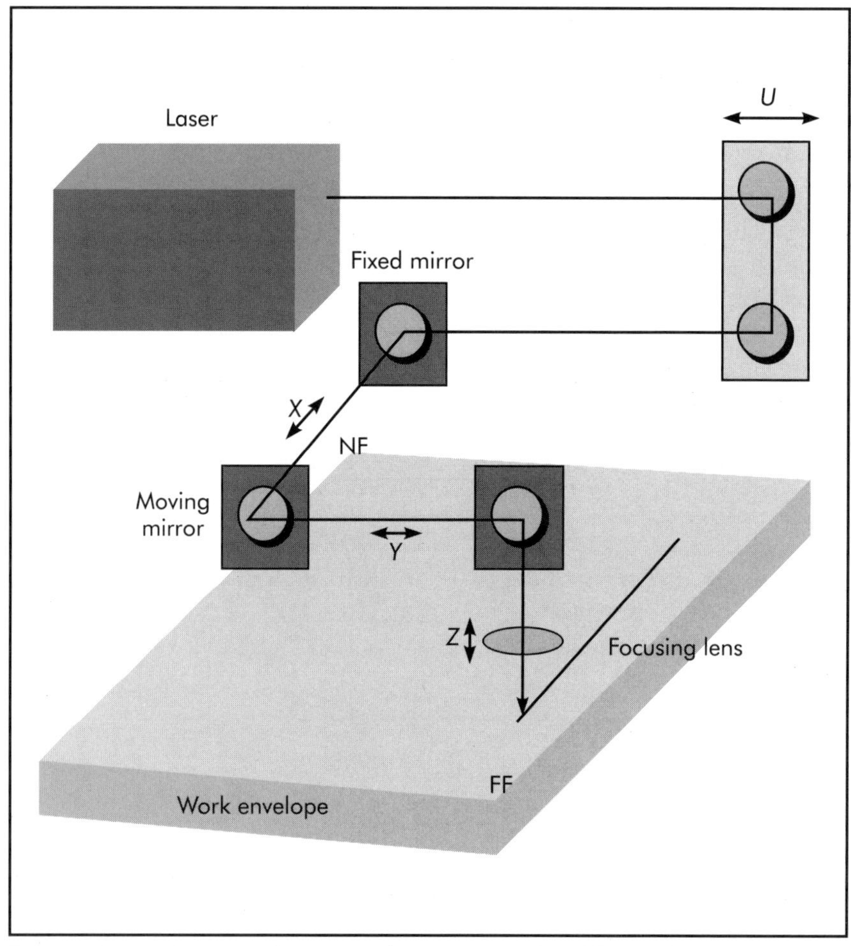

Figure 4-13. Constant-beam-path system with additional U-axis motion maintains uniform beam characteristics by keeping the total beam-path length constant across the work envelope.

for every material type and thickness. This capacity to adjust on the fly adds flexibility but complexity in part programming, and is another source of reliability and repeatability error.

The constant-beam-path system described in *Figure 4-13* requires another servo axis and at least two additional mirrors. It is superior to a collimation system in that it ensures absolute constant-beam-path length across the work envelope. However, it falls short as far as its capability to adapt the beam-focusing characteristics at the workpiece as a function of material, which a collimator's fixed choice of focal lengths (f_1 and f_2) partially allows, or that adaptive optics can enable on the fly. In *Figure 4-13*, the optical path between the laser output and workpiece goes through a U-axis-controlled detour, which is adjusted as a function of the X, Y, and Z positions to maintain a constant optical-beam-path length throughout the work envelope. This ensures constant focus characteristics from NF to FF.

GAS-DELIVERY SYSTEMS

Depending on the intended use, the specifications for global purity and control of impurities in gases for laser-cutting operations vary significantly. This impacts consumable costs as well as gas-delivery engineering design. Gases can be carried in either rigid or flexible tubing.

Rigid Tubing

Laser-gas and assist-gas delivery systems can be composed of rigid or flexible tubing. Although copper tubing is acceptable for assist-gas delivery, rigid tubing made of stainless steel is unequivocally preferable for laser-gas delivery, as it does not easily react with most gas types (especially O_2 and air). If copper tubing must be used, flux compound should be avoided in brazing and soldering as it has a tendency to de-gas slowly, thereby contaminating the laser-gas delivery for up to several days. Such contamination is a major source of resonator component failure and downtime.

Flexible Tubing

Flexible tubing can be made of polyethylene, nylon, or Teflon® for use with assist-gas or laser-gas delivery at pressures under a safe maximum level, typically about 72.5 psi (5 bar). These materials are well-suited for laser gases and low-pressure assist-gas.

For high-pressure assist-gas, such as nitrogen and air at more than 72.5 psi (5 bar), steel-mesh-reinforced flexible tubing is recommended.

Contamination by Diffusion

It must be recognized that any tubing is permeable to some degree. Metal tubes have low permeability, whereas flexible rubber and polyurethane tubing should be avoided for their relatively excessive permeability. Permeability translates into a two-way diffusion of gases through the walls of a tube. Diffusion of molecules moves from a region of high partial pressure to a region of lower partial pressure at a rate that depends chiefly on the material composing the tube and the nature of the molecule. This rate also varies with temperature and total pressure. For example, a tube containing an absolute pressure of 29 psi (2 bar) of CO_2 laser-gas mixture composed of 5% CO_2, 40% He, and 55% N_2 has partial pressures of 1.50 psi (0.1 bar) of CO_2, 11.60 psi (0.8 bar) of He, and 16.00 psi (1.1 bar) of N_2. However, the partial pressure of atmosphere gases in standard conditions are less than 0.06 psi (0.004 bar) of CO_2, almost 0% of He, 11.313 psi (0.78 bar) of N_2, and 3.046 psi (0.21 bar) of O_2.

Based on the differences in partial pressure, *Table 4-3* shows how different gas molecules diffuse between a tube and room atmosphere, which progressively changes the composition of expensive laser gas in the tube until partial pressures reach equilibrium for each gas. Diffusion is generally a slow process, but is accelerated when the total static pressure differential increases. Stainless-steel diaphragms should be specified for high-pressure gas regulators to minimize gas diffusion. For impurities such as moisture and certain hydrocarbons, a ppm level of contamination is sufficient to significantly degrade laser performance (Marie, Van Der Have, and Roe 1988). Nylon and polyethylene tubing materials are preferred, along with stainless steel (for which diffusion is lowest) for laser- and assist-gas delivery (Berkmanns 2001). PVC and Teflon® are more permeable than polyethylene.

Table 4-3. Diffusion scenarios of tubes containing high-purity laser-gas mixture (5% CO_2, 40% He, 55% N_2) and room atmosphere

Gas Type	Tube #1 Partial Pressure, psi (bar)	Diffusion	Atmosphere Partial Pressure, psi (bar)	Diffusion	Tube #2 Partial Pressure, psi (bar)
CO_2	1.50 (0.1)	⇒	<0.0580 (<0.004)	⇐	0.3626 (0.025)
He	11.60 (0.8)	⇒	<ppm	⇐	2.9008 (0.200)
N_2	16.00 (1.1)	⇒	11.3130 (0.780)	⇒	3.9885 (0.275)
O_2	ppm	⇐	3.0460 (0.210)	⇒	ppm
H_2O	ppm	⇐	% humidity in air	⇒	ppm
Total hydrocarbons	ppm	⇐	% local pollution	⇒	ppm
Total	29.00 (2.0)		14.500 (1.000)		7.2500 (0.500)

Note: Tube #1 contains 29 psi (2 bar) of laser gas flowing from a gas cylinder to a laser inlet. Tube #2 contains 7.25 psi (0.5 bar) of laser gas flowing from a blower to a resonator's cavity. The diffusion arrows follow the difference in partial pressure and not necessarily the difference in total static pressure.

Leakage

Leakage, which is at least as serious as diffusion, compromises the integrity of laser gas if the total static pressure inside a tube is lower than the atmospheric pressure surrounding it. This can be the case for tubes inside lasers operating under a partial vacuum. Leakage can be due to cracking. Flexible-tube materials are often prone to cracking when aging, bent into a tight radius, or under heat or chemical attack. Nylon and polyethylene are the most heat-resistant of all flexible-tube materials. The largest source of leakage is at fittings and valves. All fittings can be standard nylon or stainless steel, depending on the choice of tubing. Brass fittings can be used with copper tubing. A leak test can confirm a proper fit. Although convenient, quick-disconnect mechanisms should be avoided when handling high-purity gases, as they are often prone to high leak rates that increase with use.

If the total pressure inside a tube is higher than atmospheric pressure, precious laser gas wasted through leakage can lower profitability. In some cases, it also compromises the flow-rate level or the nominal gas mixture's proportions required for high-performance laser operation.

Purging and Flushing

For operations that require different types of assist-gas, a purging and flushing mechanism designed in the gas-delivery system is beneficial for productivity and quality. Preferably, common parts of a gas-delivery system should use a low volume to shorten the duration and cost of flushing sequences. Most tube-material surfaces adsorb gas molecules in their wall surface and slowly de-gas them, which can result in contamination if a type of gas molecule different than the one adsorbed in the walls is in use.

Electromagnetic proportional valves automate flushing, purging, and setup of laser gas and assist-gas types and pressure. However, electromagnetic valves must be chosen carefully, as many models have a relatively high leakage rate.

The ability to flush gas-delivery lines is crucial to raising the performance of a laser-cutting machine and increasing MTBF and preventive maintenance intervals. It enables purging of leaked impurities before they reach the laser resonator's cavity and heat exchanger circuits, particularly after each gas-cylinder exchange. The use of high-cost laser gases merits purging systems to rectify the fact that atmospheric impurities in a facility—moisture and hydrocarbons, in particular—are the main source of contamination of high-purity laser-gas delivery lines.

If not thoroughly purged, contaminated tubing continuously drip-feeds impurities to the laser (from hours to days) until a harmful level of accumulated contamination is reached. As an example, *Figure 4-14* shows how much O_2, N_2, and moisture diffusion from

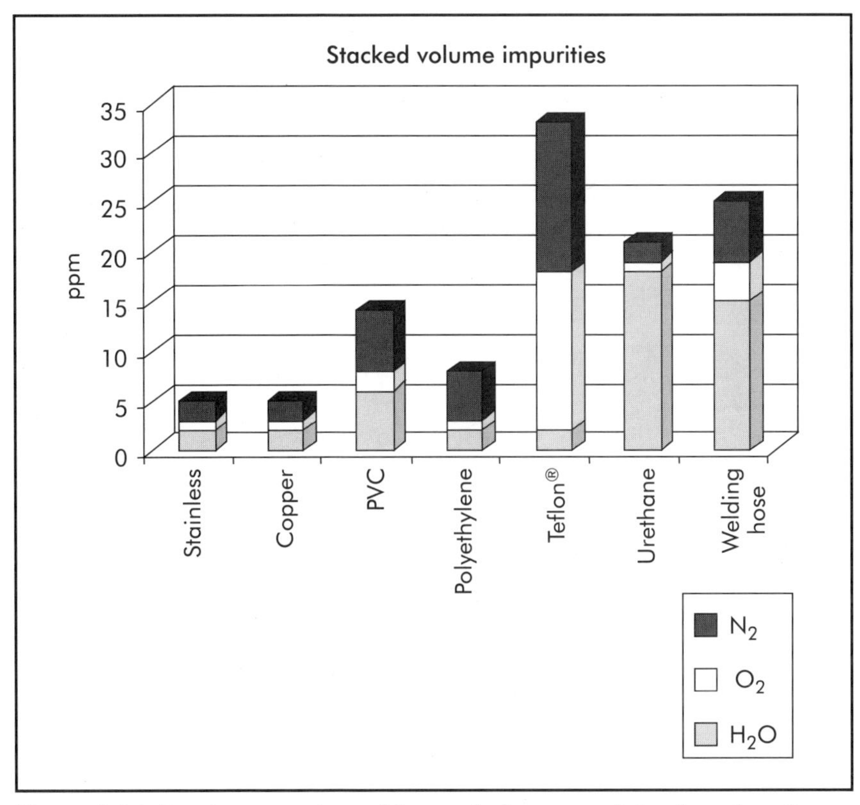

Figure 4-14. Purging gas tubes with pure helium containing less than 2 ppm of each impurity, moisture, oxygen, and nitrogen, yields these characteristic permanent impurity levels.

room atmosphere to inside gas-delivery tubing can be expected for tubes made of various materials purged with helium containing less than 2 ppm of each of the aforementioned three impurities (Berkmanns 2001). The results indicate that almost no diffusion occurs with metal tubing. For comparison, while 10 minutes of helium purging is sufficient to reach minimum moisture impurity with metals, polyethylene, and Teflon®, several hours of helium purging is necessary before stabilizing permanent impurity levels for PVC, urethane, and rubber welding hoses. H_2O moisture contamination is particularly harmful to CO_2 laser operations and should be maintained under 5 ppm by volume.

A careful evaluation of the cost associated with a state-of-the-art valve-purging system, regulator components, and tubing material concludes that they are worthwhile investments for industrial laser systems. An average return can be expected within a few hundred hours of operation. The harm from gas impurities goes beyond contaminating cavity optics and includes shortening the MTBF of power supplies and degradation of beam-mode quality, focusability, and cutting performance.

AIR-FILTER SYSTEMS

All the metal evaporated or flushed through the kerf accumulates into a large volume of metallic dust that may become a health hazard when inhaled. It also clogs motion systems, contaminates gas- and beam-delivery systems, and workpiece surfaces to the point of inducing decreased cutting performance, higher defects, and more frequent maintenance downtime for cleaning. An effective air-suction filter system should be in place to collect the dust and fumes of metals, oil, and other by-products.

SCRAP REMOVAL SYSTEMS

Some by-products of laser cutting can be too large and heavy to be collected through an air-suction filter system. Engineering scrap that is generated despite an optimized nesting pattern can quickly accumulate and needs to be evacuated. Generally, laser-cutting machines collect scrap by letting it drop through the part-support mechanism, such as the one in *Figure 4-15.* Intelligent, cost-effective nesting should generate scrap small enough to drop through a part-support grid into a collection tray or conveyor belt for evacuation into a scrap dumpster.

MOTION SYSTEMS

Articulated robots, such as the one that was shown in *Figure 1-4,* provide standard, low-cost motion systems for 3D processing. They are powered by servomotors for at least six-axis motion in a maximum flexibility setting. Maximum flexibility comes at the price of average accuracy and repeatability, ranging at about ±0.005 in. (±0.13 mm) within a limited work envelope. The work envelope limitation can be solved by enabling the robot or workpiece to slide on additional axes.

Faster and more accurate and precise than articulated robots, gantry-type motion systems are no different than those for conventional cutting systems, such as plasma and punch-cutting machines. Generally, a ball screw (*Figure 4-16*) or rack-and-pinion powered by a servomotor yields motion in a linear axis. Typical accuracy and repeatability are within ±0.001 in./ft (±0.10 mm/m) at full speed (about 2,000 in./min [51 m/min]) for motion systems.

In commercially available industrial machinery, more technologically advanced linear motors are replacing conventional systems with ball screws powered by servomotors. Linear motors use an electromagnetic interaction between a permanent magnet linear track and a coil traversed by an alternate current to produce motion of the coil along the track. The coil armature is attached to a moving part of the laser-cutting machine, such as the *Y*-axis gantry or its focusing-head assembly. A major difference with ball-screw systems is that no direct-contact friction takes place on a rotating endless screw. Indirect-contact friction takes place only between the coil armature and its guiding rail. Linear motors are precise enough to eliminate backlash and, most importantly, have no moving or rotating parts in them. Combined with the lightweight, high-stiffness construction of a *Y*-axis bridge gantry, linear motors provide high acceleration of several Gs, and high-speed

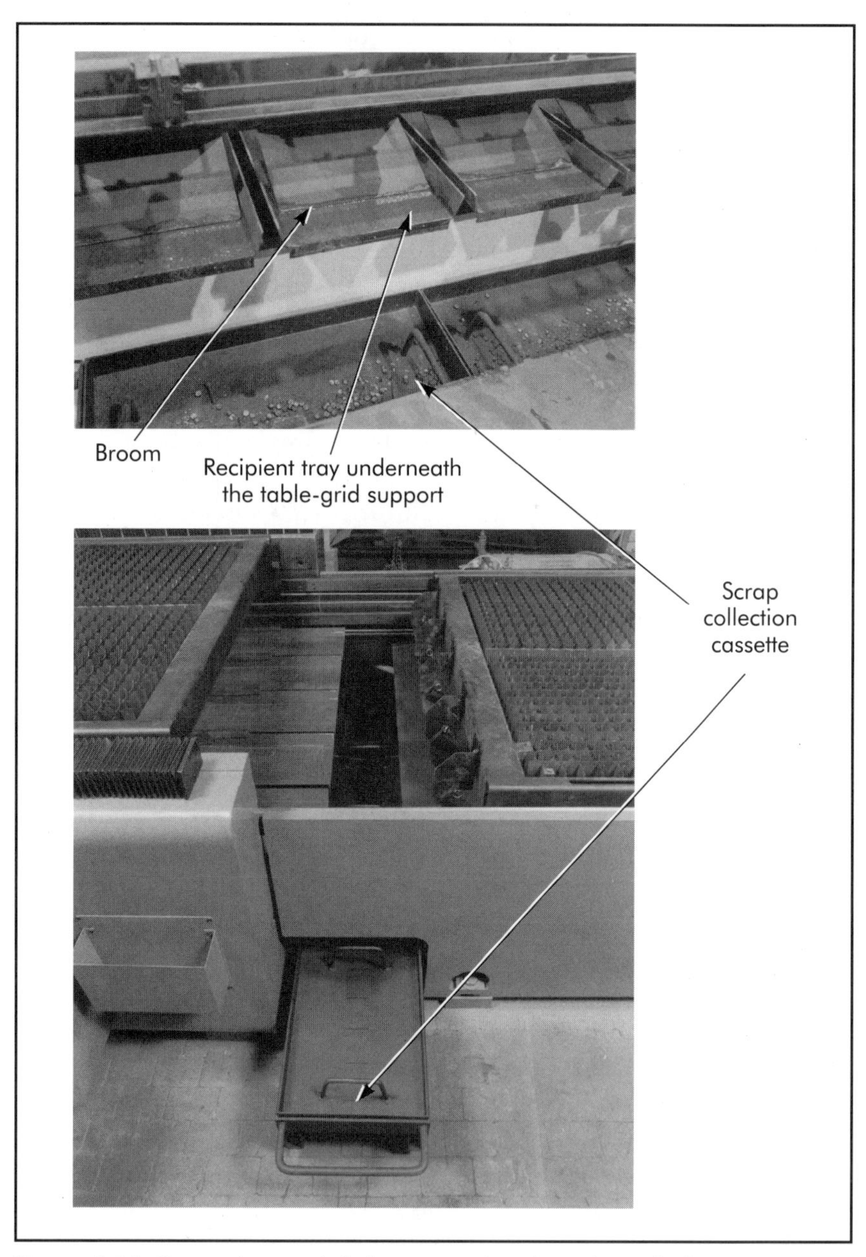

Figure 4-15. Scrap dust and skeleton remains drop through the part-support grid of the shuttle table onto a recipient tray. This tray is broomed periodically and the dust and scrap pieces are collected in a scrap cassette. The cassette can be emptied without stopping production. (Courtesy Cincinnati, Inc.)

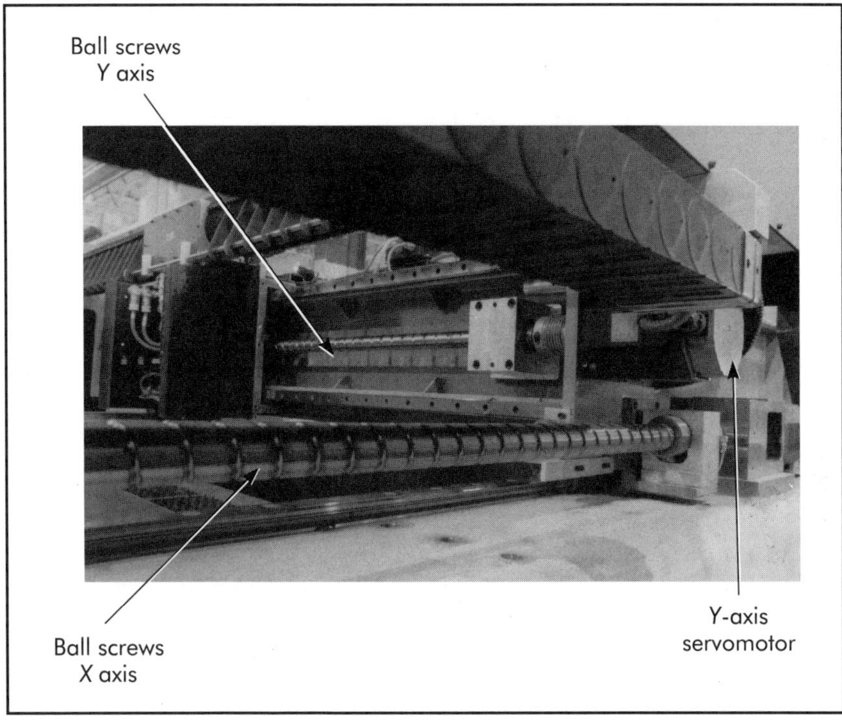

Figure 4-16. View of endless ball screws transmitting power for the X- and Y-axis motions. (Courtesy Cincinnati, Inc.)

cutting of small intricate features. They also enable very high rapid-traverse speeds of 5,906 in./min (150 m/min) to shorten cycle time and increase productivity. High-speed blanking of 0.04-in. (1.0-mm) thin aluminum sheet for automotive bodies was achieved at 1,500 in./min (38 m/min) on a linear-motor laser-cutting machine, demonstrating an edge quality superior to that of die blanking (Penn, Clarke, and Quinn 2000).

FACTORY AUTOMATION

When processing thin-gage material at high speed, material-handling time becomes a more significant percentage of cycle time. Material-handling automation to find, load, and unload raw material and stack finished cut products makes sense, particularly for high-volume production. However, thick, heavy plates are generally cut at a much slower speed, and material-handling time is less of a factor in cycle time. Due to its heavy weight, a thick plate can only be handled with care and mechanical assistance anyway, making automation to load and unload material appealing (Thompson 1999). *Figure 4-17* illustrates a popular load/unload mechanism.

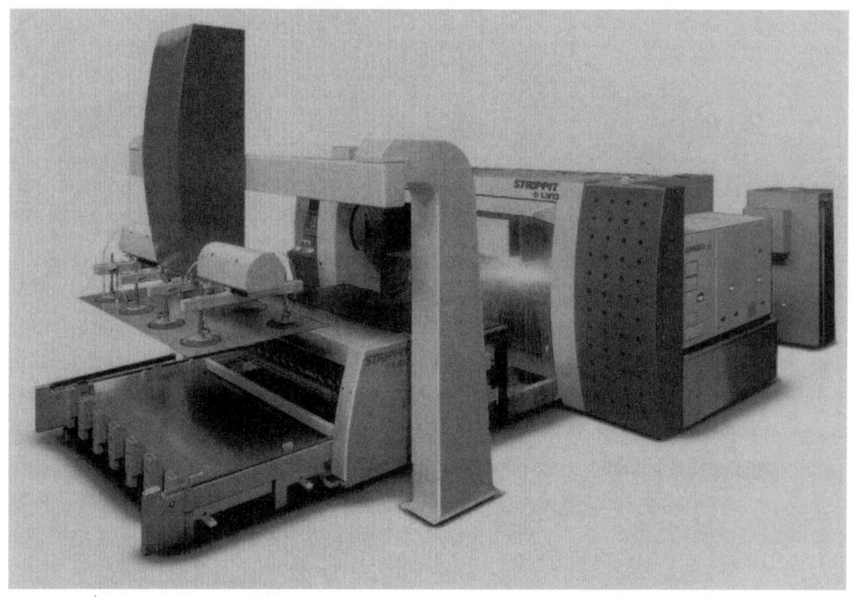

Figure 4-17. Automatic load/unload system with vacuum suction cups efficiently lifts thick plates as well as thin sheets of steel, aluminum, and other metals. (Courtesy Strippit/LVD)

Factory automation can be described as an integration of material-handling hardware and control software. It should limit human intervention in receiving and processing orders, production scheduling, computer-aided design (CAD) file part nesting, CNC machine-code programming, part programming, downloading of program codes to the machine on the floor, and machine setup. For machine setup, a cutting-parameter database is generally provided by the machine builder and is electronically accessible from the machine's numerical controller.

A close study of a metal-fabrication process map should begin with the creation of an order. With automation, several different jobs can be programmed for processing in a queue while corresponding sheets and plates are stored on an automated rack (*Figure 4-18*). Pallet-rack storage and load/unload end-effector shuttles are common options that improve productivity when coupled with processing automation. This enables changes to the setup from one application to another with minimal operator intervention. Safety precautions dictate that if remote computers can access and communicate with a machine's numerical controller on the floor, the latter should remain the master while remote computers are subordinate for operation and maintenance. The only unattended functions of remote computers should be for supervisory data collection.

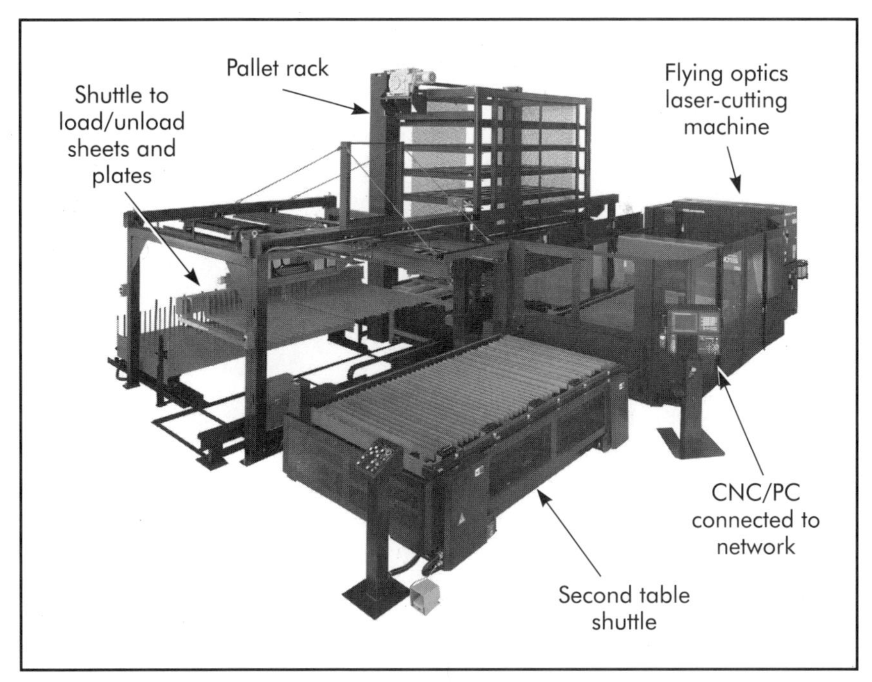

Figure 4-18. Factory automation integrates material-handling automation with order processing, CAD-file part nesting, G-code part-program computing, download to machine controls, production scheduling, cutting-parameter setup, and preventive maintenance schedules. (Courtesy Amada, Inc.)

REFERENCES

Bakken, D. 2001. "Fiberoptic Beam Delivery: Nd-YAG Lasers." *LIA Handbook of Laser Material Processing*. Ready, J. and Farson, D., eds. Orlando, FL: Laser Institute of America.

Berkmanns, J. 2001. "Laser Gases for CO_2 Laser Resonators." *LIA Handbook of Laser Material Processing*. Ready, J. and Farson, D., eds. Orlando, FL: Laser Institute of America.

Haas, G. 2002, June. "Sensors & Special Optics for Laser Cutting." Technical Forum Seminar. Advanced Thermal Processing of Metal Sheets & Plates: Cutting, Welding, & Inspection. Ohio State University, Columbus, OH. Dearborn, MI: Society of Manufacturing Engineers (SME).

Hecht, J. 1999. *Understanding Fiberoptics*, Third Edition. New Jersey: Prentice Hall.

Hoffmann, P. and Neubauer, N. 1995. "Enlarged Applicability of Laser Systems by Adaptive Beam Delivery." *Journal of Manufacturing Systems*. Vol. 24, No. 5. Dearborn, MI: Society of Manufacturing Engineers.

Marie, B., Van Der Have, P., and Roe, K. 1988, November. "Influences of Gaseous Impurities in the CO_2 Laser Cavity." International Congress on Applications of Lasers and Electro-Optics (ICALEO), Santa Clara, CA. Orlando, FL: Laser Institute of America.

Penn, W., Clarke, J., and Quinn, E. 2000. " High-speed Laser Blanking of Aluminum." International Congress on Applications of Lasers and Electro-Optics (ICALEO). Dearborn, MI, pp. B1-B7. Orlando, FL: Laser Institute of America.

Thompson, A. 1999, November. "Automated Laser Systems: New Developments in Laser-cutting Technology." Fabtech International Session 103, Chicago, IL. Dearborn, MI: Society of Manufacturing Engineers.

Methods

"Faithfulness and truth have met; together with righteousness and peace they have embraced each other. Truth shall spring out of the earth; and righteousness shall look down from heaven. The Lord shall give that which is good; and our land shall yield her increase. Righteousness shall go before Him; and shall set us in the way of His steps."

—Psalm 85

INTRODUCTION

Laser-cutting processes are high-spatial-definition derivatives from traditional thermal-cutting processes, such as plasma and flame cutting. Each process consists of applying more heat power to a workpiece surface than the workpiece can dissipate through conduction, convection, and radiative heat transfer. Consequently, the local accumulation of energy raises the temperature of the workpiece beyond its melting point. Then material removal can easily take place with the aid of pressurized assist-gas (*Figure 5-1*).

Compared to traditional thermal-cutting sources, high-power industrial laser beams can concentrate a high-power beam incident on a workpiece within a very small focus spot, typically less than 0.020 in. (0.51 mm) in diameter. This creates extremely high power densities that actually melt and even vaporize metals almost instantaneously. The double action of this liquefaction and

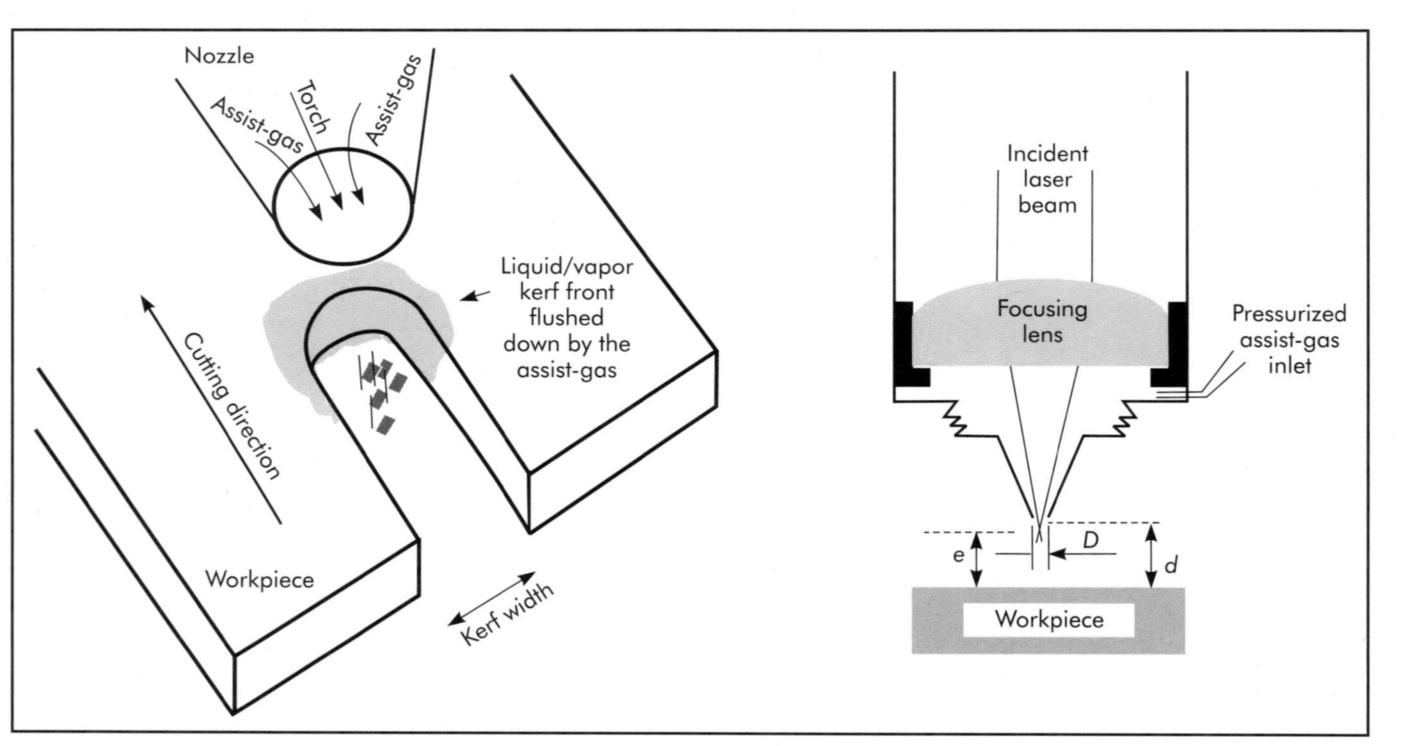

Figure 5-1. Thermal cutting process: the torch heats up the metal beyond its melting point. Liquefied and vaporized metal in the kerf front can be removed under the blowing action of pressurized assist-gas. Key parameters to be set up include assist-gas type and pressure; feed rate; laser-output peak power duty and frequency; nozzle diameter, D; nozzle standoff, d; and focus position, e, relative to the workpiece's surface.

vaporization, added to the flushing action of the assist-gas, enables the metal removal, forming a material void called *kerf*. Since the focus spot is so minute, more heat is transferred and propagates through the workpiece in the direction of the laser radiation than by conduction in its transverse directions. Other benefits include:

- higher contour definition and precision;
- superior edge quality;
- faster cutting speeds;
- a narrower heat-affected zone (HAZ), and
- a more efficient melting process.

A beam of laser light replacing a traditional torch as a source of heat requires specific elements associated with the particular nature and properties of laser light. The following sections detail specific key process input variables involved in laser-cutting methods.

ASSIST-GAS TYPES

There are four main types of assist-gases used for cutting:

- pure reactive gas, such as oxygen and hydrogen;
- pure inert gas, such as argon and helium;
- neutral gases, such as nitrogen, which are not chemically reactive with a majority of metals and are low-cost alternatives to inert gases, and
- any combination of the above, such as air (21% O_2 + 78% N_2 + 1% Ar).

In some applications, additional mist or even a water shower assists laser cutting by cooling the workpiece. *Table 5-1* summarizes the most common assist-gases used in industrial laser-cutting applications.

LASER-GAS TYPES

Laser gases for industrial, metal-cutting CO_2 lasers consist of specialty mixtures of about 3–9% CO_2, at least 30% helium, and

Table 5-1. Typical assist-gas types used in industrial laser cutting of metals

Material	Assist-gas, psi (bar)	Comment
Mild steel	Low-pressure O_2 21.76–26.11 (1.5–1.8)	Most common for 0.250 in. (6.40 mm) and thicker
Mild steel	Medium-pressure O_2 26.11–72.52 (1.8–5.0)	Most common for less than 0.250-in. (6.40-mm) thickness
Mild steel	High-pressure N_2 72.5–290.1 (5–20)	Mostly for high-speed cutting of thin sheets and to avoid oxide scales on steel cut edges
Mild steel	High-pressure air 72.5–290.1 (5–20)	Mostly for high-speed cutting of thin sheets—lower speed and lower cost than pure N_2 and increases edge oxidization
Stainless steel	High-pressure N_2 72.5–290.1 (5–20)	Most common
Stainless steel	High-pressure air 72.5–290.1 (5–20)	Lower cost than pure N_2 but increases edge oxidization and dross
Aluminum alloys	High-pressure N_2 72.5–290.1 (5–20)	For special non-oxidized cut edge and/or thick plate requirement
Aluminum alloys	High-pressure air 72.5–290.1 (5–20)	Most common for aluminum—lower cost than pure N_2 but increases dross
Copper alloys	Low-pressure O_2 21.76–26.11 (1.5–1.8)	Moderately more efficient than air
Brass	Low-pressure O_2 21.76–26.11 (1.5–1.8)	Moderately more efficient than air

Table 5-1. (continued)

Material	Assist-gas, psi (bar)	Comment
Brass	High-pressure O_2 or N_2 up to 290.1 (20)	High-speed cutting of thin sheets
Titanium alloys	High-pressure Ar	For aerospace applications, reactive O_2 and N_2 are avoided 43.5–145.0 (3–10)
Nickel alloys	Low-pressure O_2 up to 43.5 (3)	For energy industry applications, high cutting speed is enabled but with dross and edge oxidation
Nickel alloys	High-pressure N_2 43.5–145.0 (3–10)	For aerospace and energy industry applications there is slower cutting speed than with O_2 assist, but less dross and no edge oxidation

Note: The numerical values indicated are absolute pressures and not relative to atmospheric pressure. Additional gas mixtures, such as Ar/He and N_2/H_2, are sometimes useful for certain applications such as titanium or high-speed, thin-sheet cutting.

the balance nitrogen. A few CO_2 laser manufacturers specify additional O_2 and up to 6% of CO in the mix to minimize depletion of CO_2 by upsetting the balance of the chemical reaction depicted in *Equation 5-1*. Handling requires special care, since CO is highly toxic, odorless, and colorless. Xenon (Xe) is added in small proportions with some laser models to improve lasing efficiency and stability. This generally reduces consumption of laser gas and the frequency of downtime for cylinder changes.

$$CO_2 \leftrightarrow CO + 1/2\ O_2 \tag{5-1}$$

where:

CO_2 = carbon dioxide
CO = carbon monoxide
O_2 = oxygen

Some laser models require that each gas of the mixture be supplied in separate individual cylinders, as they are equipped with an onsite gas mixer to create the right proportion before feeding to the resonator cavity. Other laser models require pre-mixed gas packaged in a single cylinder with the exact proportions and impurity control levels specified by laser manufacturers.

GAS SUPPLY

Laser and assist-gases are supplied in several modes adapted to the consumption rate, flow rate, and supply-pressure requirements:

- For low consumption rates, cylinders are brought inside a plant individually or by battery of six to 16. The gas is in compressed form for most types, such as N_2, O_2, and He. CO_2 is stored in liquid form in a cylinder and can only be supplied at low pressure, below a few psi (bar). In cylinder form, gas purity can be up to 99.999% for gases such as N_2 and O_2. The maximum purity available for CO_2 is notably lower. The cylinders are generally made of steel or aluminum. A standard, industrial grade N_2 gas cylinder contains a little less than 300.31 standard cubic feet (SCF) (27.9 m^3) of gas compressed at close to 2,176 psi (150 bar). A bank of 12 cylinders with 3,600.53 SCF (334.5 m^3) total capacity can supply about eight hours of stainless-steel-cutting assist at 950 ft^3/hr (448 L/min) and flow rate of 167 psi (10 bar).

- For medium consumption rates of assist-gas, liquid Dewars can be employed indoors with standard supply pressures of up to 200 psi (14 bar) for oxygen assist-gas. Alternatively, Dewars can accommodate high supply pressures of up to 450 psi (31 bar) for nitrogen assist-gas. For medium to high consumption rates at high supply pressures, trailer tubes present a strong alternative solution. They can be 38.06 ft (11.6 m) in length, and contain the equivalent of as many as 36 cylinders of gas at a pressure as high as 2,600 psi (179 bar). They are generally installed on the outside of a facility. Tubes require less frequent non-value-added handling than cylinders and do not require a special foundation pad.
- For high consumption rates of assist-gas, such as nitrogen and oxygen, a bulk supply is more appropriate. Bulk supplies consist of large external tanks installed outside a plant. Tanks such as the one shown in *Figure 5-2* store gas in liquid form with a vaporizer, which is needed to supply gas pressure up to about 218 psi (15 bar) with standard bulk tanks and 580 psi (40 bar) with special high-pressure bulk tanks. An optional boost pump can help build up to 580 psi (40 bar) of supply pressure. Commercially available pressure-building devices with no pump or moving parts are popular alternatives to boost pumps and high-pressure tanks. Although there is an added initial cost for installation of the required concrete foundation pad, liquid gas from a bulk tank costs less per hundred cubic feet (cubic meters) than the same gas supplied from individual cylinders or tubes. A 1,500 gal (5,678 L) tank of liquid oxygen contains the equivalent of 170,000 SCF (4,814 m^3) of oxygen gas, whereas the same tank full with liquid nitrogen would contain the equivalent of 140,000 SCF (3,964 m^3) of nitrogen gas. These tanks are specially built with double-wall thermal insulation to maintain the liquid gas at its cryogenic temperature (under atmospheric pressure conditions, oxygen becomes liquid under –296° F [91 K],

Figure 5-2. Bulk tank containing liquid oxygen with its vaporizer standing on the side.

whereas nitrogen turns liquid under –321° F [77 K]). Despite this insulation precaution, liquid gas boils continuously inside a tank and loss of molecules by venting must take place to prevent pressure build-up beyond the tank's safety limit.

Some facilities have their own on-site air separator to extract N_2 from the atmosphere with adjustable industrial-grade purity of 95–99.9%. Nitrogen is collected by diffusion when air is transmitted through a special material membrane. The higher the purity of nitrogen sought after, the lower the flow-rate capacity of the unit at equal footprint. Such installations need an optional compressor to raise available pressure above 145 psi (10 bar). Assist-air is usually supplied from a shop compressor with a high-quality, high-pressure filter and dryer system.

For high-pressure laser cutting with air and nitrogen assist-gas, the needed stagnation pressure ranges between 87–290 psi (6–20 bar) at the cutting nozzle. Such stagnation pressures correspond to flow rates of 100–1,500 ft^3/hr (47–708 L/min), depending on the nozzle's exit diameter. In *Table 5-2*, room conditions are 14.7 psi (1 bar) atmospheric pressure and 80° F [300 K] temperature; 1.00 ft^3/hr = 28.3 L/hr = 0.47 L/min).

In comparison, low-pressure O_2 laser cutting of thick mild steel requires less than 29 psi (2 bar) of stagnation pressure inside the cutting nozzle of an exit diameter of 0.08 in. (2 mm) (less than 14.7 psi [1 bar] above atmospheric pressure). This corresponds to a flow rate of less than 100 ft^3/hr (47 L/min).

With laser-cutting metals, such as mild steel with O_2 assist-gas, the thicker the plate, the lower the required assist-gas pressure setting. About 21.76–26.11 psi (1.5–1.8 bar) of O_2 is all that is needed to cut mild steel plates thicker than about 3/16 in. (4.8 mm)—whereas 0.04-in. (1-mm) thick mild steel needs up to 58 psi (4 bar) of O_2 or an even higher pressure of N_2. However, when cutting thicker stainless steel and aluminum with N_2, a much higher pressure of N_2 (up to 300 psi [21 bar]) is needed.

Table 5-2. Orders of magnitude for typical flow rates for N_2 and O_2 assist-gas through different nozzle diameters at different stagnation pressures

	N_2 Pressure, psi (bar)	
	87 (6)	**290 (20)**
Nozzle diameter, in. (mm)	0.04, 0.06, 0.08 (1, 1.5, 2)	0.04, 0.06, 0.08 (1, 1.5, 2)
Flow rate, ft^3/hr (L/min)	110, 250, 450 (52, 118, 212)	400, 800, 1,500 (189, 378, 708)
	O_2 Pressure, psi (bar)	
	22.00 (1.5)	**73 (5)**
Nozzle diameter, in. (mm)	0.04, 0.06, 0.08 (1, 1.5, 2)	0.04, 0.06, 0.08 (1, 1.5, 2)
Flow rate, ft^3/hr (L/min)	25, 60, 100 (12, 28, 47)	90, 200, 350 (43, 94, 165)

Note: The indicated pressure values are absolute and not relative to atmospheric pressure. For example, 22.00 psi (1.5 bar) absolute pressure would read 7.25 psi (0.5 bar) on a scale relative to atmospheric pressure on standard pressure gages.

GAS PURITY

The purity of oxygen assist-gas is experimentally proven to impact cutting speed: from an industrial grade of 99.5% purity to a high-purity grade of 99.9% and above, a 10–30% cutting speed improvement can be expected with a CO_2 laser on mild steel (Schmidt 1996; Gabzdyl 1996; Powell et al. 1992). However, the cost to purchase high-purity oxygen is generally not matched with an upgrade of the assist-gas delivery system so it preserves the high purity all the way from the gas cylinder, tube, or bulk tank to the kerf in the workpiece. What good is a 99.99% purity gas cylinder if it is hooked up to a gas-delivery system that allows leakage, diffusion (see Chapter 4), or exposure to a polluted room atmosphere during cylinder exchange? Industrial-grade O_2 assist-gas is a lower-cost choice, but it must be accompanied with a sound gas-delivery system that can preserve the purity of the gas (Smith and Penn 2000). The same is true for inert gases such as Ar and neutral gases such as N_2. Industrial-grade purity, along with a quality gas-delivery system, should suffice for quality edges in most applications. For top-notch operations, a higher-purity grade can bring significant productivity advantages.

Degrading the purity level below industrial grade can have sharp consequences on the quality and speed of the cut. The main gas quality-control effort should focus on avoiding major contamination (absolute change of more than 0.5% in assist-gas composition). In a typical scenario, an operator can immediately switch from piercing with O_2 to cutting stainless steel with N_2. The initial cutting performance will be subpar with an increase in cut-edge roughness and dross if precautions are not taken. Troubleshooting should include ensuring that the part of the assist-gas-delivery system common to O_2 and N_2 distribution lines has been thoroughly purged of all O_2 by flushing with clean N_2. A mixture of high-purity N_2 with O_2 resident in the pipes may lead to a nitrogen purity level below 99% for a period of time. This is enough to exhibit noticeable cutting performance degradation, particularly when the programmer sets an aggressively high cutting-feed rate.

In contrast to assist-gas, the purity of laser gases is specified much higher than lower-cost industrial grade. Higher-purity gas yields a more efficient lasing mechanism and an appreciably longer life of consumable and non-consumable components in the laser. Higher-purity gas also yields higher peak power and better beam stability and mode structure.

Rather than blindly specifying a high-purity gas for CO_2 lasers, gas companies have conducted research aimed at ranking the relative impact of specific impurities in laser gas on laser performance (in other words, output power and mode characteristics, stability, repeatability, reliability, life of components, etc.). Earlier research established that the addition of small quantities of carbon monoxide (CO) enhanced the life of optics and excitation electrodes by reducing the depletion of CO_2 into CO, C, and O_2. This technique is not in widespread use due to the highly toxic nature of CO.

Gas suppliers established long ago that, rather than produce super-high-purity laser gases by specifying a low level of global impurity, it is much smarter and less expensive to control the adjusted levels of specific detrimental impurities (Marie et al. 1988). *Figure 5-3* shows that some impurities are much more harmful than others. For example, 10 parts per million (ppm) of acetylene (C_2H_2) has a similar negative effect on laser oscillation gain (efficiency) as 1,000 ppm of propane (C_3H_8) or 10,000 ppm of methane (CH_4). Even though 10,000 ppm of CH_4 is below the threshold for harming gains in laser oscillation, this high level of contamination is not recommended as it gathers on optics and glassware and accelerates degradation of the resonator cavity performance. A sound practice to ensure the control of impurities is to segregate cylinders and tanks used for CO_2 laser gases and make them non-interchangeable with the cylinders used for other applications involving gases with less purity or harmful contaminants. For example, contamination by hydrocarbons, such as C_2H_2 above the recommended ppm level, can be prevented, whereas pursuit of controlling CH_4 contamination way below a reasonable 1-ppm target level may add more cost than value.

Water moisture (H_2O), another specific impurity, destabilizes direct current (DC) and radio frequency (RF) discharges and accelerates degradation of the optical properties of cavity mirrors, some of which may have extremely hygroscopic coatings (in other words, they absorb moisture in a self-destructing reaction). The end result is a loss in efficiency that is often corrected by an increase in excitation current from the power supplies in production.

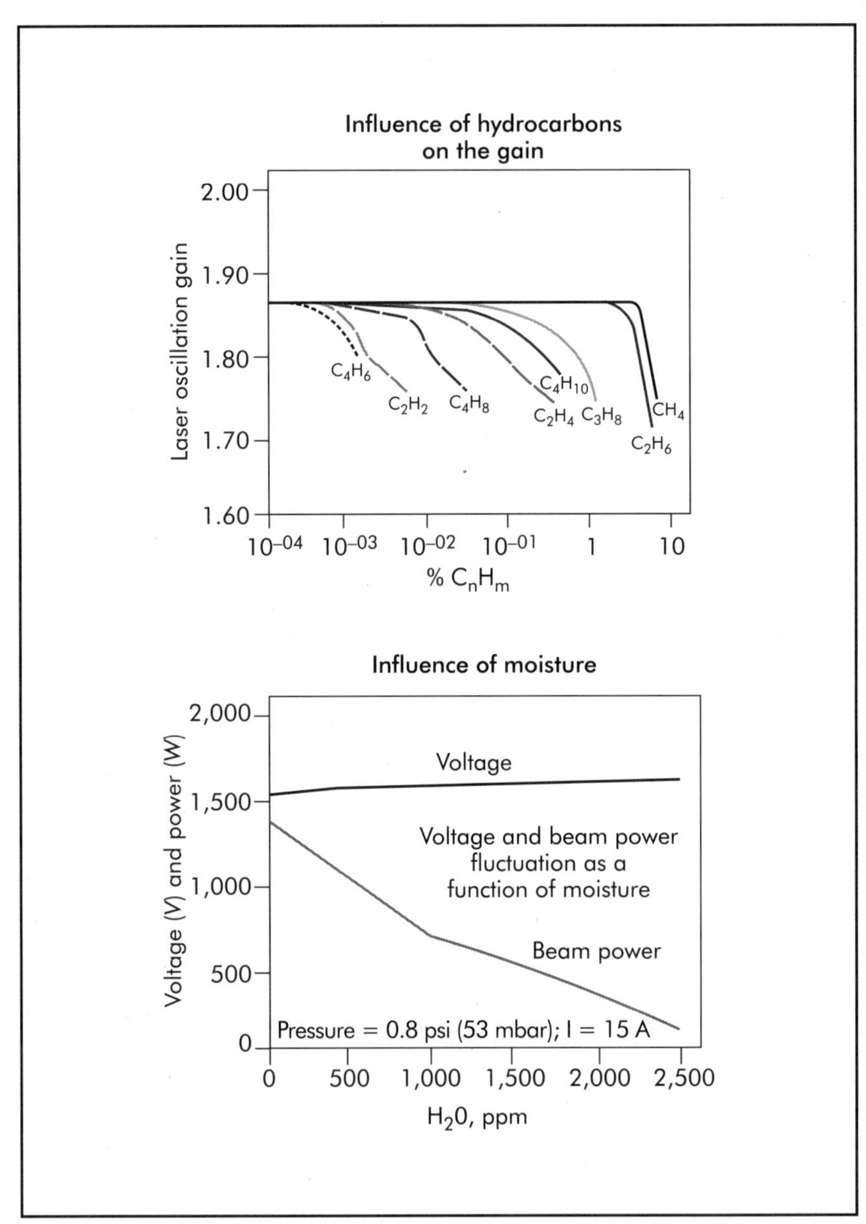

Figure 5-3. Hydrocarbons and moisture contamination in CO_2 laser-gas mix. The impact on efficiency and productivity can be measured by its influence on the laser cavity's amplification gain or output power. The threshold concentration before significant gain loss is far higher for methane (CH_4) than for acetylene (C_2H_2). (Courtesy Air Liquide America)

If the increase is demanded repeatedly at ever-increasing amplitude, it may lead to a power-supply failure. This causes not only expense but also significant downtime to identify the root cause of failure and replace failed components. Moisture contamination in the laser-gas cylinder or laser-gas distribution and circulation system must be controlled to less than 5 ppm.

Other impurities found in CO_2 gas cylinders and tanks are COS and SO_2 molecules. Fortunately, these compounds are found well below the 100-ppm level at which harm to laser oscillation gain starts. Argon impurities have no significant effect on gain unless they are a small percentage of the proportion of contamination (Air Liquide America 2002). For enhanced control of impurities, the inside walls of laser-gas cylinders undergo a special surface treatment to limit adsorption of any gas impurity on the internal walls. Less adsorption takes place on aluminum than on steel walls.

All the previous precautions to produce, prepare, store, and deliver laser gases impact productivity by increasing the mean time between cleaning of optics and the life of optics, power supplies, electrodes, and other laser resonator components. A net positive effect results in overall downtime reduction.

ASSIST-GAS DELIVERY NOZZLE GEOMETRY

Nozzle geometry plays a crucial role in the dynamics of assist-gas, which has a pivotal influence on cutting performance. From a fluid mechanics perspective, assist-gas flow flushing away hot molten metal mixed with metallic vapors through the narrow capillary formed by a kerf inevitably yields turbulence, particularly when the assist-gas flow reaches supersonic speed. Minimizing turbulence can be a benefit as it limits heat loss by convection, along with roughness and gouging in the kerf. Nozzle design should incorporate a straight section (length, L, indicated in *Figure 5-4*), at least two times larger than the nozzle's throat diameter, D, to limit turbulent flow. The larger the diameter, the more tolerant the cutting process will be to focused-beam deviation from the center of the nozzle. One major drawback is that at a constant stagnation pressure, the consumption of assist-gas grows quadratically with nozzle diameter.

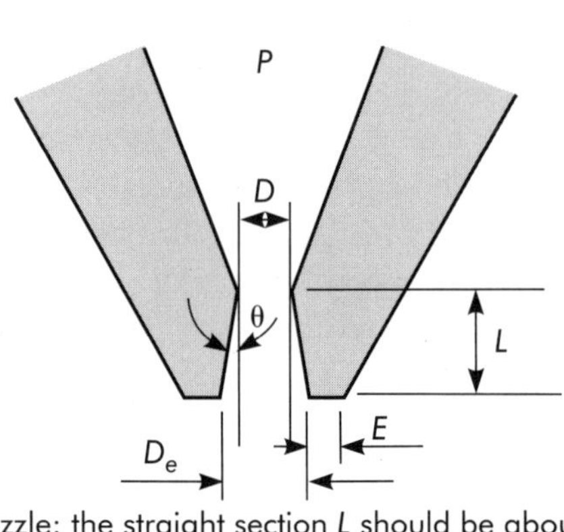

Cutting nozzle: the straight section *L* should be about twice throat diameter *D*. A thicker section *E* is preferred for high-pressure systems. Angle θ is preferably 0° for short *L* and high stagnation pressure *P*.

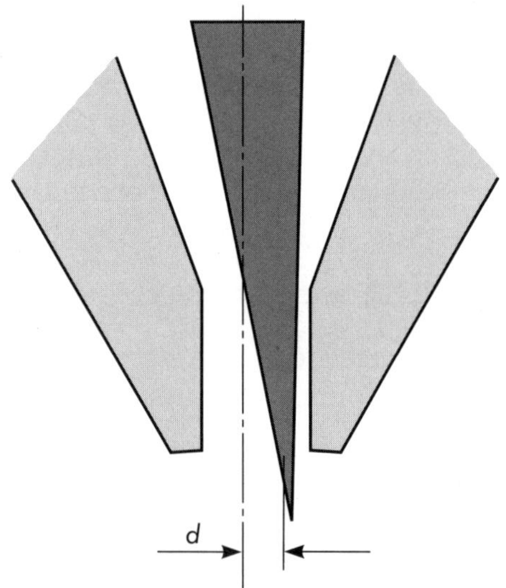

Cutting nozzle: a wider exit diameter makes the laser-cutting process more tolerant to beam-centering deviation *d*.

Figure 5-4. Nozzle geometry plays a decisive role in defining which assist-gas dynamics determine cut-edge quality. Stagnation pressure, P, and throat diameter, D, are determining factors of flow rate.

A gas at stagnation pressure, P_0, flowing through the nozzle orifice of a throat diameter reaches supersonic speed at the narrowest section of the nozzle geometry (the nozzle's throat) as soon as:

$$\frac{P_0}{P_a} \geq \left(\frac{\gamma+1}{2}\right)^{\frac{\gamma}{\gamma-1}} \quad (5\text{-}2)$$

where:

P_0 = stagnation pressure inside the nozzle
P_a = atmospheric pressure outside the nozzle exit
γ = ratio of specific heat coefficients of the assist-gas (see Appendix C)

For laser-cutting assist-gas molecules, the vibrational modes of the molecules are frozen for temperatures below 1,340° F (1,000 K) ($Z \approx 0$ at 80° F [300 K] room temperature). *Table 5-3* compares theoretical and experimental data for the specific heat ratios of common assist-gases.

In a supersonic flow regime, gas molecules travel faster than the speed of sound. An initial shock wave is generated when the flowing assist-gas collides with the ambient atmosphere, starting at the lip formed by the exit of the nozzle. It develops the form of a barrel as shown in *Figure 5-5*. Another shock wave called Mach disk closes this barrel downstream. Eventually the reflection of

Table 5-3. Theoretical and experimental data for specific heat ratio of common assist-gas (Atkins 1993)

	Theoretical γ High Temperature >3,140° F (>2,000 K)	Theoretical γ Room Temperature 80° F (300 K)	Experimental γ Room Temperature 80° F (300 K)
O_2	1.29	1.40	1.40
N_2	1.29	1.40	1.41
He	1.66	1.66	1.66
Ar	1.66	1.66	1.66
CO_2	1.15	1.40	1.30
H_2O	1.17	1.33	
Air	1.29	1.40	1.44

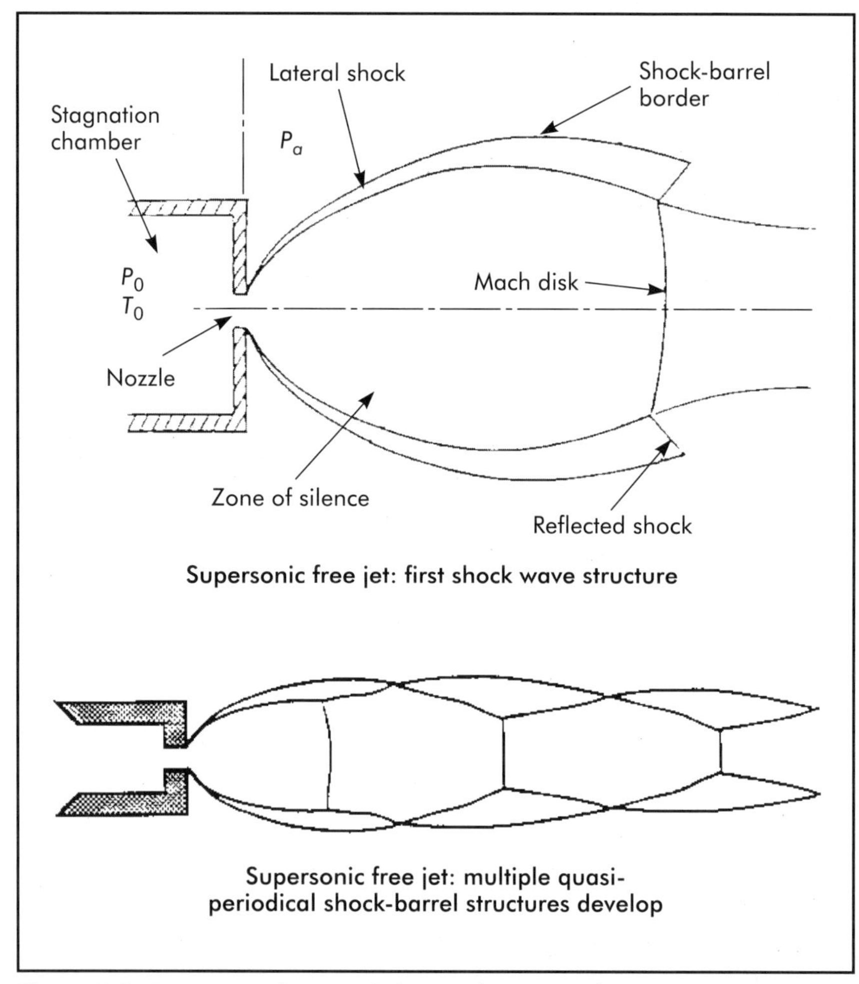

Figure 5-5. Supersonic flows colliding with matter always generate at least one shock wave. In free jets, a shock-barrel structure contains a silence zone isolated from ambient atmosphere by a lateral shock barrel and a front shock called a Mach disk.

the lateral barrel shock wave against the Mach disk shock wave creates another shock barrel and Mach disk structure similar to the first one, and subsequent ones in a quasi-periodic pattern. Because of its supersonic nature, mechanical perturbation downstream of a supersonic flow cannot affect an upstream event. Mechanical perturbation includes all physical phenomena involving mass transfer, as opposed to optical perturbations, such as light radiation. For example, heat can propagate by mechanical perturbation, such as convection, and optical perturbation, such as radiative heat transfer. As such, if a supersonic flow of assist-gas impinges a 3,140° F (2,000 K) vaporized metal in the kerf, the assist-gas temperature upstream of the kerf cannot be convectively heated by the kerf. Were it not for the kerf's radiative heat, the temperature of the nozzle assembly and assist-gas it contains would not rise above room temperature.

A study of the first shock-barrel structure in *Figure 5-5* reveals features and characteristics that could serve as a model for subsequent downstream shock barrels. The initial shock barrel is limited on the side by a lateral shock-wave barrel and in its downstream front by the Mach-disk shock wave positioned at distance x_M from the nozzle exit of throat diameter D. A well-accepted empirical equation for x_M shows that it is directly proportional to D and grows proportionally to the square root of stagnation pressure P_0 (Ashkenas and Sherman 1965).

$$\frac{x_M}{D} = 0.67\sqrt{\frac{P_0}{P_a}} \tag{5-3}$$

where:

x_M = distance from the nozzle exit
D = throat diameter

The volume flow rate in standard cubic feet per hour (SCFH) through the nozzle can be computed by the following equations (also see *Table C-1* of Appendix C).

For subsonic flows:

$$V_f = \beta_{sub}\frac{P_0 D^2}{\sqrt{T_0}}\sqrt{\left(\frac{P_a}{P_0}\right)^{\frac{2}{\gamma}} - \left(\frac{P_a}{P_0}\right)^{\frac{\gamma+1}{\gamma}}} \tag{5-4}$$

For supersonic flows:

$$V_f = \beta_{sup}\frac{P_0 D^2}{\sqrt{T_0}} \tag{5-5}$$

where:

V_f = volume flow rate, SCFH (1 SCFH = 0.47 L/min)

P_0, respectively P_a = stagnation pressure in the cutting head, respectively the ambient atmospheric pressure, both in Pascals (Pa) (10^5 Pa = 14.7 psi). Note that P_0 and P_a are absolute pressures: a pressure that reads 7.4 psi (0.5 bar or 0.5 10^5 Pa) for P_0 would actually mean a value of 22.1 psi (1.5 bar or 1.5 10^5 Pa), whereas the atmospheric pressure, P_a, is 14.7 psi (1 bar or 10^5 Pa).

D = nozzle throat diameter, m (1 in. = 0.0254 m)

T_0 = temperature of the assist-gas in the cutting head, K

The volume flow rates are converted to SCFH. Values for β_{sup} and β_{sub} are provided in *Table C-4* of Appendix C for common assist-gases. As an example, for nitrogen assist-gas, β_{sup} = 3,174 and β_{sub} = 12,265, whereas for oxygen, β_{sup} = 2,969 and β_{sub} = 11,473.

Table 5-4 illustrates computations for flow rate and position, x_M, of Mach disk for two different nozzle diameters and assist-gases. In the case of O_2 assist-gas, stagnation pressure of 21.76 psi (1.5 bar) in a nozzle is not sufficient to generate a supersonic regime as verified in *Equation 5-2*; therefore, no shock waves are generated. A mostly laminar flow exists in this condition, until it encounters the hot liquid-vapor metal of the kerf front.

Flow rates can be measured quite accurately with simple, commercially available devices. However, the user must be cautious as flow-meter scales are generally calibrated for a specific gas or group of gases. For example, a floating-ball-type flow meter with a scale calibrated for measuring the flow rate of gas #1 in SCFH also may be used to measure the flow rate of gas #2. To obtain the real measurement for gas #2, the value read on the scale should be multiplied by:

$$\sqrt{\frac{m_1 P_2 T_1}{m_2 P_1 T_2}}$$

Table 5-4. Flow rates and position, x_M, of Mach disk for two different stagnation pressures

Assist-Gas	Molar Mass, g	γ	*D*, in. (mm)	P_0, psi (bar)	Pressure Threshold Supersonic Regime, psi (bar)	Mach Disk Position, x_M, in. (mm)	Flow Rate, SCFH (L/min)
O_2	32	1.40	0.06 (1.5)	147 (10)	27.800 (1.89)	0.125 (3.18)	385.71 (181.9)
N_2	28	1.40	0.06 (1.5)	147 (10)	27.800 (1.89)	0.125 (3.18)	412.34 (194.5)
H_2	2	1.40	0.06 (1.5)	147 (10)	27.800 (1.89)	0.125 (3.18)	1,542.83 (727.7)
Air	29	1.40	0.06 (1.5)	147 (10)	27.800 (1.89)	0.125 (3.18)	405.17 (191.1)
CO_2	44	1.40	0.06 (1.5)	147 (10)	27.800 (1.89)	0.125 (3.18)	328.93 (155.2)
Ar	40	1.67	0.06 (1.5)	147 (10)	30.000 (2.05)	0.125 (3.18)	365.82 (172.6)
He	4	1.67	0.06 (1.5)	147 (10)	30.000 (2.05)	0.125 (3.18)	1,156.84 (545.6)
H_2O	18	1.33	0.06 (1.5)	147 (10)	27.000 (1.85)	0.125 (3.18)	505.19 (238.3)
Assist-Gas	**Molar Mass, g**	**γ**	***D*, in. (mm)**	**P_0, psi (bar)**	**Pressure Threshold Subsonic Regime, psi (bar)**	**Mach Disk Position, x_M, in. (mm)**	**Flow Rate, SCFH (L/min)**
O_2	32	1.40	0.06 (1.5)	22.00 (1.5)	27.800 (1.89)	NA	59.17 (27.9)
N_2	28	1.40	0.06 (1.5)	22.00 (1.5)	27.800 (1.89)	NA	59.17 (27.9)
H_2	2	1.40	0.06 (1.5)	22.00 (1.5)	27.800 (1.89)	NA	221.38 (104.4)
Air	29	1.40	0.06 (1.5)	22.00 (1.5)	27.800 (1.89)	NA	58.14 (27.4)
CO_2	44	1.40	0.06 (1.5)	22.00 (1.5)	27.800 (1.89)	NA	47.20 (22.3)
Ar	40	1.67	0.06 (1.5)	22.00 (1.5)	30.000 (2.05)	NA	51.26 (24.2)
He	4	1.67	0.06 (1.5)	22.00 (1.5)	30.000 (2.05)	NA	162.11 (76.5)
H_2O	18	1.33	0.06 (1.5)	22.00 (1.5)	27.000 (1.85)	NA	72.95 (34.4)

Note: The pressures indicated are absolute: 22 psi means a reading on the gage of 7.4 psi relative to atmospheric pressure.

where:

P_1, T_1 = pressure and temperature, respectively, used during scale calibration with gas #1 of molar mass, m_1, per the manufacturer of the flow meter, Pa (K)

P_2, T_2 = static pressure and temperature, respectively, of the measured gas #2 of molar mass, m_2, in the flow meter, Pa (K)

Table 5-5 gives values for this factor for common gases if $P_1 = P_2$ and $T_1 = T_2$. This table gives a conversion approximation. An accurate reading can be obtained with a thorough on-site calibration.

It is interesting to derive from *Equation 5-5* that in a supersonic regime, the relative percent of variation of volume flow rate:

$$\frac{\Delta(\text{flow rate})}{\text{flow rate}}$$

is directly proportional to pressure variation. It is double the relative variation in diameter and negatively proportional to half the temperature relative variation as per the following derivation for a supersonic regime:

$$\frac{\Delta(\text{flow rate})}{\text{flow rate}} = \left|\frac{\Delta P_0}{P_0}\right| + \frac{1}{2}\left|-\frac{\Delta T_0}{T_0}\right| + 2\left|\frac{\Delta D}{D}\right| \tag{5-6}$$

So, if

$$\frac{\Delta(\text{flow rate})}{\text{flow rate}} = -5\%$$

is specified as the maximum allowable range of flow rate for good cutting performance, it can be reached with ±5% pressure variation, ±10% temperature variation, or ±2.5% nozzle-diameter variation. A low pressure of 27.412 psi (1.89 bar) of O_2 means ±1.45 psi (±0.1 bar) assist-gas-pressure control is necessary. This high sensitivity to variation of O_2 pressure is consistent with experimental results (Schmidt 1996).

The same allowable ±5% of flow-rate variation is much more forgiving at 145 psi (10 bar) of N_2 assist-gas because stagnation pressure must be controlled to within ±7.25 psi (±0.5 bar) when everything else is constant. Similarly, a ±5% flow-rate variation

Table 5-5. Flow-meter scale reading conversion

Gas for Meter Calibration Scale	Measured Gas				
	O_2 (32 g)	N_2 (28 g)	Ar (44 g)	Air (29 g)	He (4 g)
O_2 (32 g)	1.000	1.073	0.895	1.051	2.830
N_2 (28 g)	0.932	1.000	0.834	0.980	2.638
Ar (44 g)	1.118	1.199	1.000	1.175	3.162
Air (29 g)	0.951	1.021	0.851	1.000	2.692
He (4 g)	0.353	0.379	0.316	0.371	1.000

Example: A flow meter with a scale calibrated for nitrogen (N_2) is used to measure the flow rate of Argon (Ar). The scale reads 100 ft^3/hr. The pressure and temperature for the measurement are the same as the ones used to calibrate with N_2. The real flow rate is then $100 \times 0.834 = 83.4$ ft^3/hr. In the same conditions, a flow of helium (He) also reads 100 ft^3/hr. The real flow of helium is obtained by $100 \times 2.638 = 263.8$ ft^3/hr or $83.4 \times 3.162 = 263.8$ ft^3/hr.

means that when replacing a 0.08 in. (2.0 mm) nozzle with a spare one, the difference between their diameters must be within ±0.002 in. (±0.05 mm); a 0.04 in. (1.0 mm) nozzle would allow half this tolerance. With such high sensitivity to nozzle-diameter variation, it seems wise to choose large-diameter nozzles whenever economical.

A ±5% allowable flow-rate variation also means that at room temperature of 80° F (300 K), the temperature of the assist-gas must be maintained to within ±54° F (±30 K). This indicates that variations in morning versus afternoon room temperatures have little chance to make a difference in cutting performance. However, during cold winter days, transitioning to a heated facility after an unheated environment overnight may make a difference (at least initially). This risk is favorably lessened by the fact that the nozzle assembly remains in such close proximity to the workpiece that radiative heat transfer from the kerf maintains the cutting head and the assist-gas inside it at an elevated temperature, which varies only slightly with room temperature.

In the case of a subsonic assist-gas flow rate, such as with low-pressure O_2 laser cutting, the variation in flow rates with respect to P_0 and P_a is more complex. From *Equation 5-4* it can be deduced that when neglecting variations in atmospheric pressure, P_a, (see Appendix C) for a subsonic regime:

$$\frac{\Delta(flow\ rate)}{flow\ rate} = \frac{1}{2}\frac{\gamma-1}{\gamma}\left[1+\frac{1}{1-\left(\frac{P_a}{P_0}\right)^{\frac{\gamma-1}{\gamma}}}\right]\left|\frac{\Delta P_0}{P_0}\right| + \frac{1}{2}\left|-\frac{\Delta T_0}{T_0}\right| + 2\left|\frac{\Delta D}{D}\right| \quad (5\text{-}7)$$

implying that

$$\frac{\Delta(flow\ rate)}{flow\ rate} \geq \left|\frac{\Delta P_0}{P_0}\right| + \frac{1}{2}\left|-\frac{\Delta T_0}{T_0}\right| + 2\left|\frac{\Delta D}{D}\right|$$

Just like in the supersonic regime, a subsonic regime with 5% variation in flow rate can be met with 10% relative temperature variation or 2.5% relative nozzle-diameter variation. However, a 5% variation in stagnation pressure yields more than 5% flow-rate variation (see Appendix C).

NOZZLES

Nozzles are consumables and care must be taken to limit their cost. Most nozzles are made of copper alloy that is easily machined. Copper alloy resists damage by laser radiation, since it is particularly reflective to high-power infrared light rather than absorbing it. Nozzle tips, such as those shown in *Figure 5-6*, are small end-pieces screwed or installed at the bottom tip of a laser head. They are easily replaceable and have low downtime and maintenance costs. Nozzle tips can be destroyed by collisions with raised objects on a table, or when processing with a centering deviation that makes the laser beam hit and heat the nozzle until it melts. They also can be destroyed when an accumulation of hot spatters sticks to them and clogs their exit diameter until burning starts as the focused laser-beam path is intersected.

Figure 5-6. (a) CO_2 laser-cutting example. (b) YAG laser-cutting example. (c) Nozzle tips are consumables that are easily mounted to a laser-cutting head. Their proximity to the workpiece exposes them to hot metal spatters, which clog and damage their exit holes. (Courtesy Rofin-Sinar)

Nozzle Standoff

From *Table 5-5*, the distance between the kerf and nozzle exit ultimately has a decisive impact on edge quality. If a Mach disk shock wave is positioned at the kerf, the shock wave resulting from its reflection on the kerf's top edge will induce violent disturbances of molten-metal flow down the kerf. Reflected shock waves might even deflect some flow of assist-gas away from the kerf's front. Publications describe the quasi-periodical nature of variations in measured assist-gas pressure as a function of distance from the nozzle exit (Powel 1998; Fieret and Ward 1986). This quasi-periodicity coincides with that of the barrel-shock structures evidenced in *Figure 5-5*.

The accuracy of theoretical calculations with actual assist-gas purity measurements along the assist-gas flow stream at several distances from the nozzle exit predicts the Venturi effect illustrated in *Figure 5-7*, which sucks surrounding atmospheric air into the kerf (O'Neill, Gabzdyl, and Steen 1992). Pressure variations due to shock-wave reflections and Venturi contamination combine to yield slower cutting speed, rougher edge surfaces, and gouging when the gas dynamics in the kerf become excessively unstable, or when insufficient assist-gas penetrates the front of the kerf with the laser beam. Gouging, dross, and surface roughness become even more pronounced with thick material that has

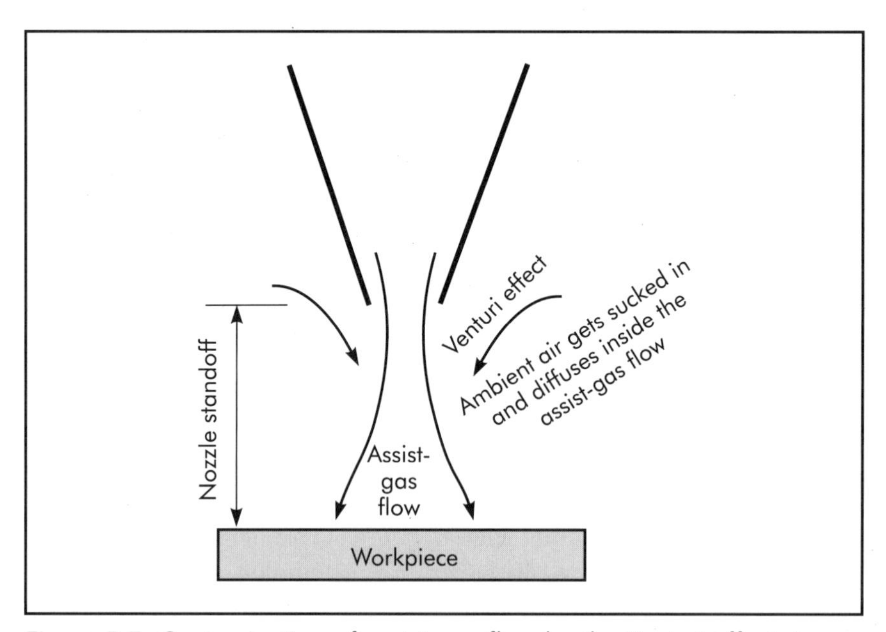

Figure 5-7. Contamination of assist-gas flow by the Venturi effect. Larger nozzle standoff distances promote more severe contamination.

high thermal conductivity. In these situations, the faster conduction cooling and solidification rate of molten metal before expulsion by pressurized assist-gas yields a rougher edge surface and more dross. To avoid positioning the kerf's top edge near the Mach disk, the nozzle standoff should be set shorter than the distance to the position of the first Mach disk (predictable by *Equation 5-3*). A distance of up to 90% of the nozzle diameter is recommended. If the nozzle is positioned too close to the kerf, it becomes exposed to more spatters and intense radiation generated by the heated metal and reflections of the laser beam back toward the nozzle. When the temperature of the nozzle and cutting-head assembly rises excessively, it contributes to the thermal distortion of the cutting-head assembly and beam misalignment. The temperature gradient of assist-gas immediately exiting the nozzle lip may also rise, inducing refractive deflection of the laser beam when it traverses the assist-gas on its way down to the workpiece. The overall consequences are downtime and an increased scrap rate due to the degradation of cutting performance, as well as shorter life of nozzle tips and focusing lens consumables.

Nozzle standoff is set up using numerical control and can be adjusted on the fly with a closed-loop, height-sensing probe during cutting. The height sensor can be a contact or noncontact probe. It measures the absolute distance between a reference point on the nozzle and the workpiece or its variations. The measurement then feeds back to the computer numerical controller (CNC), which processes the information and commands a servo-controlled, Z-axis adjustment to maintain the standoff constant through the entire workpiece surface. Any relief and non-uniformity of the sheet/plate flatness is then traced by the head to maintain constant standoff distance (see *Figure 4-8*).

Many height sensors are based on capacitive technology. Higher-cost optical and interferometric measurement systems produce an electrical signal proportionate to the distance between the sensor and metallic workpiece. If a height sensor is not calibrated properly, or its response time is too slow relative to the surface profile change at the motion feed rate, then nozzle standoff distance may vary from its nominal setup during cutting. A resultant change in the assist-gas flow dynamics and focus position yields unwanted variations in edge quality. Proper calibration can be established manually by comparing with a well-known spacer, or automatically with a CNC-programmed sequence using the accurate *Z*-axis, servo-controlled motion as a reference.

Unfortunately, the signal from capacitive sensors can be poisoned with electronic noise due to plasma radiation originating from the kerf front. The noise becomes more intense with high peak power. Nominal nozzle standoff and its tolerance vary with material type, thickness, edge-quality specification, laser type (for example, the value of M^2), characteristics of a laser beam incident on a focusing lens (f/D value), nozzle geometry, and assist-gas characteristics. Each cutting-system manufacturer supplies a database of cutting parameters including standoff values determined after extensive cutting-parameter developments. A typical nozzle standoff of 0.08 in. (2.0 mm) can be expected when cutting thick, mild-steel plates with low-pressure oxygen assist-gas and a 0.08-in. (2.0-mm) diameter nozzle. A 0.04 in. (1.0 mm) standoff is typical for high-pressure, nitrogen-assist laser cutting of thin mild steel with a 0.04-in. (1.0-mm) diameter nozzle.

Nozzle Alignment

For cutting curvilinear contours, the best cutting performances occur when the nozzle's circular aperture is machined with perfect axis symmetry. For applications that operate with a non-circular aperture of the nozzle, the wall geometry should be machined to accurately reflect the designed contour and symmetries. Even with perfectly axis-symmetric nozzles, it is essential that the laser beam be closely centered with respect to the nozzle exit aperture. This will contribute to maintaining steady cutting performance, regardless of the orientation of the cutting direction vector throughout the work envelope. Each time laser-mode tuning and external beam alignment in the beam-delivery system are performed, the laser beam has a slightly different pointing direction, which yields a beam-centering deviation, d, as illustrated in *Figure 5-4*. Beam-centering deviations also can occur after a nozzle tip or focusing lens is replaced. Lens or nozzle adjustments are the two main methods used to center a beam back to zero deviation. These adjustments are illustrated in *Figure 5-8*.

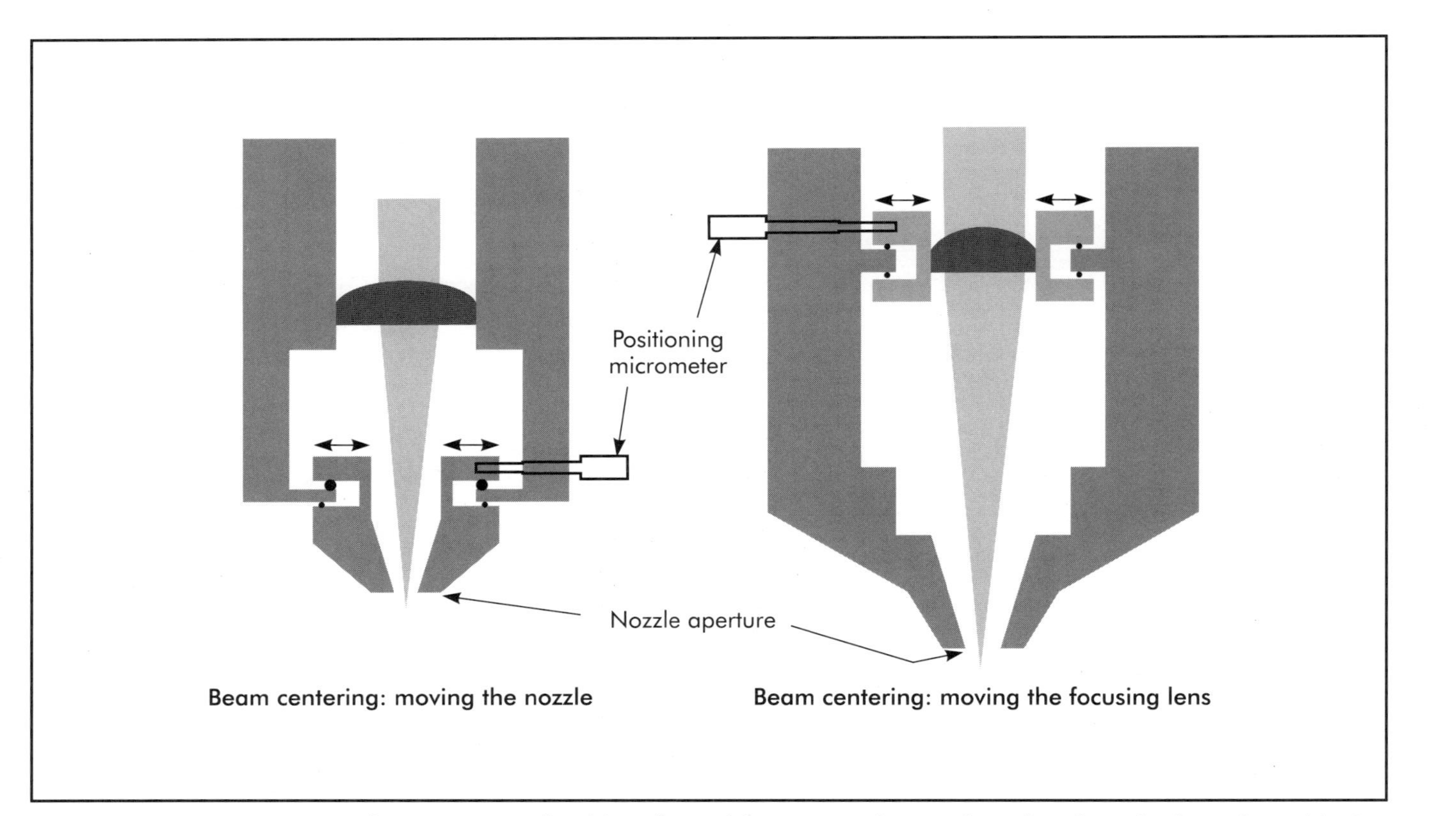

Figure 5-8. Beam-centering alignment is preferably achieved by moving the nozzle rather than the focus lens. Moving the lens can enhance astigmatism by misaligning the beam and focus lens axes.

In practice, alignment is achieved with the following simple shoot-and-adjust technique.

1. The laser resonator is operated at full power with the shutter closed to transition it into a hot state.
2. The lips of the nozzle apertures are first painted with a marker. Then, a piece of light-colored electrical tape is pressed to adhere onto the nozzle aperture against the marker's ink.
3. The laser output is set at low power for very short pulse duration. Power setting and pulse duration vary depending on the manufacturer.
4. Assist-gas pressure is turned on to build sufficient positive pressure to protect the focusing lens from eventual fumes, but not so strong as to pull the tape away.
5. The laser is turned off, the shutter is opened, and a pulse shot is immediately commanded. One shot of the focused beam is sufficient to pierce a hole through the tape.
6. The tape is removed and the marker's imprint (representing the nozzle aperture) and the pierced hole (representing the position of the focused laser beam) can be observed. If the hole is not at the center of the nozzle aperture, an adjustment of either the lens or nozzle assembly is necessary, and another iteration of this process can start at step 2. Otherwise, beam centering is successfully completed.

One shortfall of the centering technique is that some laser resonators, particularly at the high end of the power spectrum, have better pointing stability than others. For any industrial laser, a net difference in beam mode and pointing direction can be observed between the hot and cold states. For this reason, it is preferable to choose laser resonators with small differences between hot and cold modes. A larger aperture nozzle results in better reliability and reproducibility of the laser-cutting process, which may counterbalance the higher assist-gas consumption and cost.

Figure 5-9 shows the appearance of contaminated mirror surfaces of focusing lenses. The laser optics and the optics and conduits of the beam-delivery system get progressively dirty too, until cleaning or replacing them becomes necessary. As a result, the optical properties of an entire beam-delivery system change inevitably with time, possibly altering beam-to-nozzle centering be-

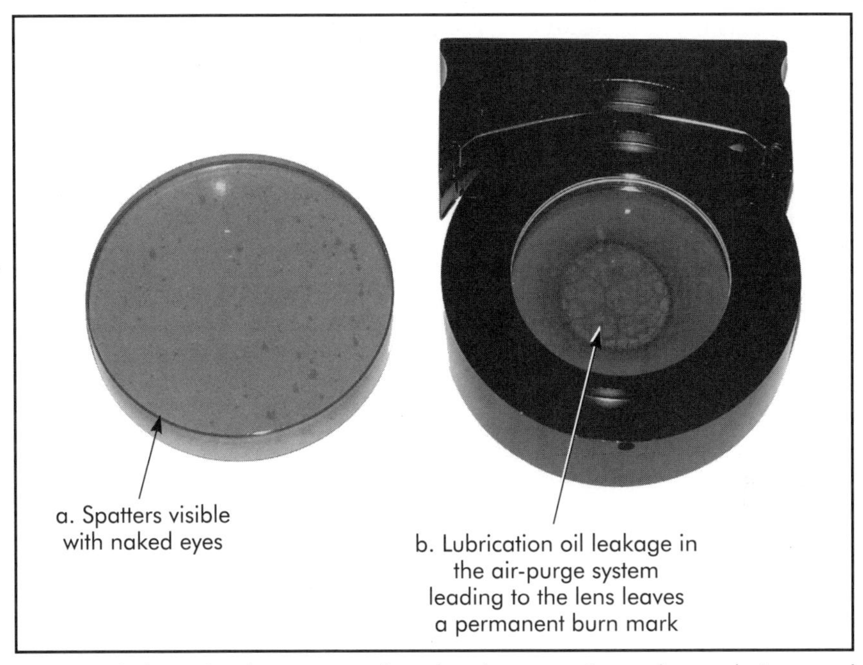

Figure 5-9. Focusing lenses are often the closest optics to the workpiece and are therefore exposed to metal spatters that contaminate their surfaces progressively. (a) Some spatters can be cleaned out only when close to the lens periphery. (b) When not cleaned, mirror-surface contamination leads to complete baking and destruction of the optics beyond reparability.

cause of induced thermal lensing. Beam-centering tolerance should be maximized by using large-diameter nozzles whenever economical with regard to gas consumption. Since nozzle-tip changes are performed more frequently than preventive maintenance on external and laser optics, adjustment of beam centering is performed anyway. Each adjustment inherently corrects the negative effect of degrading optics' properties.

WATER AND MIST ASSIST

When laser cutting thick plates of a metal with low thermal conductivity, such as mild steel, the feed rate is slow and maximum-output peak power is preferred. This combination yields an accumulation of heat and increased temperature of the workpiece. Thermal expansion may prevent parts that have been cut to drop freely from narrow kerf contours for collection. This forces manual intervention and downtime to hammer parts out and adjust cutting parameters.

By the time a part cools to room temperature, cut contours are being deformed due to two factors. The first is convection cooling of fin-like features, which is much less efficient than conduction cooling of features with large radii, thus yielding thermally induced bending and warping. The second factor relates to internal tensions in a metal such as springback. Absorption of heat by a metal can release internal stresses, making a perfectly straight cut path yield a curvilinear cut contour (see *Figure 5-10*). To remedy these problems, some manufacturers recommend an optional water spray to cool the workpiece. Less messy than water spray is a medium-to-high pressure mist shower around the kerf, which has a very efficient convection cooling effect.

The proportion of water vapor in the mist can be lower than room temperature humidity if specially dehumidified dry air is supplied. A larger proportion of water or other cooling compound in a mist results in enhanced convection cooling of the workpiece. Care must be taken to prevent the mist shower from contaminating the assist-gas, particularly low-pressure O_2. The design of a mist shower should be such that the arrays of nozzle holes delivering the mist point axis-symmetrically away from the central assist-gas flow, as shown in *Figure 5-11*. Mist jets flowing at a stronger rate than the O_2 assist-gas flowing out of the cutting nozzle result in a Venturi effect, which aspirates the O_2 assist-gas. In these conditions, the O_2 assist-gas flow contaminates the mist rather than the other way around.

FOCUS CHARACTERISTICS

The focus characteristics of a laser beam on a workpiece are key to controlling a cutting process. A good explanation of these characteristics should be part of standard training for operators, maintenance personnel, designers, and product engineers. Appendices A and B provide the details of beam generation and propa-

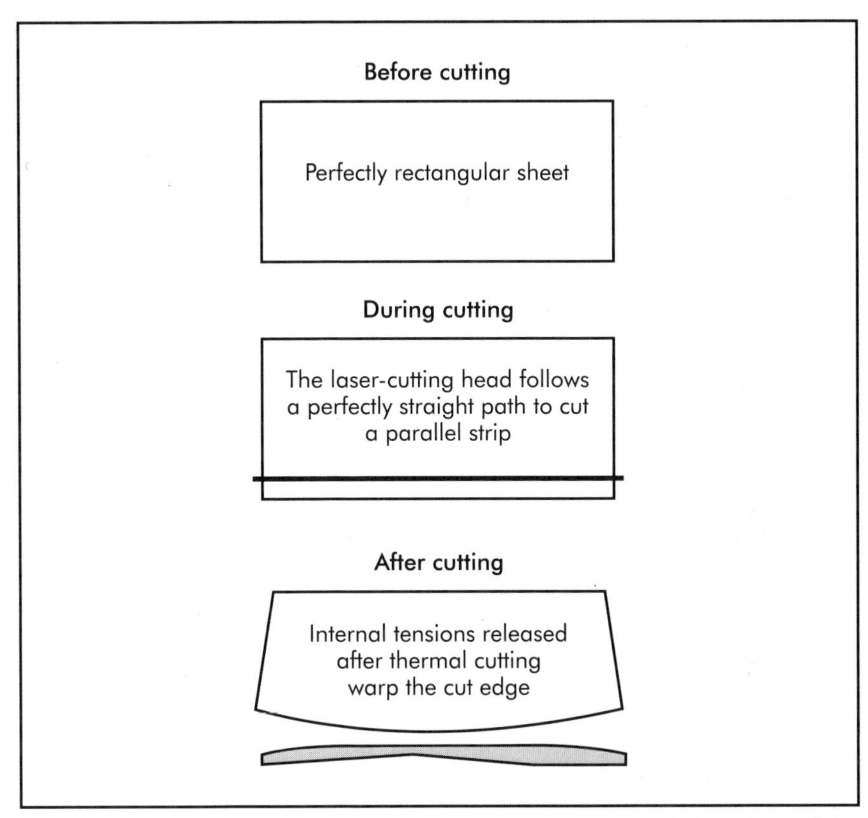

Figure 5-10. High heat input at low speed leads to thermal distortion of the cut contour, particularly features of narrow width, such as thin strips and fins. However, even part contours without these features can suffer thermal distortion if internal tensions in the metal are not released prior to thermal processing.

gation. The following sections focus on the essentials for setup and troubleshooting.

Beam-delivery System

Figure 5-12 describes an example of a beam-delivery system with six optics: a collimator composed of two mirrors of focal lengths f_3 and f_4, two bending flat mirrors with infinite focal lengths, one adaptive mirror of adjustable focal length f_2, and a focusing lens

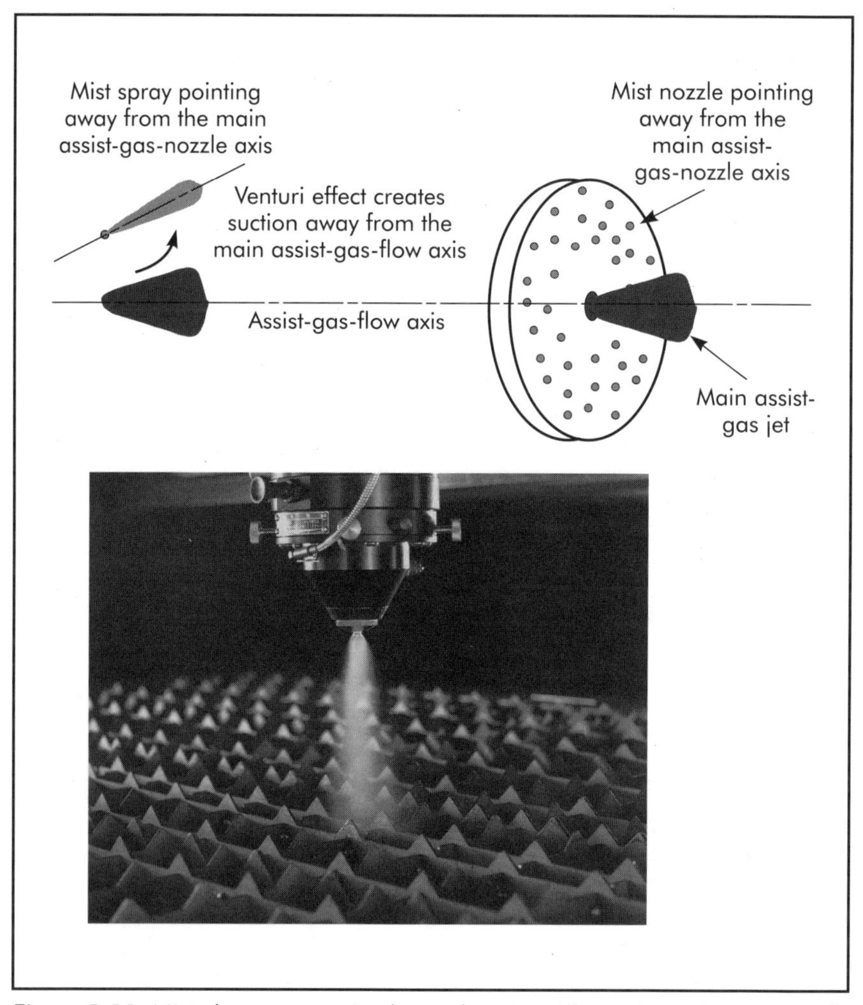

Figure 5-11. Mist shower to assist thermal cutting. The main assist-gas nozzle aperture is directed toward the kerf. Mist nozzles distributed axis symmetrically around the main assist-gas nozzle spray the workpiece surface with air/water mist. The hole apertures of the mist nozzle are pointing away from the kerf, thereby producing Venturi suction of the main assist-gas away from the kerf. This Venturi effect prevents contamination of the main assist-gas by mist in the region of the kerf's front. (Courtesy Amada)

of focal length f_1. *Table 5-6* shows how the choice of focal length is mostly a function of the workpiece's thickness whether for CO_2 or YAG laser systems.

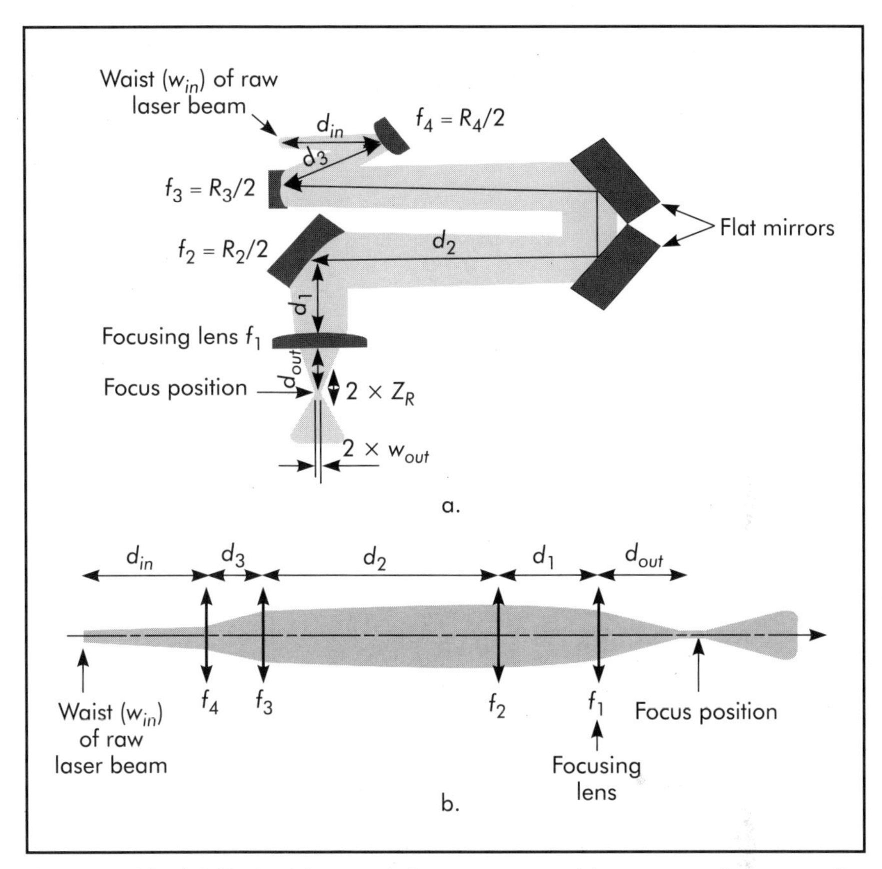

Figure 5-12. (a) Typical beam-delivery system with at most three non-flat mirrors and a focusing lens. The raw incident laser beam has a known waist, w_{in}, and location, d_{in}, which are obtainable from the laser manufacturer. The optical-path distances between optics are denoted d_1 through d_3. Since the flat mirrors have infinite focal lengths, they can be simply ignored and distance d_2 represents the total optical-path distance between f_2 and f_3. The distance between focusing lens f_1 and the focus position is d_{out}; $2 \times w_{out}$ is the diameter of the focused beam spot; $2 \times Z_R$ is the Rayleigh range around the focus spot. (b) The beam-delivery system depicted in (a), when unfolded, is equivalent to this sequence of lenses.

The optical-path distances, d_1, d_2, and d_3 are shown in *Figure 5-12,* as well as distance, d_{in}, between the incident beam's waist position and the first non-flat mirror optic, f_4; ($2 \times w_{in}$) denotes the diameter of the incident beam at its waist.

Table 5-6. Typical effective focal lengths used in metal cutting

Material Thickness, in. (mm)	CO_2 Laser System Effective Focal Length, in. (mm)	YAG Laser System Effective Focal Length, in. (mm)
<1/8 (3.2)	3.75 (95.3)	3.00 (76.2)
<3/16 (4.8)	5 (127)	5 (127)
<1.00 (25.4)	7.5 (191)	NA
<1-1/4 (31.8)	10 (254)	NA

Note: Most CO_2 laser systems use 5-in. (127-mm) focal length for up to 3/16-in. (4.8-mm) thick metal cutting and 7.5-in. (191-mm) focal length for thicker gages. Below 1/8 in. (3.2 mm) workpiece thickness, even shorter 3.75 in. (95.3 mm) lenses can be used for higher feed-rate CO_2 laser cutting. Above 3/4 in. (19.1 mm) thickness, a 10-in. (254-mm) focal-length lens performs better than a 7.5 in. (191 mm) lens.

Beam-focus adjustment downstream of the focusing lens is characterized by parameters such as: focus-spot diameter ($2 \times w_{out}$) and focus position (d_{out}) relative to the focusing lens (f_1) and Rayleigh range (Z_R). These parameters are bound by the following relationships (see Appendix B) for a laser beam of wavelength, λ, and of beam quality, M^2. The radius of the beam's cross section as a function of optical distance z downstream from the focusing lens is denoted by $W_{out}(z)$. For a flying-optics machine, optical distances d_1, d_2, and d_3 vary with the cutting head's axes position (Z, Y, and X) on the work envelope.

$$d_{out} = \frac{-\beta\delta - \alpha\gamma\dfrac{\pi^2 w_{in}^4}{M^4\lambda^2}}{\delta^2 + \gamma^2\dfrac{\pi^2 w_{in}^4}{M^4\lambda^2}} \tag{5-8}$$

$$Z_R = \frac{\dfrac{\pi w_{in}^2}{M^2\lambda}}{\delta^2 + \gamma^2\dfrac{\pi^2 w_{in}^4}{M^4\lambda^2}} \tag{5-9}$$

$$w_{out}^2 = \frac{w_{in}^2}{\delta^2 + \gamma^2 \frac{\pi^2 w_{in}^4}{M^4 \lambda^2}} \tag{5-10}$$

$$W_{out}(z) = w_{out}\left[1 + \left(\frac{z - d_{out}}{Z_R}\right)^2\right]^{\frac{1}{2}} \tag{5-11}$$

In which:

$$\alpha = (1 - \frac{d_1}{f_2})(1 - \frac{d_3}{f_4}) - (d_2 + d_1 - \frac{d_1 d_2}{f_2})(\frac{1}{f_3} + \frac{1}{f_4} - \frac{d_3}{f_3 f_4}) \tag{5-12}$$

$$\beta = (1 - \frac{d_1}{f_2})\left[d_{in} - \frac{d_3 d_{in}}{f_4} + d_3\right] + (d_2 + d_1 - \frac{d_1 d_2}{f_2})\left[1 - \frac{d_{in}}{f_3} - \frac{d_{in}}{f_4} - \frac{d_3}{f_3} + \frac{d_3 d_{in}}{f_3 f_4}\right] \tag{5-13}$$

$$\gamma = (1 - \frac{d_3}{f_4})(-\frac{1}{f_1} - \frac{1}{f_2} + \frac{d_1}{f_1 f_2}) + (-\frac{1}{f_3} - \frac{1}{f_4} + \frac{d_3}{f_3 f_4})\left[1 - \frac{d_2}{f_1} - \frac{d_2}{f_2} - \frac{d_1}{f_1} + \frac{d_1 d_2}{f_1 f_2}\right] \tag{5-14}$$

$$\delta = (\frac{d_1}{f_1 f_2} - \frac{1}{f_1} - \frac{1}{f_2})\left[d_{in} - \frac{d_3 d_{in}}{f_4} + d_3\right] + \left[1 - \frac{d_2}{f_1} - \frac{d_2}{f_2} - \frac{d_1}{f_1} + \frac{d_1 d_2}{f_1 f_2}\right]\left[1 - \frac{d_{in}}{f_3} - \frac{d_{in}}{f_4} - \frac{d_3}{f_3} + \frac{d_3 d_{in}}{f_3 f_4}\right] \tag{5-15}$$

Note that α and δ are dimensionless, whereas β is proportional to a distance and γ is inversely proportional to a distance. A mirror can be eliminated from the above equations simply by setting its focal length, f, to an infinite value, making it equivalent to a flat mirror or no mirror at all. *Figure 5-13* illustrates the case where the beam is approximated to a perfectly collimated incident beam with a constant diameter equal to the waist diameter ($D = 2 \times w_{in}$) at the focusing lens. The previous equations can be used to determine the position and diameter of the focus point simply by setting: $d_{in} = d_3 = d_2 = d_1 = 0$ and $f_2 = f_3 = f_4 = \infty$. This yields: $\alpha = 1$, $\beta = 0$, $\delta = 1$, and $\gamma = -1/f_1$, and the following approximations (see Appendix B):

$$d_{out} = f_1; \; w_{out} = \frac{M^2 \lambda f_1}{\pi w_{in}}; \; Z_R = \frac{M^2 \lambda f_1^2}{\pi w_{in}^2} \tag{5-16}$$

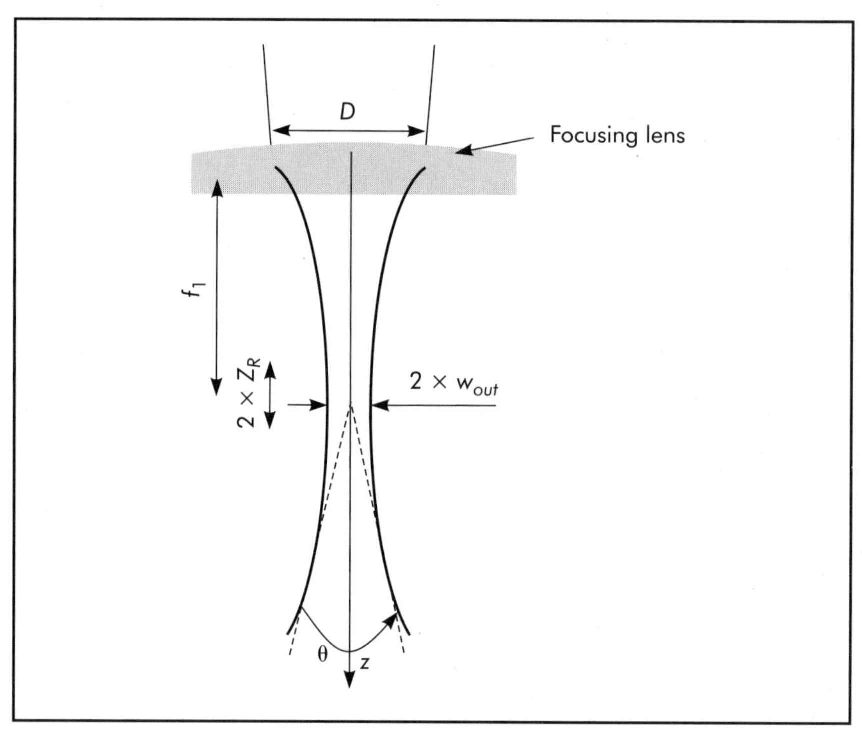

Figure 5-13. The laser beam incident on the focusing lens of focal length, f, has a diameter, D. The focus beam has a diameter $2 \times w_{out}$. The Rayleigh range ($2 \times Z_R$) represents a length within which the beam diameter increases by less than about 40% with respect to the focused beam diameter. The full angle divergence of the focused beam is represented by θ.

The full angle divergence of the beam is obtained by:

$$\tan\theta = \frac{2\lambda M^2}{\pi w_{out}} \quad (5\text{-}17)$$

For small values of angle, θ:

$$w_{out}\theta = \frac{2M^2\lambda}{\pi}$$

where:

λ = wavelength of laser-beam radiation
w_{in} = beam waist upstream of the lens, which is approximated by the diameter of the laser beam incident on the lens of focal length f_1
θ = beam's full angle of divergence
M^2 = beam quality factor, also called M-square or K or $1/k$, whose absolute minimum possible value is 1

Equation 5-16 shows that for focusability evaluation the so-called f-number (*f*/*D*, the ratio of focal length to beam diameter) is more important than the focal length taken alone regardless of the laser resonator type and characteristics.

Table 5-7 shows typical values of M^2 for industrial multikilowatt lasers. M^2 is a measure of mode composition of a laser beam and its divergence once it exits the cavity. The Rayleigh range represents a length around the beam waist or extension around the

Table 5-7. Typical values of M^2 for industrial multikilowatt lasers

Application	CO_2 (M^2)	YAG ($w\theta$)
Cutting metals	<3.5	<50 mm-mrad
Welding metals	<8.0	<100 mm-mrad

Note: Beam quality is evaluated in terms of the product of beam diameter, *w*, and the beam's full divergence angle, θ, which is expressed in mm-mrad units rather than in dimensionless terms of M^2.

focus point of diameter $2 \times w_{out}$, within which the beam radius remains smaller than

$$\sqrt{2} \times w_{out}$$

A smaller f-number (f/D) induces a smaller focus-spot diameter ($2 \times w_{out}$) and a smaller Rayleigh range (Z_R). For best cutting capability, a maximized Rayleigh range is preferred for focus-positioning tolerance, while a minimized diameter ($2 \times w_{out}$) is preferred for higher power density. These two conflicting requirements must lead to a delicate balance and choice of f/D, as well as choice of laser resonator characterized by M^2, λ, and indirectly by radius w_{in}. For applications aimed at high-speed cutting of thin sheets, preference can be given to lasers with a small M^2 factor close to a minimum value of 1, whereas a larger M^2 factor yields a larger Rayleigh length, which is favorable to better cutting performance on thick gage. Typical values for $2 \times w_{out}$ and $2 \times Z_R$ are listed in *Table 5-8* for CO_2 lasers.

Cooling

Transmissive optics, such as focusing lenses, are generally cooled by conduction from the edge flanges in contact with a water-cooled mount ring as shown in *Figure 5-14*. This cooling method works well in industrial high-power laser-cutting operations, but it has some disadvantages. A cool edge temperature coupled with a hot center where a laser beam impinges yields a temperature gradient that the lens must be able to withstand without excessive thermal lensing. *Thermal lensing* it a change in focusing properties due to distortion in the lens caused by thermal stresses. The thermal lensing effect increases when a beam's power and power-distribution gradient rise.

Efficiently water-cooled, industrial high-power lasers need about 3 minutes of beam off time to transition from hot mode and be ready to fire in cold mode. Conversely, they need about 3 minutes to transition from cold mode to a steady hot-mode status. Thermal lensing occurs when a laser beam is turned on and the shutter is opened after more than about 3 minutes of beam-off downtime. Optics must sustain cold and hot operation without

Table 5-8. Typical values for $2 \times w_{out}$ and $2 \times Z_R$ with CO_2 lasers of different quality factor M^2 can be summarized in the quadrant for M^2 and f/D

	M^2 = 1	2	4		M^2 = 1	2	4
λ = 10.6 μm				λ = 10.6 μm			
f/D = 5				f/D = 3.73			
$2 \times w_{out}$ (mm)	0.07	0.13	0.27	$2 \times w_{out}$ (mm)	0.05	0.10	0.20
$2 \times Z_R$ (mm)	0.34	0.67	1.35	$2 \times Z_R$ (mm)	0.19	0.38	0.75
	M^2 = 1	2	4		M^2 = 1	2	4
λ = 10.6 μm				λ = 10.6 μm			
f/D = 7.5				f/D = 5.6			
$2 \times w_{out}$ (mm)	0.10	0.20	0.40	$2 \times w_{out}$ (mm)	0.08	0.15	0.30
$2 \times Z_R$ (mm)	0.76	1.52	3.04	$2 \times Z_R$ (mm)	0.42	0.85	1.69

	f/D Small	f/D Large
M^2 small	thin gage high speed	medium gage medium speed
M^2 large	medium gage slow speed	thick gage slow speed

significant optical characteristic alteration due to thermal lensing. Thermal lensing may also occur when transitioning from low-duty cycle pulsed piercing to continuous wave (CW) cutting.

Figure 5-14 illustrates different temperature gradient profiles in lenses at equal power. A laser beam with a narrow Gaussian mode induces more thermal lensing than a beam with a wide top-hat mode. In summary, thermal lensing is always present. However, it may be manifested at varying magnitudes. Under nominal conditions, thermal lensing should be at a tolerable level that contributes to the definition of a machine's cutting capability.

Focusing Lens

The most-used focusing optic in industrial laser cutting of metals is a focusing lens. Use of focusing mirrors is reserved for those

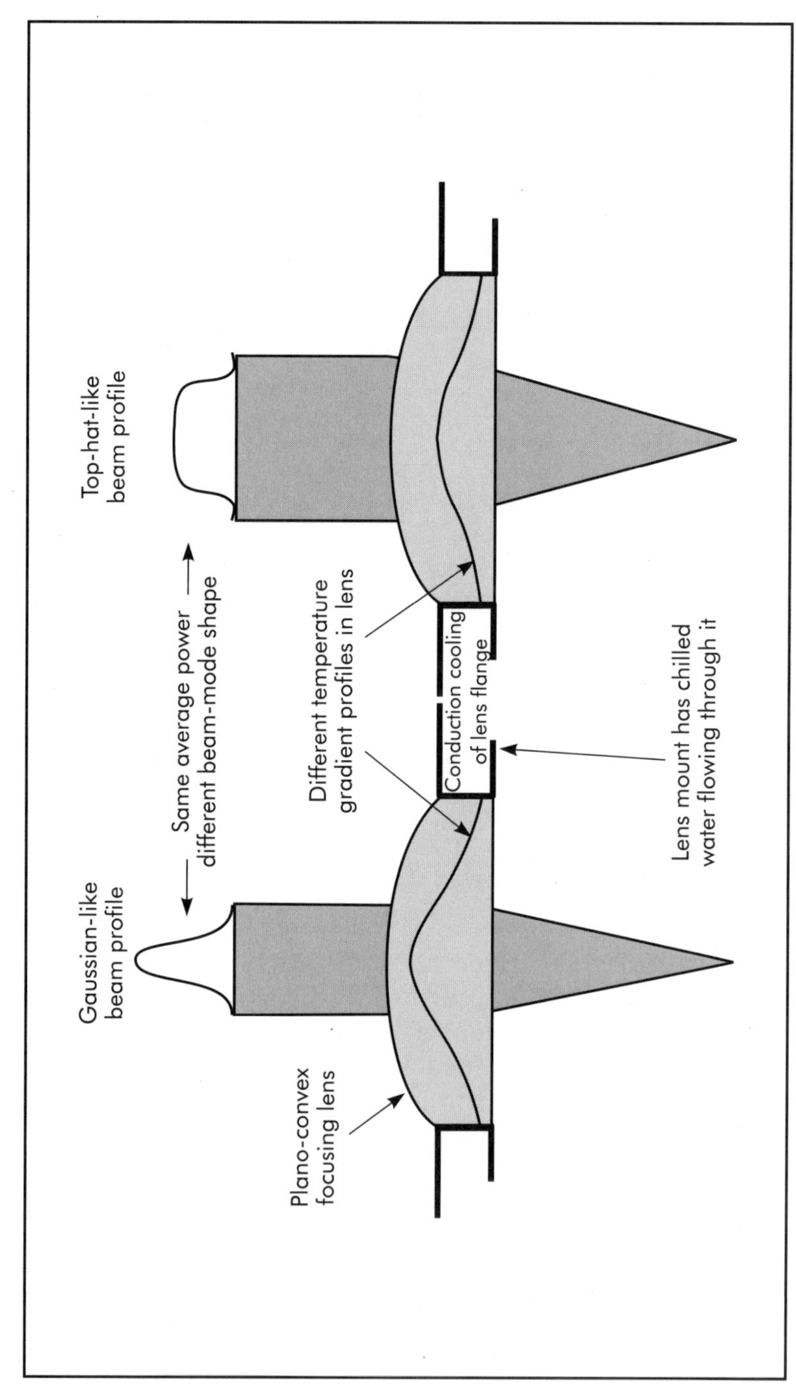

Figure 5-14. At the same average laser power and same conduction cooling through the lens flange, a narrow Gaussian-like beam profile produces a steeper temperature gradient in a focusing lens than a top-hat-like beam.

high-power processes of more than 6-kW average output power (YAG or CO_2 laser). This is because reflective optics are much easier to directly and uniformly water cool than transmissive optics. A lens introduces more aberration and less astigmatism than a mirror at equal focal length, but a lens generally focuses to a smaller spot than a mirror. The use of a focusing mirror complicates the ability to provide backup pressure for utilizing coaxial assist-gas flow. Ancillary nozzle arrangements have been developed to provide relatively uniform assist-gas flow with a focusing mirror.

YAG laser systems use focusing lenses made of quartz with special anti-reflective coating and focusing mirrors made from fused silica. Quartz's transmissivity and fused silica's reflectivity approach 99.5% transmissivity at a wavelength of 1.06 μm. Mirrors in industrial high-power CO_2 laser systems are made most often of copper or silicon substrate with various coatings designed to enhance their reflectivity at 10.6 μm wavelength. Industrial high-power CO_2 laser systems use focusing lenses made mostly of zinc selenide (ZnSe) with anti-reflective coating. Gallium arsenide (GaAs) substrate is used for CO_2 laser-system focusing lenses less frequently. Special optional coatings applied on lenses can reduce back-reflections toward the laser cavity.

One important specification for a focusing lens is its thickness, which needs to be strong enough to sustain high-pressure assist-gas. Lens manufacturers recommend and provide appropriate lens thicknesses based on the application. Assuming a 90% clear pressure aperture, a 1.5-in. (38-mm) diameter ZnSe lens with focal length of 5.0–7.5 in. (127–191 mm) and 0.16 in. (4.0 mm) thickness can sustain up to about 116 psi (8 bar) pressure. The same lens with a thickness of 0.3 in. (8 mm) can sustain up to almost 508 psi (35 bar).

Focusing lenses are mainly of two kinds shown in *Figure 5-15*: a most popular plano-convex type; and a higher-performing positive-meniscus type that yields a smaller focus spot due to a reduction of spherical aberrations. The benefit of decreased aberrations is obtained at a higher cost per meniscus lens than per plano-convex lens. By construction, lenses do not intrinsically induce as much astigmatism as focusing mirrors. However, they cannot prevent astigmatism. *Astigmatism* is an optical anomaly exhibited

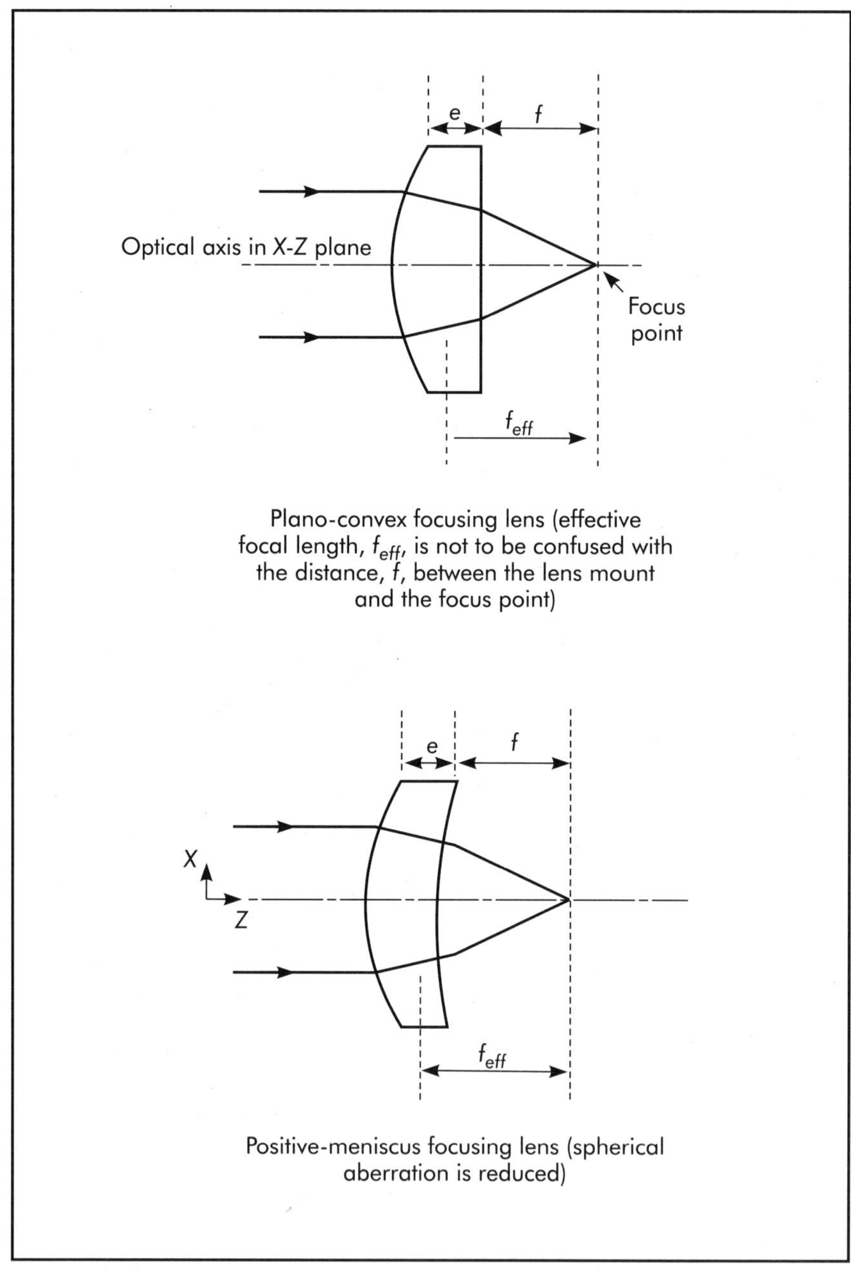

Figure 5-15. Focusing lenses are mainly of two kinds: the most popular plano-convex type; and the better-performing positive-meniscus type that enables a smaller focus spot with reduced spherical aberrations.

by differing focal length and focusing strength in different planes. It can result from a misalignment of the incident laser-beam axis with respect to the optical axis of the focusing optic, or from a lack of axis-symmetry of either the focusing optic or the laser-beam mode.

A focusing optic includes any converging or diverging lens or mirror along the beam-delivery system. *Figure 5-16* illustrates a condition of astigmatism resulting in different focus positions (Z) with respect to distance to the focusing lens in two transverse directions. Position Z_2 corresponds approximately to the specified

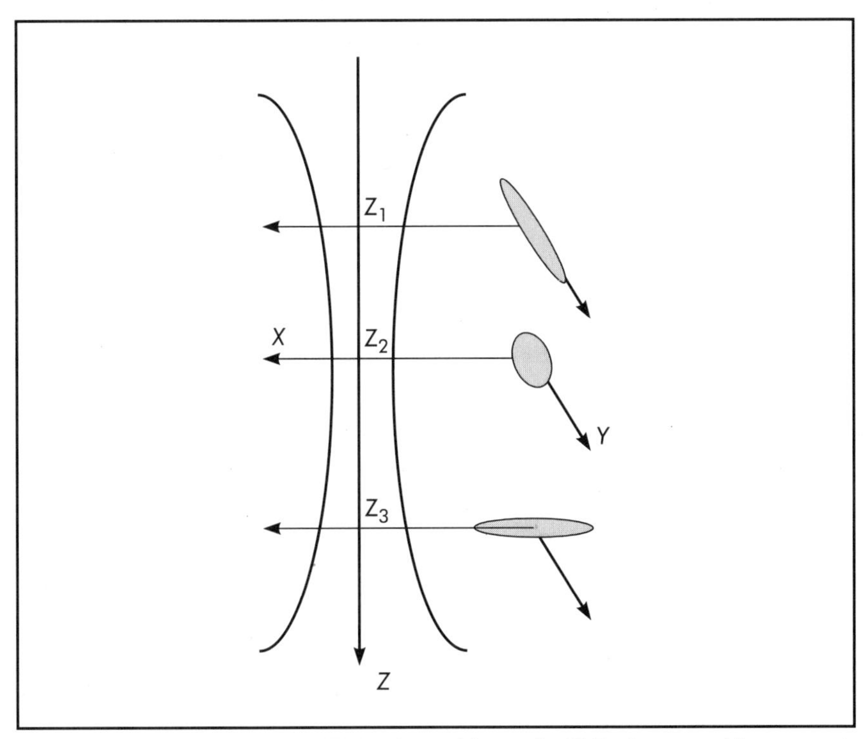

Figure 5-16. Focus position Z_1 is viewed from the X-Z plane and focus position Z_3 is viewed from the Y-Z plane; the actual focus spot is oblong at both positions. The width and length of the oblong focus spots at positions Z_1 and Z_3 are not necessarily identical. Position Z_2 is the location that yields the smallest circular focus spot. Far upstream from focus position Z_1 and far downstream from focus position Z_3, the beam's cross-section appears circular again.

focal length of the lens and yields a circular focus spot. At position Z_1 above Z_2, the focused laser-beam spot is oblong with its width possibly narrower than the diameter of the circular spot at Z_2. The oblong spot at Z_1 has its longitudinal axis parallel to the Y axis. At position Z_3 below Z_2, the focused laser-beam spot is oblong as well, with its width possibly narrower than the diameter of the circular spot at Z_2. The oblong spot at Z_3 has its longitudinal axis parallel to the X axis.

Cutting parameters should be chosen conservatively so as to tolerate some astigmatism, since the beam-pointing direction is not absolutely constant. Pointing direction varies with the life of the optics in the laser cavity and beam-delivery system, and with the alignment's precision, which is dependent on the skills and experience of the maintenance engineering team. In nominal conditions, astigmatism remains under control at an acceptable minimum level.

Focus Position

Focus position, depicted in *Figure 5-17*, can be controlled by adjustment of the standoff distance between the focusing lens and the workpiece surface. Lens standoff can be adjusted manually during setup or automatically by the power of servo or stepping motors, without necessarily altering the nozzle standoff. For thin-gage cutting, the focus position is generally placed on the workpiece surface. The focus position is generally placed beneath the workpiece surface for medium-thickness cutting. For thick-gage cutting, the focus position may be placed above the workpiece surface for best edge quality in mild steel. However, experimental development specific to stainless steel (Eguchi, Hayashikawa, and Hongu 2000) departs from this statement. It confirms that positioning the focus spot below the surface at about half the material thickness, as shown in *Figure 5-17*, is advantageous to reduce dross formation, particularly on thicker plates. As a matter of fact, positioning the focus close to the bottom surface of the workpiece advantageously and optimally reduces dross formation when cutting stainless steel and aluminum. However, for thick-plate cutting, a

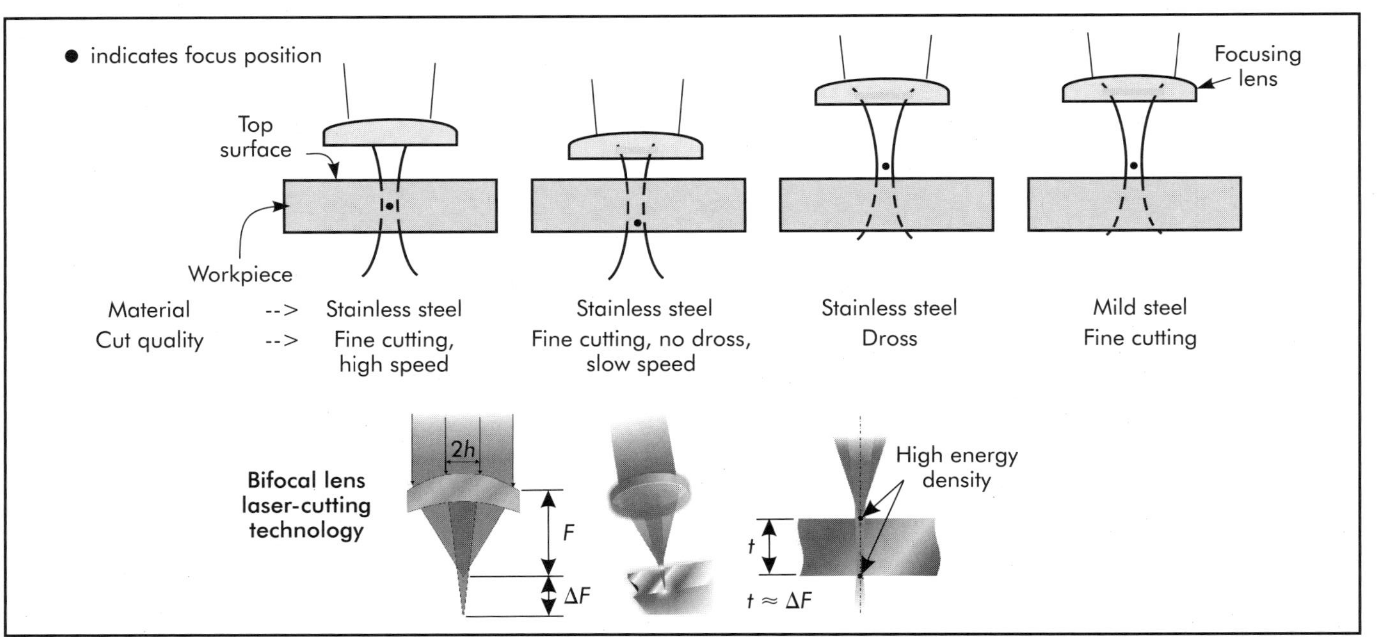

Figure 5-17. Comparison of mild steel (with O_2 assist-gas) and stainless steel (N_2 assist-gas) showing focus positions for laser cutting of 0.5-in. (12-mm) thick steel with a 4-kW CO_2 laser and 7.5-in. (191-mm) focusing lens. The focus position for cutting thick stainless steel is preferably about halfway below the workpiece surface as a compromise to yield a dross-free, fine-cut edge at a reasonable cutting speed. With mild steel, the best cut-edge quality is obtained with the focus position at about 0.08 in. (2.0 mm) above the workpiece's top surface. Using bifocal focusing lenses, it is possible to position one focus point near the bottom surface of the workpiece to eliminate dross and another focus point near the top to maintain high cutting speeds. (Courtesy Air Liquide)

focus position near the bottom means a defocused beam with low power density near the top of the workpiece, which consequently slows cutting speeds. Bifocal technology (Caristan et al. 2003) utilizing two focus points aligned in the laser-pointing direction enables placement of one focus point near the bottom of the workpiece for dross reduction and another near the top surface to yield higher cutting speeds.

The focus position is located at a distance from a lens equal to about the focal length of that lens. It must be recognized that laser-beam output can have fluctuating characteristics such as diameter, divergence, and M^2 number. These characteristics may vary with the age of the cavity optics, actual peak power, duty, and frequency. Consequently, the focus position and characteristics may vary significantly enough to impact a cutting process.

A simple experimental method can accurately confirm a focus position by measuring kerfs in thin stainless-steel cutting with N_2 assist-gas at maximum laser power and moderate to slow speed. The use of stainless-steel material for this test is preferred because of its low heat conductivity, which coupled to the fact that it is thin gage (0.04 in. [1 mm] or less), allows more precise equality of the width of kerf to the beam-spot diameter on a workpiece surface. Maximum output power emulates real production conditions. Using N_2 assist-gas limits heat-input dissipation by conduction in a workpiece compared to the O_2 exothermic combustion-assist process. Several kerfs are produced on a thin stainless-steel sheet, each at different Z-axis positions separated by small increments. The kerf width should show a pattern going from wide to narrow and wide again. An interpolation can predict which Z-axis position will produce the narrowest kerf. An experimental test should confirm this prediction. The narrowest kerf indicates the beam-focus spot positioned at the workpiece surface in known relationship with the Z-axis position reading.

Another simple method to find the focus position is to scan the laser beam across a thick, flat, wood surface at a known incline angle. The burn trace incurred by the wood exhibits a width that varies with the height position on the incline. The position of the narrowest width indicates the focus position.

Depth of Focus

Depth of focus is a practical measure of the tolerance of the laser-cutting process to focus position variations relative to the workpiece surface across the entire work envelope. The computed Rayleigh range, Z_R, gives a reasonable trend prediction of the depth of focus. The Rayleigh range depends on the f-number, M^2 number, and laser wavelength (see *Equations 5-9* and *5-16*). Focus position varies with these parameters as well (see Appendix B). Implicit in the f-number is a dependency on the characteristics of a beam incident on a focusing lens, for example diameter and divergence. These characteristics vary with optical-path length due to the natural divergence of a laser beam even when reduced by the effect of collimation. From the near field (NF) end of a work envelope to its opposite diagonal far field (FF) end, the optical-path length can change 19 ft (6 m) or more on a flat-bed machine. Focus position and Rayleigh range change accordingly. In terms of cutting performance, the Rayleigh range gives a wide approximation of practical tolerance to focus-position variations. Such practical tolerances are measured experimentally and are generally much smaller than the theoretically computed Rayleigh range. The depth of focus tolerance measures the overlap of the practical ranges from NF to FF as illustrated in *Figure 5-18*.

LASER OUTPUT

Laser output is characterized by three main parameters: peak power, pulse duty, and pulsing frequency as illustrated in *Figure 5-19*. *Pulse frequency* represents the number of pulses of output energy emitted per second. *Pulse duty* is the percentage of ON time per pulse period; 100% duty corresponds to continuous-wave (CW) output. *Peak power* is the maximum output power within a pulse of energy, generally referred to as commanded power, P_0.

With some laser resonators, even when commanding zero power, a non-zero output base power is obtained. This base power may become a quality issue, as it may be enough power to mark metal surfaces with visible traces even during rapid traverse motion. Back reflections enhance such markings on highly reflective metals such

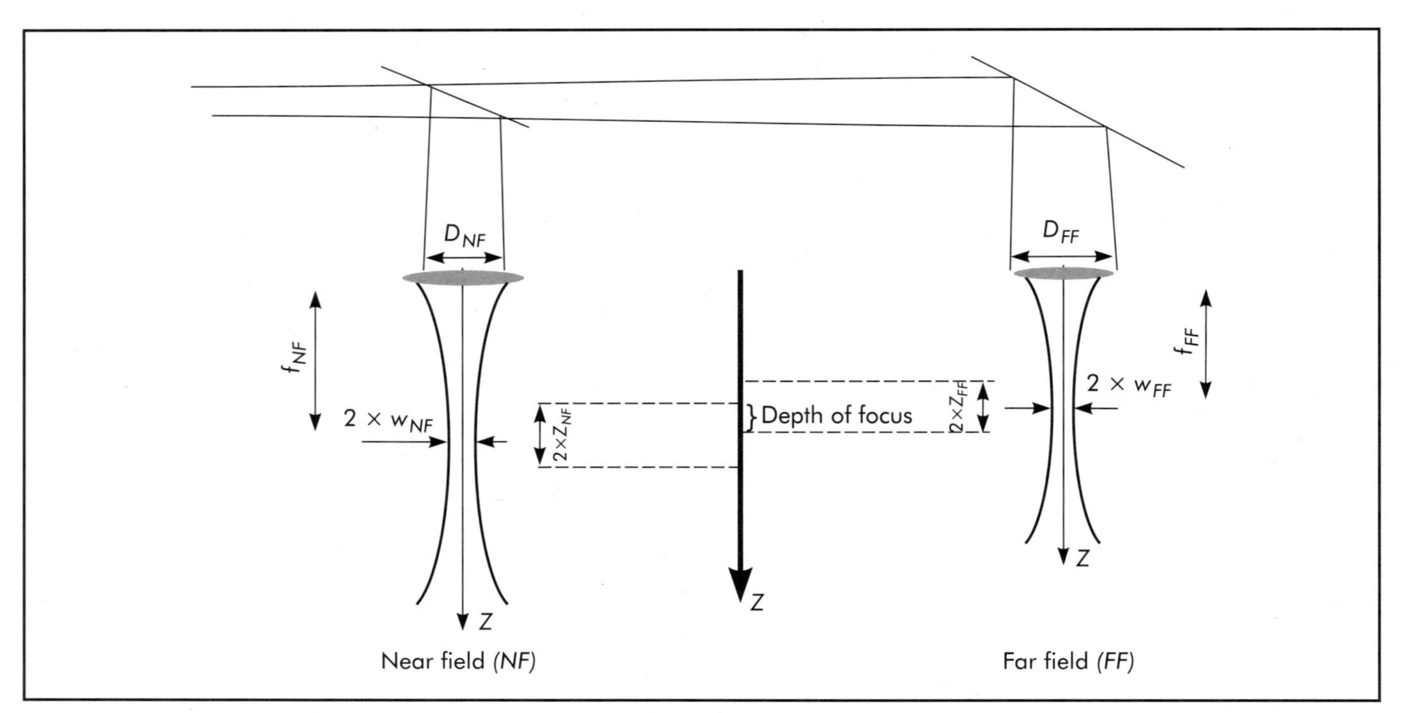

Figure 5-18. In the near field (NF), the beam incident on the focusing lens has a diameter, D_{NF}, which is smaller than the diameter, D_{FF}, in the far field. Expectably, the focus-spot diameter, $2 \times w_{NF}$, is larger than $2 \times w_{FF}$ in the far field and the tolerances to focus position ($2 \times Z_{NF}$ and $2 \times Z_{FF}$) are also different. Since the focus positions f_{NF} and f_{FF} relative to the lens also change, there is an optimum Z position and a small window of overlap (or depth of focus) in which cutting performance can tolerate variations in position Z.

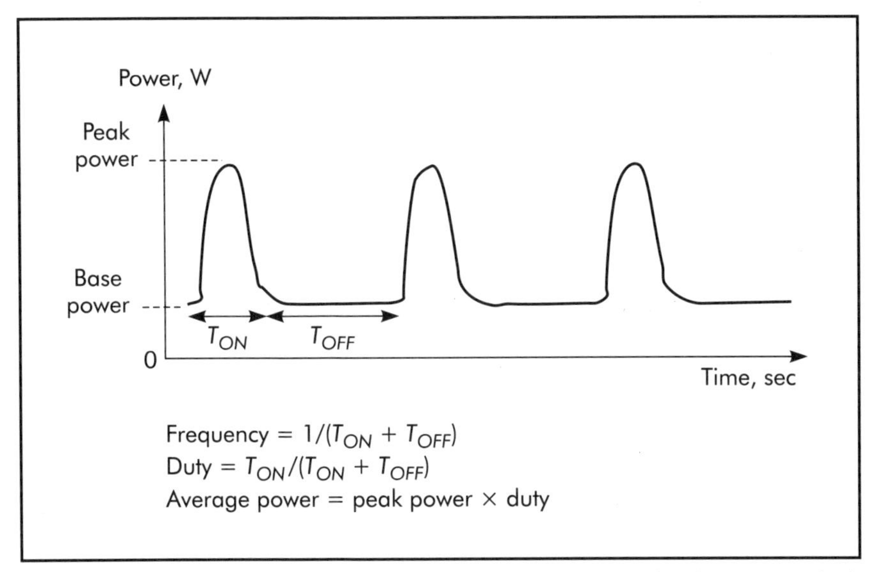

Figure 5-19. Most laser-cutting systems offer simple pulsed output, which can be characterized by peak power, pulse duty, and pulse frequency. More sophisticated pulsing patterns are possible for special applications. Base power is residual power available even when zero power is commanded. It can be intentionally set at a relatively high level to optimize cutting performance.

as stainless steel and copper and aluminum alloys. Some applications require absolutely no marking. To avoid these marks, the laser-cutting head can be raised to defocus the beam during rapid traverse, or the shutter can be closed during rapid traverse. The latest electronic technologies enable near-zero-output power when commanding zero power. However, certain applications may benefit from an elevated base power level.

Knowing the pulse frequency and duty and assuming perfectly square pulse waves, actual peak power, P_a, can be derived from an average power measurement, P_{avg}, by dividing the latter by the duty factor. For example, if P_{avg} is measured at 700 W ±40 W with an electronically controlled duty of 40%, then it can be inferred that P_a = 1,750 W ±100 W. If the corresponding commanded power, P_c, is 2,000 W, then a discrepancy of 150–350 W exists. This may explain noticeable cutting performance shortcomings. The discrepancy between P_c and P_a has several potential causes:

- The average power measurement device may need re-calibration or the measurement procedure needs improvement.
- The power sensor internal to the laser and power-supply controls used to deliver appropriate voltage and current to the laser's pumping mechanism is not properly calibrated. This can happen each time the laser optics start to age, and worsens until cleaning or replacement of the optics is needed, unless on-line measurement, closed-loop controls are in place with the laser-power supplies. It can also happen when power supplies get replaced or repaired.
- P_c is the commanded peak power at the laser-output coupler mirror. Each optic of a beam-delivery system absorbs about 1% of power when new and clean. This absorption worsens sharply when an optic's surface becomes dirty, sometimes leading to thermal lensing. The laser beam impinging on an optic's surface will burn all minerals and hydrocarbons on its surface and coming from ambient air humidity or adjacent processes such as welding fumes and painting emissions. Burn marks alter optical properties and enhance laser-power absorption by the optic to a point of no return if maintenance cleaning is not performed early enough.

Certain hydrocarbons emitted from acrylic fumes and some glues exhibit strong absorption of CO_2 laser radiation at 10.6 μm wavelength. If present in ambient air and along the beam-delivery path, their absorption adds to the optics absorption, resulting in further reduced actual peak power at the workpiece and a larger discrepancy between P_c and P_a.

Laser-beam Mode

Laser-beam modes can be monitored by sophisticated beam-cross-section scanning and analysis instruments. More economical and faster is burning a clear transparent block of acrylic, such as seen in *Figure 5-20*, by shooting at it with the laser's raw unfocused beam for a few seconds. The CO_2 laser radiation ablates and vaporizes the acrylic proportionate to the power-distribution pattern across the laser beam's cross-section. This reveals an imprint representative of the power distribution across the laser beam's cross-section. It should be noted that when acrylic burns are used to assess beam characteristics, a set burn time should be consistently utilized. The power distribution will exhibit certain characteristics, which vary from manufacturer to manufacturer. In general, the mode burn is characterized by its diameter and axis-symmetry. Axis-symmetry is essential for isotropic cutting performance, that is, uniformity in all cutting directions. If non-axis-symmetry is achieved intentionally, then the beam-spot orientation with respect to cutting direction must be adjusted on the fly during cutting. A flat-top characteristic mode-burn profile with symmetrical and mildly slanted walls is preferred to a narrow sharp-peak feature exhibiting dissymmetry. The latter condition damages lenses and mirrors quicker and enhances thermal lensing. The relationship between M^2 and beam mode (see Appendices A and B) can help explain the beam-propagation patterns exemplified in *Figure 5-21*.

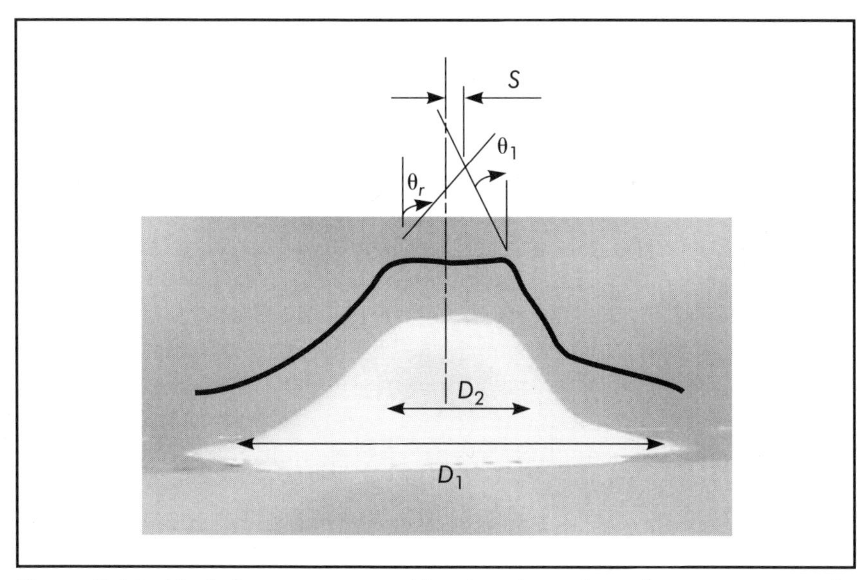

Figure 5-20. Mode burns generated by shooting a laser beam on an acrylic block. Several mode-burn characteristics can be looked for: D_1 is the diameter of the total imprint; D_2 is the diameter of the top-hat part; θ_1 and θ_r are angles defining the top-hat section's symmetry; S is a measure of the dissymmetry. Generally, an educated visual inspection of these angles and measurement of D_1 will be sufficient for evaluation by an operator.

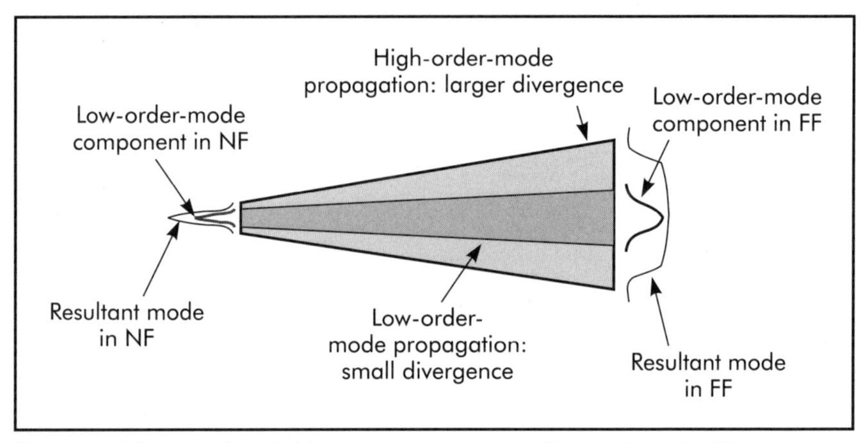

Figure 5-21. An industrial laser beam is generally multi-mode. The percentage of representation of each mode varies. Most individual modes add power within the smaller radius of the lowest-order mode. The diameter of the low-order mode may include a larger percentage of energy in the near field (NF) than in the far field (FF).

Polarization

Laser-beam polarization is a physical electromagnetic feature of laser light that has a measurable impact on cutting performance. There are two scientifically accepted interpretations for light (see Appendix A). The corpuscular interpretation states that *light* is an emission of mass-less particles called photons traveling at the speed of light. The electromagnetic interpretation states that light is an electromagnetic wave propagating at the speed of light.

Considering the electromagnetic interpretation, one of light's electromagnetic components is an electric field represented by the vector field, E, in *Figure 5-22*. This vector's direction and amplitude are oscillating in a plane perpendicular to the direction of propagation of the light it represents. If only its amplitude oscillates and its direction remains fixed, then the light is linearly polarized. If its amplitude is constant and its direction rotates uniformly, then the light is circularly polarized. It is demonstrated theoretically and can be accepted that circularly polarized light has performance that on average does not depend on the direction of cutting. This is generally not the case with linearly polar-

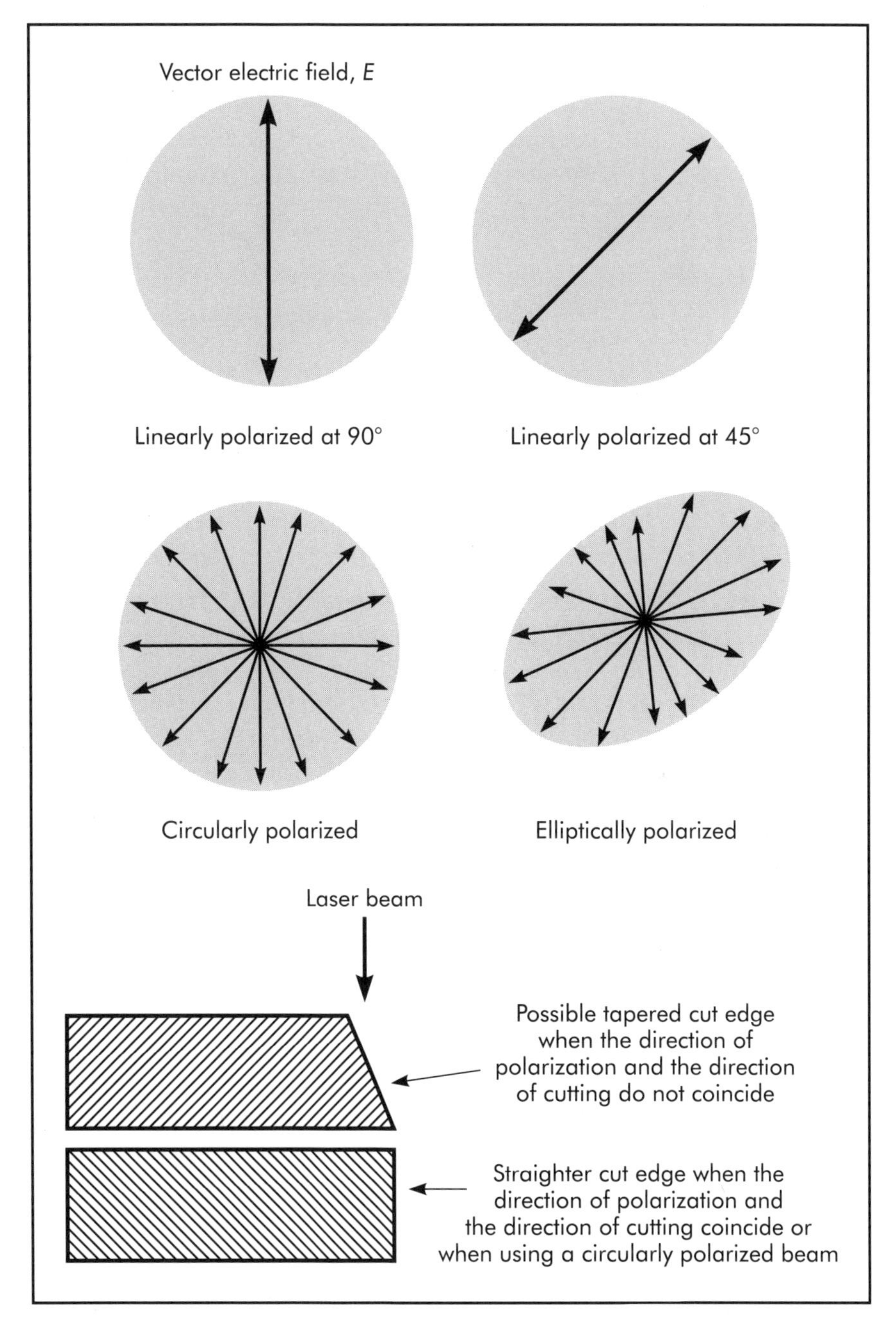

Figure 5-22. The laser beam's direction of propagation is perpendicular to the plane of view of this page. The arrows represent the vector electric field.

ized light when cutting metals. When penetrating the kerf front, the direction of polarization with respect to the cutting direction affects cutting performance. A circularly polarized laser beam performs uniformly in all directions across the work envelope. A linearly polarized beam yields edges with a more pronounced slant angle when the direction of polarization is perpendicular to the cutting direction.

In YAG lasers, linear polarization occurs when the end surfaces of the YAG crystals are cut at Brewster angle θ_B. If n_2, respectively n_1, represents the refractive index of the crystal, respectively the refractive index of room atmosphere ($n_1 = 1$ for air), then the Brewster angle is given by:

$$\theta_B = \arctan\frac{n_2}{n_1} \tag{5-18}$$

Linearly polarized laser light can be generated in industrial CO_2 lasers when Brewster angle windows and/or multiple 45°-incidence reflector mirrors are used in the cavity. Multiple reflector mirrors advantageously enable the folding of a long intra-cavity laser-beam path into several shorter segments that can be packaged within the small footprint of the cavity enclosure (see *Figure 4-4*).

Figure 5-23 illustrates a ray of light impinging on a surface. Together, the incident ray and the direction perpendicular to the surface define a plane of incidence. The vector polarization can be expressed as the sum of an s-component perpendicular to the plane of incidence and a p-component parallel to the plane of incidence.

It is known from Fresnel equations (Luxon and Parker 1992) and demonstrated by experiments (VDI- Gesellschaft Produktiontechnik 1990) that, depending on the angle of incidence, θ_1, the parallel polarizations can have a reflectance, $R_{//}$, much smaller than the reflectance, $R_{\perp}$, of the perpendicular polarization (see *Figure 3-6*). The incident beam is refracted at angle θ_2 shown in *Figure 5-23* and given by Snell's law:

$$\theta_2 = \arcsin\left(\frac{n_1}{n_2}\sin(\theta_1)\right) \tag{5-19}$$

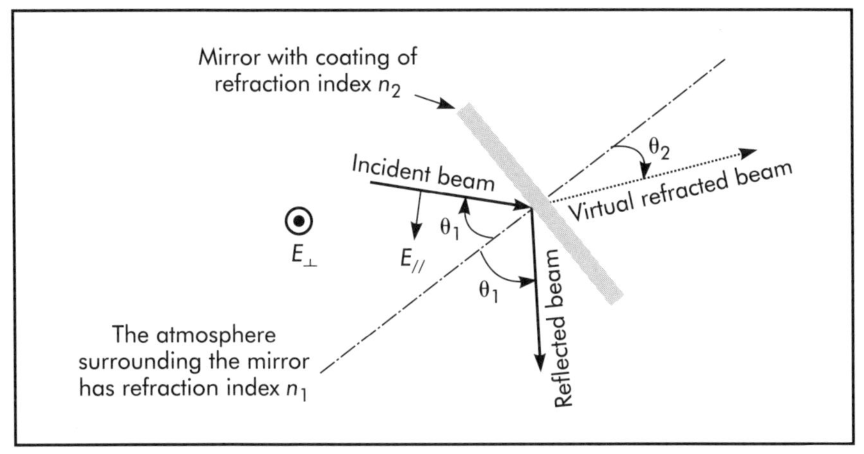

Figure 5-23. Incident and reflected beams define a plane of incidence that coincides with the plane view of this page. The component of the electric field, E, in the plane of incidence defines the parallel polarization component, $E_{//}$, of the laser beam. The component of the electric field oriented in a direction perpendicular to the plane of incidence defines the perpendicular polarization of the laser light beam. The amplitude of $E_{//}$ gets more attenuation after each reflection on a mirror than the perpendicular polarization component. After several reflections in the beam-delivery system, a linearly polarized transmitted beam may exhibit an ever stronger anisotropy of its polarization.

where:

n_1 = refractive index of the atmosphere surrounding the mirror ($n_1 = 1$ for air)
n_2 = refractive index of the mirror's coating layer
θ_1 = angle of incidence on the mirror

deriving (Luxon and Parker 1992):

$$R_{//} = \left(\frac{\tan(\theta_1 - \theta_2)}{\tan(\theta_1 + \theta_2)} \right)^2 \text{ and } R_\perp = \left(\frac{\sin(\theta_1 - \theta_2)}{\sin(\theta_1 + \theta_2)} \right)^2 \quad (5\text{-}20)$$

where:

$R_{//}$ = reflectance of parallel polarization
$R_\perp$ = reflectance of perpendicular polarization

The Brewster angle condition of *Equation 5-18* corresponds to $\theta_1 + \theta_2 = 90^\circ$, which yields $R_{//} = 0$: only the perpendicular linear polarization component survives in the reflected beam. For normal incidence, $\theta_1 = 0^\circ$, it can be demonstrated that (Modest 2001; Petring 1994; Luxon and Parker 1992):

$$R_{//} = R_{\perp} = R = \left(\frac{n_1 - n_2}{n_1 + n_2} \right)^2 \tag{5-21}$$

The polarization relates to a physical parameter that is called the phase of the electromagnetic wave. A 180° phase shift in the reflected beam, compared to the incident beam phase, is to be expected if $n_2 - n_1 > 0$, but no phase shift is to occur if this relation is not fulfilled. Such phase shift rotates the polarization by an equal angle amount. This peculiarity is helpful for the design of anti-reflective coatings.

The preceding results help explain how the output beam for a multikilowatt industrial CO_2 laser with multiple reflectors in the cavity becomes mainly linearly polarized by having the perpendicular polarization phagocyte all lasing energy at the expense of the parallel polarization.

In industrial multikilowatt laser installations, a linearly polarized beam can be transformed into a circularly polarized beam using a so-called quarter-wavelength $\lambda/4$ phase-shift mirror. The mirror has multi-layer coatings with optical bi-refringence properties, such as potassium di-hydrogen phosphate (KDP) crystal.

Bi-refringence is a characteristic by which the optical properties (for example, refractive index) are different for the parallel and perpendicular polarization components of light with respect to the plane of incidence. The thickness of each coating layer determines the phase shift applied to the polarization. When a beam's linear polarization is at 45° incidence with respect to the optic axis of a bi-refringent coating, it can be broken down vector-wise into a parallel polarization carrying half the energy and a perpendicular polarization carrying the other half. The energy is normally distributed between the two polarization components at a ratio of $\cos\theta/\sin\theta$, which for $\theta = 45^\circ$ means 50/50. With a quarter-wavelength, $\lambda/4$ phase shift-mirror, the parallel polarization is forced to rotate 90°, whereas the phase of the perpendicular polarization remains unchanged. In addition, the refractive index for the two polarizations is different due to the bi-refringence properties of the coating. The speed of propagation of these two polarization components of light through the coating are also different, thus contributing to an actual continuous rotation of the resultant polarization of the resultant beam reflected by the phase-shift mirror. Because the incident direction of polarization is at 45° from the optic axis, the two polarization components have the same amplitude. Therefore, the resultant reflected beam has constant amplitude while rotating its polarization (a consequence of the Malus Law). The resultant polarization is circularly polarized. If the incident direction of polarization is not aligned at exactly 45° from the optic axis, then the resultant reflected beam has an elliptical polarization. Therefore, cutting performance potentially changes as a function of the orientation of the longitudinal axis of the polarization ellipse with respect to the cutting direction.

FEED RATE

Feed rate is the most reliably controlled cutting parameter. Servo and numerical control technologies precisely apply the commanded linear cutting speed whether in 2-D for flat-bed cutting machines or for 3-D shaped processing. However, special care must be given to corner radius and corner angle features. Due to machine inertia and finite servo power capability, feed rate should be "clamped" by radius, that is, restricted proportionally to the square root of a feature's radius.

Start of Cut

Start-of-cut parameters differ from rectilinear cutting parameters. Assuming that a workpiece is pierced through before a cut starts, motion accelerates from zero feed rate to the commanded feed rate. Laser-power-output parameters must start from low levels and increase to commanded values, similar to a sequence starting immediately after dwell time, accelerating from position

O to position *B* in *Figure 5-24*. Progressive acceleration until the commanded feed rate is met must begin slowly enough to not lose a cut due to the bottom part of the kerf front lagging (see *Figure 5-25*).

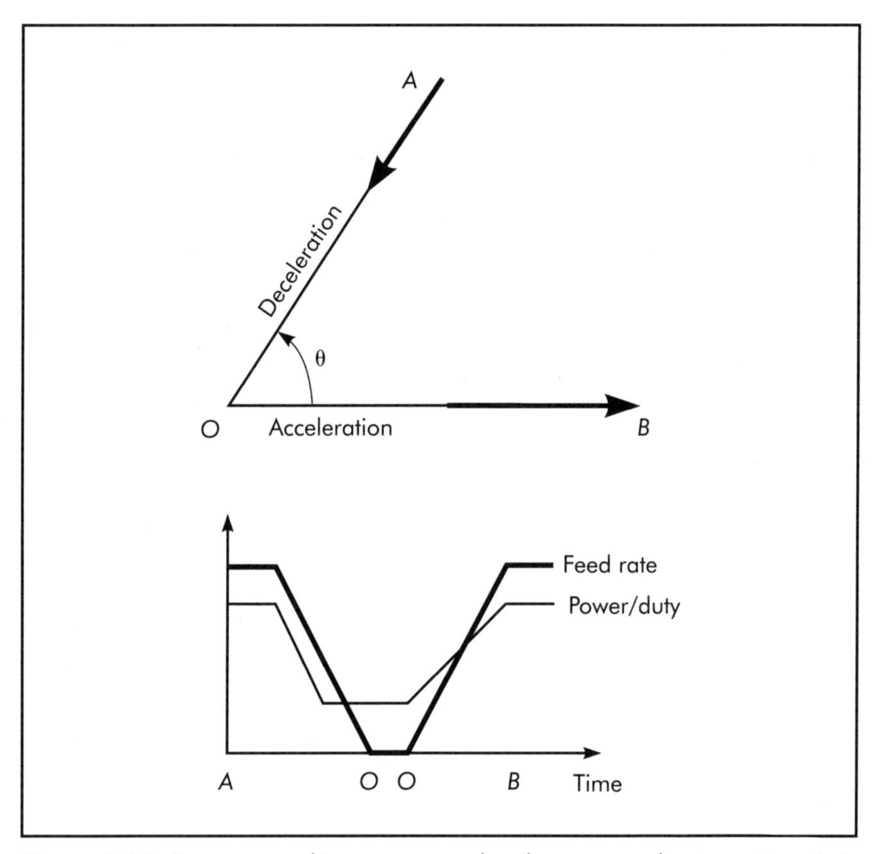

Figure 5-24. To process this corner angle, the approach at position A is made at the commanded feed rate. Between positions A and corner angle O, the machine must decelerate until it reaches zero feed rate at point O. Duty and possibly frequency and peak power must be adjusted correspondingly from their commanded values down to the minimum necessary to complete cutting. The machine should dwell at point O enough time for the kerf-lagging front to catch up with the laser-beam position. Then acceleration in the new direction can begin up to the commanded feed rate to position B. Power, duty, and frequency are increased accordingly up to commanded values.

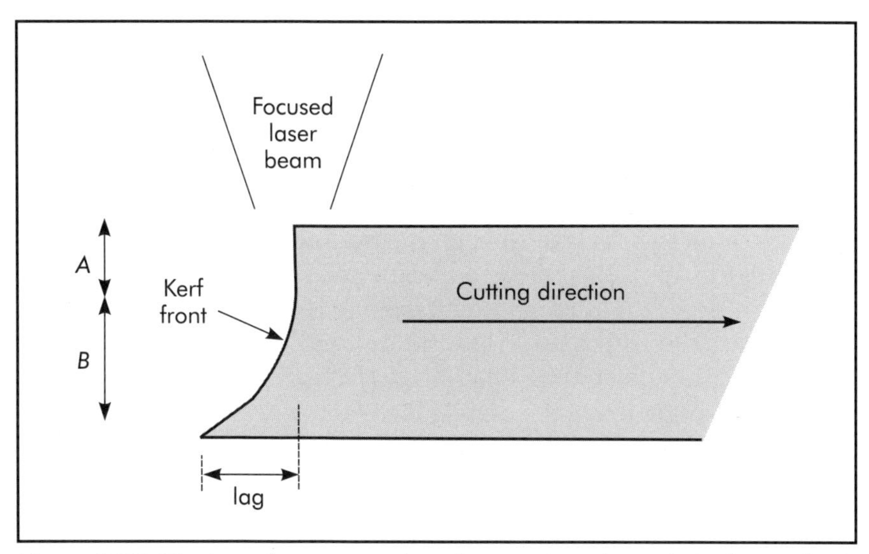

Figure 5-25. The laser beam vaporizes the metal up through thickness depth A and then the assist-gas blows molten metal down the kerf's front through depth B. As the focused laser-beam spot moves relative to the workpiece during cutting, its positions coincide with the top part of the kerf's front. The bottom part of the kerf's front lags the top part. The larger the lag amount, the smaller the cut-to-break ratio, A/B.

End of Cut

End-of-cut parameters differ from rectilinear cutting parameters. The motion goes from the commanded feed rate down to zero. Laser-output parameters must correspondingly vary from commanded values to zero power similar to the sequence leading from position *A* to position *O* in *Figure 5-24*. For thicker plates, dwell time at the end of a cut may be necessary to enable the lagging part of the kerf front to catch up with the laser-beam position and completely through-cut before turning off the power completely.

Corner-angle Processing

For corner angles, feed rate decelerates to zero in one direction before accelerating back to the commanded feed rate in a new direction. Corner-angle parameters differ from rectilinear cutting parameters essentially due to a change in direction and amplitude of the velocity vector. *Figure 5-24* illustrates this change for a corner-angle feature. The energy input to the workpiece, that is, peak power, duty, and frequency, must be adapted on the fly to account for velocity changes and temperature patterns of the workpiece as they relate to each particular cut feature. The control of heat input is critical to obtain good edge quality throughout each feature (Kanaoka and Yuyama 1996).

Theoretically, duty could be the only adjustable parameter as maximum peak power is preferred and frequency adjustments have minimal benefit in most cases. However, actual laser-output response to commanded peak power and duty may produce nonlinear and growing variations, particularly when commanded duty cycles approach low levels. So, it may become advantageous to also alter commanded peak power and duty as a function of feed rate. This adjustment minimizes heat buildup in a fin corner angle and still completes the cut with minimum gouging.

Note from *Figure 5-24* that, particularly for thicker plates, dwell time at the corner may be necessary to enable the lagging part of the kerf front shown in *Figure 5-25* to catch up with the laser beam's position and complete the through-cut at point *O* before accelerating in a new direction. For that reason, commanded laser peak power and duty must be maintained at low levels during the dwell time. *Table 5-9* gives examples of typical parameters for corner-angle processing of mild steel with a 2-kW CO_2 laser.

Corner-radius Processing

Corner-radius parameters differ from rectilinear cutting parameters when a radius of a curved feature goes below a threshold value. The threshold radius depends on the mechanical characteristics of a machine, material, and cutting-parameter settings. Low inertia and high stiffness are preferred for moving gantry parts to allow tight radii to be processed at maximum feed rate with acceptable contour accuracy. The power-sizing capability of servomotors utilized for a motion system with given inertia will determine how much to restrict the motion's acceleration by radius.

Table 5-9. Typical parameters for 90° corner-angle processing

	Corner Position, O			Deceleration and Acceleration Phases				Cutting		
Thickness in. (mm)	Pulse Frequency Hz	Pulse Duty %	Dwell Time sec	Length in. (mm)	Commanded Cutting Feed Rate, in./min (m/min)	Pulse Frequency Hz	Pulse Duty %	Feed Rate in./min (m/min)	Pulse Frequency Hz	Pulse Duty %
0.25 (6.5)	10	10	1	0.12 (3.0)	3.94 (0.1)	10	10	59.06 (1.5)	1,000	75
0.50 (12.5)	10	10	1	0.08 (2.0)	3.94 (0.1)	10	20	31.50 (0.8)	700	80

Note: 2-kW peak power CO_2 laser, 7.5-in. (191-mm) focal length, 0.08-in. (2-mm) nozzle aperture, absolute 21.8 psi (1.5 bar) of oxygen assist-gas, nozzle standoff of 0.08 in. (2 mm), and focus position on the workpiece top surface

Figure 5-26 illustrates how feed rate can be reduced proportionally to about the square root of a radius once the latter is below a certain threshold. Commanded peak power, duty, and frequency can adequately mirror feed-rate variations.

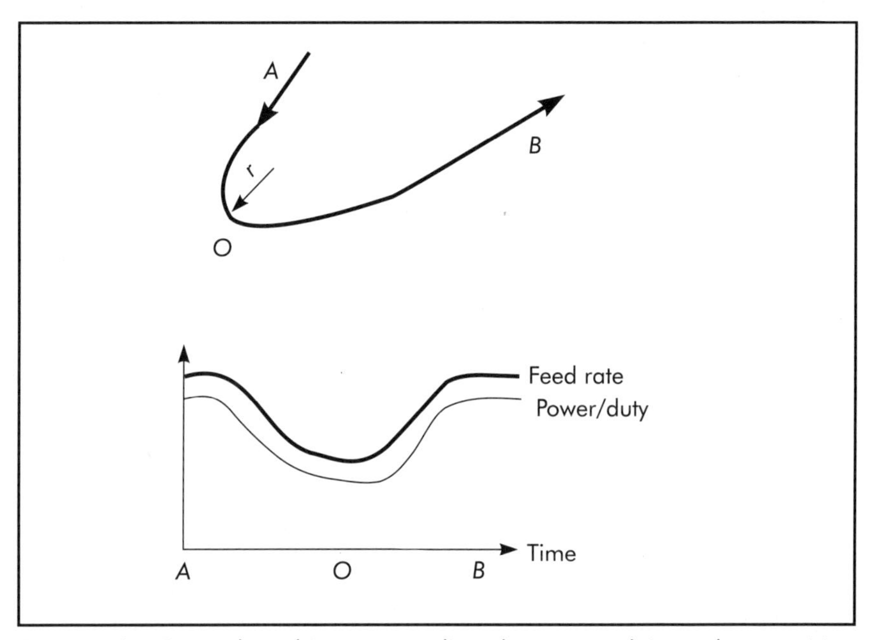

Figure 5-26. To produce this corner radius, the approach is made at position A at the commanded feed rate. Between positions A and corner radius O, the machine decelerates down to a feed rate computed by the motion controls as a function of radius, r. A well-known analogy is that of a race car. If a car drives too fast on a curve with a tight radius, it may lose track and veer off the road.

PIERCING

Thermal cutting processes need a free workpiece edge to start from, similar to sawing processes. This free edge can be found in the outer periphery of a workpiece. Or, it can be generated by piercing a hole through the metal. Cutting can start from that hole. In thin-gage metal, this hole is pierced by a single-millisecond, maximum-peak-power pulse of a focused laser beam on the workpiece. With thicker metals, several pulses of energy are needed to progressively drill or "peck-pierce" through the workpiece. The assist-gas for piercing is generally the same as for cutting and at about the same pressure. If it does not hinder quality, oxygen can be used to pierce through a metal while nitrogen or air might be used for cutting and vice versa.

Piercing of thick-gage metal generally occurs at a duty as low as 5–30% and a repetition frequency rate as low as 5–300 Hz. Examples of total piercing time and piercing parameters with a 2-kW CO_2 laser on mild steel are given in *Table 5-10*. Piercing 1.00-in. (25.4-mm) thick mild steel with a 4-kW CO_2 laser and oxygen assist-gas may take more than 20 seconds per pierce. One method to accelerate piercing of thick plates consists of operating at maximum CW power with the help of a cross-jet air knife between the nozzle and workpiece to flush recoiled metal fumes and spatters during the process. The CW piercing method with a 4-kW laser on 1.00-in. (25.4-mm) thick mild steel may take just a couple of seconds instead of more than 20 seconds, but yields a much wider pierced hole. It also results in a large temperature increase around the hole in the workpiece, sometimes necessitating water/mist cooling before effective cutting can start. To reduce the heat input, air can be used in lieu of oxygen. Air assist-gas will slow the piercing process by a second or two. In all cases, since piercing time fluctuates significantly because of changing surface conditions or material, a sensor to detect when piercing is completed enables a shortened average cycle.

REFERENCES

Air Liquide America. 2002. www.airliquide.com. Web technical report: "Lasing Gases for CO_2-type Laser—R & D Problematic and Approach." Houston, TX: Air Liquide America.

Ashkenas, H. and Sherman, F. S. 1965. *Proceedings of the 5th RGD (Rarefied Gas Dynamics) Conference*, vol. II, p. 84. J.H. de Leeuw, ed. New York: Academic Press.

Atkins, P. W. 1993. *The Elements of Physical Chemistry*. New York: W. H. Freeman and Company.

Table 5-10. Typical piercing parameters on mild steel

Thickness in. (mm)	Initial Pulse Frequency Hz	Initial Pulse Duty %	Pulse Frequency Increments Hz	Pulse Duty Increments %	Time Between Increments sec	Number of Increments	Total Piercing Time sec
1/4 (6.5)	10	20	1	1	0.1	10	3
1/2 (12.5)	10	10	1	1	0.1	20	10

Note: 2-kW peak power CO_2 laser, 7.5-in. (191-mm) focal-length lens, and oxygen assist-gas

Caristan, C., Vaidya, V., Camy-Peyret, F. 2003. "Laser Beam Propagation Caustics through Bifocal Lenses." International Congress on Applications of Lasers and Electro-Optics (ICALEO), Jacksonville, FL. Orlando, FL: Laser Institute of America.

Eguchi, S., Hayashikawa, H., and Hongu, H. 2000. "Experimental Study on High-speed Cutting of Thick Stainless Steel by 4-kW CO_2 Laser." Poster paper. International Congress on Applications of Lasers and Electro-Optics (ICALEO), Dearborn, MI. Orlando, FL: Laser Institute of America.

Fieret, J., and Ward, B. A. 1986, June. "Circular and Non-circular Nozzle Exits for Supersonic Gas Jet Assist in CO_2 Laser Cutting." Proceedings of the 3rd International Conference on Lasers in Manufacturing, Paris, France. Heidelberg, Germany: IFS Publications/ Springer Verlag.

Gabzdyl, J. T. 1996. "Effects of Gases on Laser Cutting of Stainless Steel." International Congress on Applications of Lasers and Electro-Optics (ICALEO), Section C, pp. 39-44. Orlando, FL: Laser Institute of America.

Kanaoka, M., Murai, T., and Yuyama, T. 1996. "Automatic Condition Setting of Materials Processing CO_2 Laser." International Congress on Applications of Lasers and Electro-Optics (ICALEO), Section C, pp. 1-9. Orlando, FL: Laser Institute of America.

Luxon, James T. and Parker, David E. 1992. "Industrial Lasers and Their Applications." Englewood Cliffs, NJ: Prentice Hall.

Marie, B. Van Der Have, P., and Roe, K. C. 1988, November. "Influences of Gaseous Impurities in the CO_2 Laser Cavity." International Congress on Applications of Lasers and Electro-Optics (ICALEO), Santa Clara, CA. Orlando, FL: Laser Institute of America.

Modest, Michael F. 2001. "Reflectivity and Absorptivity of Opaque Surfaces." *LIA Handbook of Laser Material Processing*, pp. 175-182. John F. Ready and Dave Farson, eds. Orlando, FL: Laser Institute of America.

O'Neill, W., Gabzdyl, J. T., and Steen, W. M. 1992. "The Dynamical Behavior of Gas Jets in Laser Cutting." International Congress on Applications of Lasers and Electro-Optics (ICALEO). Orlando, FL: Laser Institute of America.

Petring, Dirk. 1994. "Anwendungsorientierte Modellierung des Laserstrahlschneidens zur Rechnergestuzten Prozeßoptimierung." Ph.D. thesis. Aachen, Germany: University of Aachen.

Powell, J. Ivarson, A. Kamalu, J. Broden, G., and Magnusson, C. 1992. "The Role of Oxygen Purity in Laser Cutting of Mild Steel." International Congress on Applications of Lasers and Electro-Optics (ICALEO). Orlando, FL: Laser Institute of America.

Powell, John. 1998. *CO_2 Laser Cutting*. New York: Springer Verlag.

Schmidt, W. 1996. "Gases and Gas-supply Systems for Increased Productivity of Laser Processing." International Congress on Applications of Lasers and Electro-Optics (ICALEO), Section C, pp. 48-57. Orlando, FL: Laser Institute of America.

Smith, David and Penn, Wayne. 2000, November. "The Effects of Oxygen Purity & Nozzle Configuration on Laser-beam Cutting." Fabtech International, Cleveland, OH. Dearborn, MI: Society of Manufacturing Engineers.

VDI Gesellschaft Produktiontechnik (ADB). 1990. "Materialbearbeitung mit dem Laserstrahl im Gerate—und Maschinenbau—Leitfaden fur den Anwender." Dusseldorf, Germany: Springer VDI Verlag.

six

Man

"Work must be inspired by the right ideals, and education must not simply teach work, but life based on those ideals."

—W.E.B. DuBois

INTRODUCTION

Automation eases, speeds, and increases consistency and reproducibility of operations by reducing output variations. Unfortunately, automation is more often associated with a reduction of human labor than with a transfer of needs from one skill set to another. The transition from conventional cutting to laser cutting cannot occur without properly skilled workers. Human resources must adapt by showing transferable skills and increasing versatility through continuous training programs. The following sections review the human inputs influencing laser metal-cutting operations.

TRAINING

Due to precision and safety requirements, nearly 100% of laser metal cutting occurs through numerically controlled machinery. Manual motion-handling applications exist and more are under development, however, they are only marginally accepted. Converting processes from a traditional cutting operation to laser cutting requires not only capital investment in new machinery, but also the minimum knowledge and skill sets summarized in *Table 6-1*. Operators must have in-depth knowledge of laser resonators, laser material processing, optics, and beam propagation. Operators may not be found with such educational background as still too few academic institutions offer a specific industrial laser metal processing curriculum. Among the few recognized institutions are the Laser Institute of America (LIA), Society of Manufacturing Engineers (SME), University of Wisconsin, San Jose State University, the Fraunhofer Institute (Kuepper 1994), the Ohio State University (Shivpuri 2002), the Edison Welding Institute, Penn State University's ARL center (Martukanitz 2000), the Welding Research Institute at the University of Osaka (Matsu-nawa 1994), the Institut de Soudure Laser Center (Goussain and Chehaibou 1994), the CREOL Center of the University of Central Florida (Stickley 1994), and others around the world. These institutions provide continuous education programs, seminars, training, and certification that can bridge the knowledge gap. Some laser machine manufacturers offer laser-cutting and part-programming and maintenance training to address custom methods that may be required for a specific laser-cutting system.

Operators bear a special role since they are involved with setup and are closest to the machines. Sometimes experience has no substitute. That is why any departure from established procedures and setup should be recorded and discussed by the production team. Operators often show ingenuity at fixing problems and generating a scheduled manufacturing output even when it means altering methods. Two scenarios can be envisioned:

1. The method alteration is legitimate, optimizes the process, and yields a better product. The knowledge of the operator must be shared and recorded for future use. A risk analysis should be conducted to establish whether or not this optimization raises the sensitivity to noise, and reduces tolerances to variations in environmental conditions, machine maintenance status, and material. This analysis must confirm that the optimization is reproducible and quantifies the long-term impact on productivity, safety, quality, profitability, and the environment.

Table 6-1. Various skills/training requirements for laser cutting of metals operations

Skill Set	Who
Laser resonator principles	Operators, maintenance, service, procurement, sales, manufacturing engineering
Optics and beam propagation	Operators, maintenance, service, manufacturing engineering
Metal properties—metallurgy	Operators, maintenance, service, purchasing, sales, product engineering, manufacturing engineering
Laser material processing	Operators, maintenance, service, production planning, sales, product engineering, manufacturing engineering
Numerical control programming	Maintenance, service, manufacturing engineering
Part programming	Operators, maintenance, service, product engineering, manufacturing engineering
Laser safety	Operators, maintenance, service, manufacturing engineering
Product design	Production planning, sales, purchasing, product engineering, manufacturing engineering
Machine operation and maintenance	Operators, maintenance, service

2. The method alteration is not legitimate and what appears like an improvement might have drastic consequences in downstream operations. One example is heat-affected zone (HAZ) recast metallurgical-structure change, which is not visible to the operator. This change may contribute to catastrophic failure when the final product is in use.

With both scenarios, documenting changes becomes vital. This can be achieved with new software automation products pertaining to supervisory control, data collection, treatment and analysis, recommended actions, and archiving. Decision-making based on such information belongs to the human capital of the operation.

PRODUCT DESIGN

Laser cutting presents advantages and disadvantages compared to other cutting methods. The literature is rich in technology and economics comparisons between laser cutting, water-jet cutting, plasma cutting, oxyfuel cutting, die blanking, and other conventional metal-cutting processes (Julian 2002; Powell 2001; Mombo Caristan 2000; Guha 2000; Woodward 1999; Belforte and Levitt 1992). Product engineers can design parts to avoid disadvantages and exploit advantages. For example, optimizing a part's design for laser cutting may yield contour features that are incompatible with general guidelines for die-cutting processes. Die-cutting prefers parts to be designed with straight segments and corner angles to save on the die's initial cost and maintenance costs. Laser cutting performs better and faster with curvilinear features and corner radii instead of corner angles. In most applications, neither straight segment nor corner angles are necessary. However, they are designed as such by product engineers who are versed in the requirements of traditional metal-cutting technologies, such as die cutting, and who use CAD and nesting software programmed to optimize traditional methods. In the end, the parts will be designed to save time and cost according to traditional cutting technologies, even though they may be manufactured with laser cutting.

Curvilinear features can improve formability for stamping applications. Corner angles are known sources of defects such as wrinkling, buckling, and splitting. These defects force purchasing agents to procure oversized panels with wide binder stock to allow for engineering scrap where wrinkles and splits can develop away from the final part and from which it will be trimmed before use. As an illustration of the severity of this waste of material, the average volume of engineering scrap in automobile bodies surpasses a staggering 40%. For reference, automobile body production consumes close to 16 millions tons of sheet metal annually in North America, at an average material cost of about $400/ton. Metal savings alone, by reducing wrinkling, buckling, and splitting for narrower binder stocks, justifies laser cutting as an attractive alternative to die blanking, provided product engineers and die engineers optimize their developed blanks with appropriate curvilinear features.

PRODUCTION PLANNING

Cutting mild steel with N_2 instead of O_2 assist-gas eliminates the need for non-value-adding washing and cleaning to remove hard oxide scales from the cut edges. This also eliminates the need for re-lubrication after washing. Setting a nesting pattern that increases the number of common line cutting serves to drastically reduce processing time. Nesting patterns that yield engineering scrap skeleton that is too cumbersome to unload automatically slows down productivity and should be avoided by manufacturing engineers.

Production planners should take into account the delivery requirements of the customer and maintenance requirements for operations. They must also schedule manufacturing for a minimized number of setup changes involving operator intervention. To that end, a good understanding of laser-cutting machine setup and procedures becomes necessary.

REFERENCES

Belforte, D. and Levitt, M. 1992. "Laser vs. Nonlaser Process Comparison." *The Industrial Laser Handbook*, pp. 31-35. New York: Springer-Verlag.

Goussain, J. C. and Chehaibou, A. 1994. "Institut de Soudure Laser Center." International Congress on Applications of Lasers and Electro-Optics (ICALEO). Orlando, FL: Laser Institute of America.

Guha, Jayanta. 2000. "Water-Jet Cutting Applications." SME Conference on Comparative Cutting, Arlington Heights, VA, March 7-8. Dearborn, MI: Society of Manufacturing Engineers.

Julian, Al. 2002, June. "Comparative Economics of Thermal Cutting Technologies." Technical Forum Seminar (AFFT/SME), Advanced Thermal Processing of Metal Sheets & Plates: Cutting, Welding, & Inspection, Ohio State University, Columbus, OH. Dearborn, MI: Society of Manufacturing Engineers.

Kuepper, F. 1994. "Fraunhofer Resource Center for Laser Technology." International Congress on Applications of Lasers and Electro-Optics (ICALEO). Orlando, FL: Laser Institute of America.

Martukanitz, Richard. 2000, November. "Introduction to Industrial Lasers & Their Uses." Fabtech International, Session 202, Cleveland, OH. Dearborn, MI: Society of Manufacturing Engineers.

Matsunawa, Akira. 1994. "Laser Processing Centers and Their Research Projects in Japan." International Congress on Applications of Lasers and Electro-Optics (ICALEO). Orlando, FL: Laser Institute of America.

Mombo Caristan, J. C. 2000, November. "High-Speed Laser Cutting for Automotive Sheet Metal Blanking Production." Fabtech International Conference Reading, Cleveland, OH, Session 208. Dearborn, MI: Society of Manufacturing Engineers.

Powell, John. 2001. "Comparison of CO_2 Laser Cutting with Other Profiling Techniques." *LIA Handbook of Laser Material Processing*. John F. Ready and Dave Farson, eds. Orlando, FL: Laser Institute of America.

Shivpuri, Rajiv. 2002, June. "Laser Applications in Sheet-Metal Forming." Technical Forum Seminar (AFFT/SME), Advanced Thermal Processing of Metal Sheets & Plates: Cutting, Welding, & Inspection, Ohio State University, Columbus, OH. Dearborn, MI: Society of Manufacturing Engineers.

Stickley, Martin. 1994. "Lasers and Optics Activities at CREOL." International Congress on Applications of Lasers and Electro-Optics (ICALEO). Orlando, FL: Laser Institute of America.

Woodward, Kevin. 1999, August. "Thermal and Water-jet Cutting." *Metal Center News*.

seven

Measurement

"Everything that can be counted does not necessarily count; everything that counts cannot necessarily be counted."

—Albert Einstein

INTRODUCTION

Measurements play a key role in automation, supervisory control, troubleshooting, and process improvement to increase productivity, quality and, hopefully, profitability. They involve the collection of input and output data to be processed into information rather than relying on "anecdotal" reporting. Information is analyzed to derive executable actions to improve and control operations. The integrity of the executable actions depends on the objectivity demonstrated at all steps of the measurement process, from selection of which data to collect, how these data are sampled and processed, to the analysis criteria used. Imprecise and inaccurate measurements are the only things worse than no measurement at all. For this reason, gages must be regularly tested for calibration, repeatability, and reproducibility. Measurements would not be necessary if laser-cutting operations could produce perfect products, specified by perfect customers, with perfect material, by perfect employees, with a perfect laser-cutting method, and a perfect machine. Evidently, that is too great of an expectation.

Ideally, measurements should be automated, thus eliminating human error from the process. Such automation costs increase with the number of sensors and gages that must be purchased, calibrated, maintained, and installed with signal connection to the laser-cutting machine's control or an auxiliary PC. Each signal, data acquisition, sampling frequency, and data treatment require incremental CPU time and storage memory. This can slow operations if excessive CPU time for measurement activity must be shared with the machine's numerical control.

VARIABLE AND ATTRIBUTE DATA

Measurement data comes in two main categories: variable or attribute. Variable data describes a continuously measured signal sampled individually or by subgroups. For example, thermocouples measuring the inlet and outlet temperatures of the water used to cool the laser and its components deliver continuous variable signals to the data processor. These temperatures can be sampled individually and punctually at regular intervals of time, such as every 60 seconds, yielding one data entry recorded per minute. Or, they can be sampled by subgroups in which five measurements are taken every 12 seconds and averaged over a minute, every minute, to yield one data entry recorded per minute. These two sets of recorded data, one for individual temperatures and one as a subgroup average temperature, are statistically very different and will exhibit distribution profiles sharing the same average but different standard deviations as shown in *Figure 7-1*. A distribution of averages is generally narrower than a distribution of individual data, that is, there is a smaller standard deviation, σ, for a distribution of averages. Most readers are familiar with statistical process control (SPC) control charts. They plot subgroup averages and ranges (X-bar and R charts), particularly for a subgroup size smaller than 10. A *range* is simply the difference between the maximum and minimum values within a subgroup.

Attribute measurement data belong to either type I or II. Attribute data are counted rather than measured. Type I attribute data result from the counts of a number of items in a category such as from go/no-go gages. Type II attribute data result from

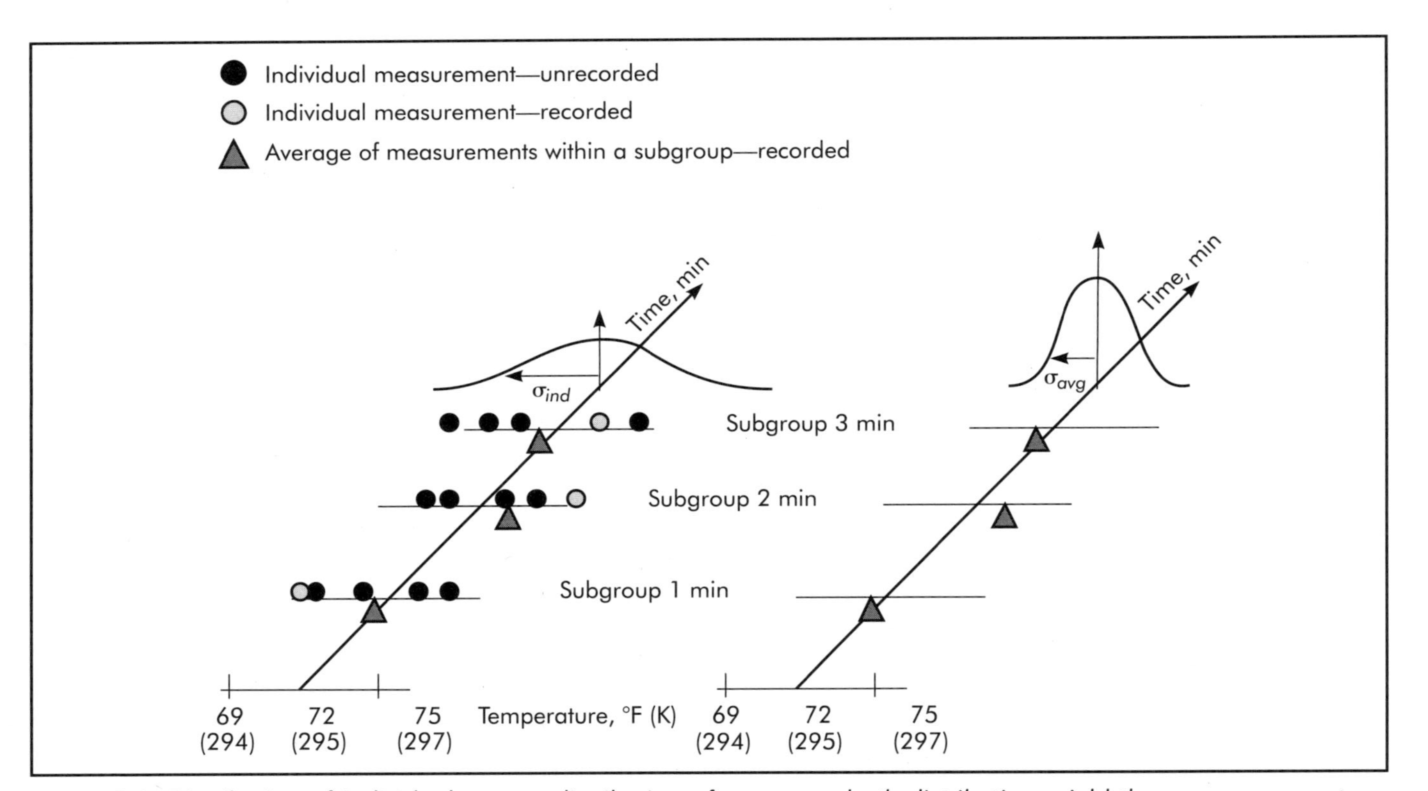

Figure 7-1. Distribution of individuals versus distribution of averages: both distributions yield the same average temperature. The distribution of individual measurements yields a standard deviation, σ_{ind}, larger than the standard deviation, σ_{avg}, of the distribution of averages.

counts of discrete event occurrences. *Figure 7-2* illustrates the difference between the two types of attribute data.

Table 7-1 provides guidance to select a control chart type (ANSI/ASQC 1996). Types of control charts for variable data include X-bar and R charts, X-bar and S charts for subgroup sizes larger than 10, and X moving R if the subgroup size is equal to one. For attribute data, c-charts, u-charts, np-charts, and p-charts can be selected based on whether the attribute data is type I or II, and whether the sample size is constant or variable.

INPUT AND OUTPUT MEASUREMENTS

Inputs in the 6M categories (material, man, method, measurement, machine, and Mother Nature) must be ranked by order of importance by the team managing a laser-cutting operation. The recording of the top key inputs can then be done either manually or automatically if the resources for such automation are approved. The list of gages, sensors, and data available in any facility but not treated automatically is impressive. It includes date and time, cumulative number of hours of operations, various temperature gages (including plant temperature, humidity, and barometric pressure), efficiency of the laser-power supplies' pumping mechanism (power delivered by laser-power supplies versus average laser-output power), material type, cutting parameters, machine X-Y-Z position, and number of hours of operation per focusing lens and nozzle tip. Ideally, as much of this data as possible should be compiled in SPC charts as information resources until the operation is clearly demonstrated to be under control with optimized productivity, efficiency, and quality. Practically, machines and manufacturing processes should be designed to require the least amount of measurements for process control.

The funneling down to a limited and manageable number of the most important signals to be monitored must be done judiciously. As much as resources permit, the start-up operation can monitor as many signals as possible. The top key signals by importance will then be decided based on historical analysis of variations. The remaining inconsequential signals will be dropped at a later date. Signals that do not show significant variations should

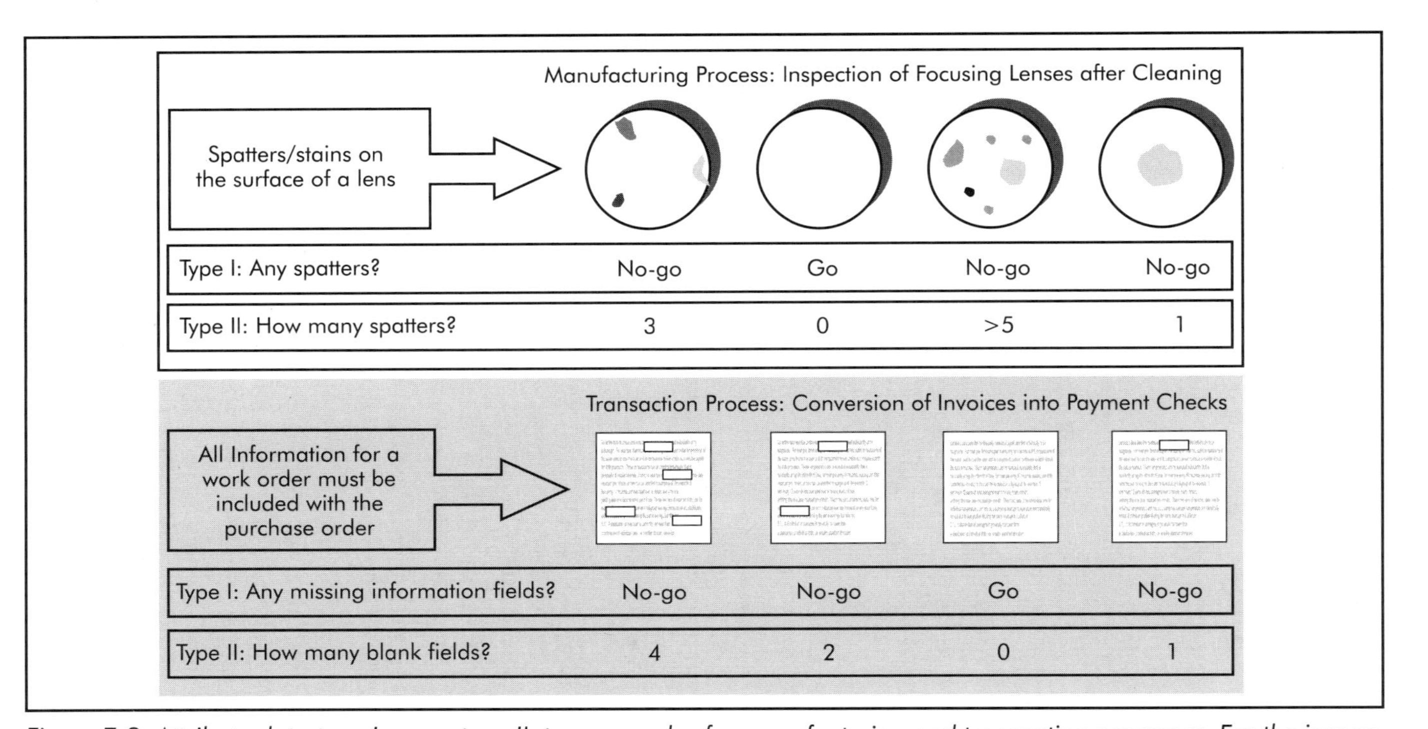

Figure 7-2. Attribute data type I versus type II: two examples for manufacturing and transaction processes. For the inspection of focusing lenses, type I attribute "Any spatter?" could consider the severity of a spatter, while type II attribute "How many spatters?" could disregard the severity of each spatter. A spatter at the periphery of a lens is less severe than one at the center; the severity increases with the size of the spatter. For the conversion of invoices into payment checks example, in type II, counting the number of missing information fields quantifies the severity of the problem.

Table 7-1. Selection of a control chart type is based on the type of measurement data available (ANSI/ASQC 1996)

Chart Type	Variable Data		
	Sample Size = 1	Sample Size ≤ 10	Sample Size > 10
X moving *R*	X		
X-bar and *R*		X	
X-bar and *S*			X

Chart Type	Attribute Data Type I		Attribute Data Type II	
	Constant Sample Size	Variable Sample Size	Constant Sample Size	Variable Sample Size
np	X			
p		X		
c			X	
u				X

be considered under control and will no longer need measurement and monitoring. It is important to realize that significant variations are inclusive of substantial variations, and substantial variations are not necessarily significant variations.

Alternatively and preferably, a six-sigma team effort can establish key process-input variables to be monitored for improvement of critical output variables. Design of experiments helps identify the combinations of key input variables that predominantly influence the selected key output variables. If the improvement is not deemed sufficient, a subsequent six-sigma project can be reiterated. This may change or add to the selection of signals to be measured and monitored.

Output data to be measured include part-contour accuracy and edge-quality parameters such as dross height, cut-edge roughness, angle of striations on cut-edge roughness, cut-edge taper, and kerf width at the top and bottom, along with supervisory control data such as machine uptime versus idle time, cycle time, and scrap rate. Current commercially available factory-management software enables various degrees of automation of diverse data collection, its treatment and processing, and information management and storage.

REFERENCE

ANSI/ASQC. 1996. Standard B1-B3-1996. "Guide for Quality-control Charts—Control-chart Method of Analyzing Data—Control-chart Method for Controlling Quality During Production." Washington, DC: American National Standards Institute.

eight

Mother Nature

"Nature does nothing without purpose or uselessly."

—Aristotle

The high definition and precision of a laser-cutting process increases its sensitivity to small disturbances from Mother Nature, namely, temperature, humidity, barometric pressure, and pollution levels inside a facility. A simple experiment consists of opening and closing the overhead doors of a heated facility in winter to enable truck traffic. The laser resonator will respond immediately to the cold wind by altering its output. If it is not operating in a closed-loop power control, the laser-output power may immediately drop or rise noticeably. In the middle of a cavity or laser-power-supply tuning procedure, such variation in temperature is enough to cause imprecise tuning. Similarly, the water chiller, which is designed with much less over-engineering protection than most industrial laser resonators, responds to temperature changes by exhibiting noticeable variation in efficiency between hot summer afternoons and cold winter mornings.

Most pressure gages measure a pressure relative to the local environmental pressure. Therefore, when measurement precision within ±1.000 psi (±0.07 bar) is required, gage calibration based on the local geographical elevation, barometric pressure, and temperature matters. It is well known by pilots and mountain climbers that for every 1,000 ft (305 m) of altitude, the temperature decreases 3.6° F (2° C) and the barometric pressure decreases about 0.5 psi (26 mm Hg) (Harris et al. 1998). Pressure measurements at mile-high elevation in Denver, Colorado may differ from sea-level measurements by as much as 2.90 psi (0.2 bar).

Hot summer humidity may contribute to dew on water-cooled optics in the beam-delivery system and on the external surface of the output-coupler (OC) mirror of a resonator cavity. Fortunate are those who can afford air-conditioned facilities. For all others, what cannot be controlled, can at least be monitored. Adverse environmental conditions may feel uncomfortable for humans, but most industrial laser machines are designed to operate at both ends of extreme conditions of temperature, atmospheric pressure, and humidity. However, the processes generally respond to variations in environmental conditions with variations in outputs. Process parameters and methods must be as tolerant as possible to such variations, or they must be optimized with each condition change. Good documentation over the years can reveal the true impact of weather on operations, downtime, productivity, profitability, and quality.

REFERENCE

Harris, Mark D., Terrio, James, Miser, William F., and Yetter, Joseph F. 1998, April 15. "High-altitude Medicine." *American Family Physician*. Leawood, KS: American Academy of Family Physicians.

Part II: Outputs

Quality

"Life is an error-making and an error-correcting process, and nature in marking man's papers will grade him for wisdom as measured both by survival and by the quality of life of those who survive."

—Jonas Salk

INTRODUCTION

Process-output variables are categorized in this book in five comprehensive domains: environment, safety, quality, productivity, and profitability. Laser processing, as a relatively young technology for the metal-fabrication industry, is the subject of special scrutiny resulting in an exceptionally good safety record among all manufacturing operations. Productivity, quality, and profitability are recognized key outputs that compete with each other for precedence. Within each of these five categories, key process-output variables (KPOV) can be identified and customarily ranked for each enterprise and application. A small job shop that produces small batches of various orders may obtain a different KPOV ranking than a large-volume production manufacturer that supplies large batches of fewer part numbers. However, both groups tackle the same base manufacturing process driven by the same higher-level 6M categories (material, man, method, measurement, machine, and Mother Nature) of key process-input variables (KPIV).

CRITICAL-TO-QUALITY PARAMETERS

A cutting job is measured by how well the customer's critical-to-quality (CTQ) parameters are addressed. CTQ parameters are not limited to engineering quality specifications. As an example, from a procurement perspective, part-delivery lead time might be the most important quality issue, whereas from a user perspective, contour accuracy may be the most critical criteria for satisfaction. This chapter will mainly address engineering specifications pertaining to the cut part from the point of view of a laser-cutting machine operation.

Among all CTQ parameters, edge quality plays a central role for manufacturers. There are no internationally or even nationally recognized standards for laser-cut-edge quality. Machine builders evaluate edge quality differently, and each end-user sets their own edge-quality specifications. German DIN standard 2310, parts 1–6 covering cut edges obtained with thermal processes including laser cutting, represents the closest attempt to specifying a cut-edge-quality standard. In the automotive industry, the American Society for Testing and Materials (ASTM) edge-quality standards for die-blanked and sheared sheet-metal edges and burrs, and the shear-to-break ratio could be amendable and extendable to laser-cut-edge standards.

VARIATION

In manufacturing operations, variations represent the enemy. They are due to either common causes or special causes. Examples of common causes include accidental interferences, whereas special causes encompass predictable or controllable events that must be dealt with.

Special causes often cause subtle, long cycle trends over a period of several hundred to several thousand hours of operation between maintenance intervals. For example, mirror and lens contamination is a typical special cause of progressive performance degradation. Mirrors and lenses require cleaning or replacement at regular intervals. In today's highly automated machinery, another special cause and underestimated source of sudden cutting quality degradation is material variation. Variations in surface finish, flatness, and thickness of the raw sheets or plates negatively affect cutting quality.

As competition among laser-cutting-machine builders intensifies, marketing pressures call for publishing and claiming the fastest feed rate and maximum-thickness-cutting performance. This has led to inflated claims proven only in laboratory conditions with specified best-quality material and expert application engineers. When the environment "noise" levels change, so does cutting performance. Operators get involved in a downward spiral of adjusting parameters in attempts to reproduce published performances. The extended downtimes for these adjustments make it counterproductive to the intended result. More conservative parameters, feed rate, and reasonable performance expectations could eliminate these patterns of "tweaking" behavior and still yield a higher net output at a higher net quality.

The fishbone diagram in *Figure 9-1* lists a multitude of process-input variables that can influence laser-cutting-operation output. *Figure 9-2* itemizes process-output variables in each of the five general domains. For each set of CTQ parameters, corresponding KPOVs can be assigned and ranked. KPIV identification helps when failure-mode analysis is eventually required.

EDGE QUALITY

Generally speaking, each end-user defines laser-cutting quality or performance as a custom compromise of the following features, based on an importance ranking dictated by the customer and application.

- The process must have maximum cutting-speed capability based on a specific range of thickness.
- The process must deliver the best edge quality for a specific range of thicknesses and materials. Edge quality can be scientifically measured by edge-surface roughness. For specialized applications, such as aerospace, it is also measured by metallurgical microscopy of the nature and width of the heat-affected-zone (HAZ) recast layer. The bevel angle of the kerf

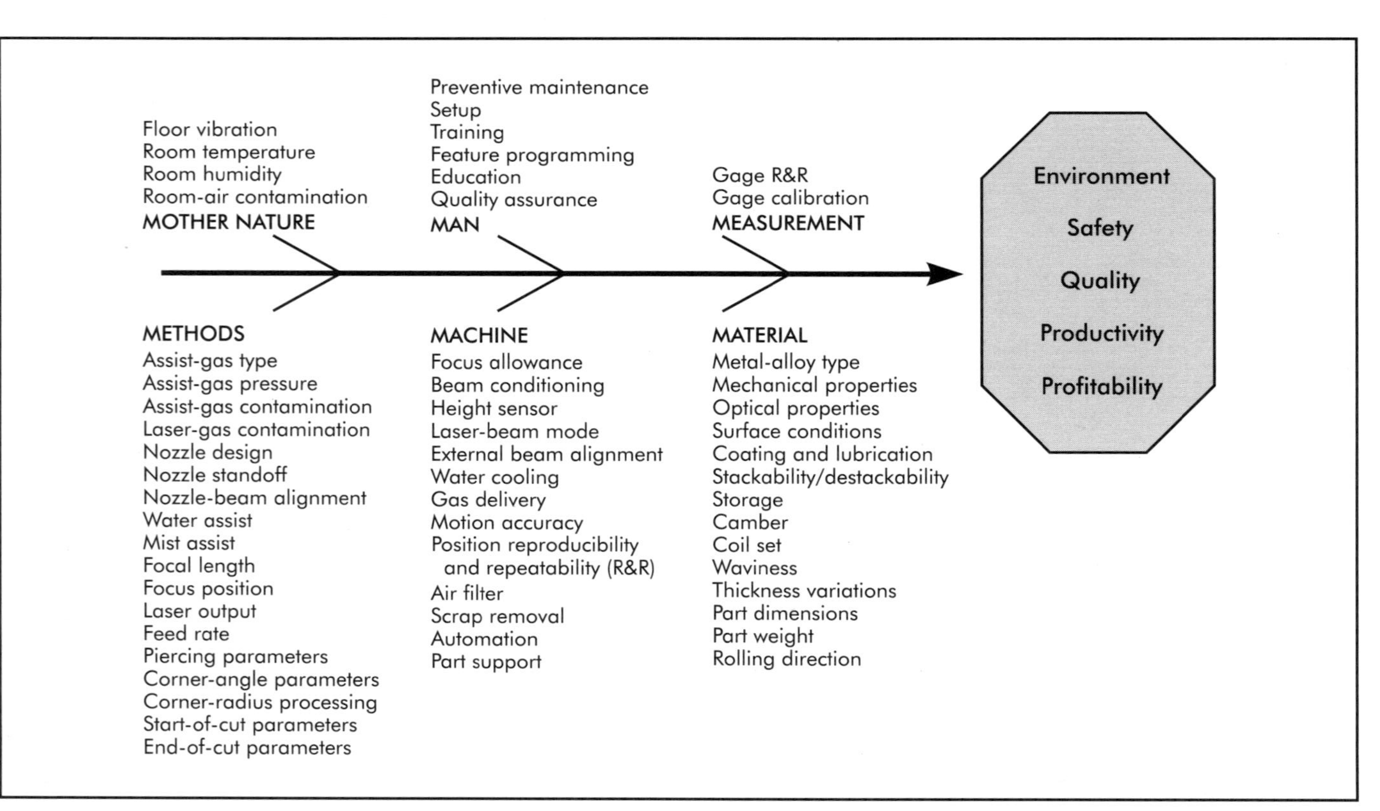

Figure 9-1. Comprehensive troubleshooting must consider all potential key process-input variables for each out-of-control output variation.

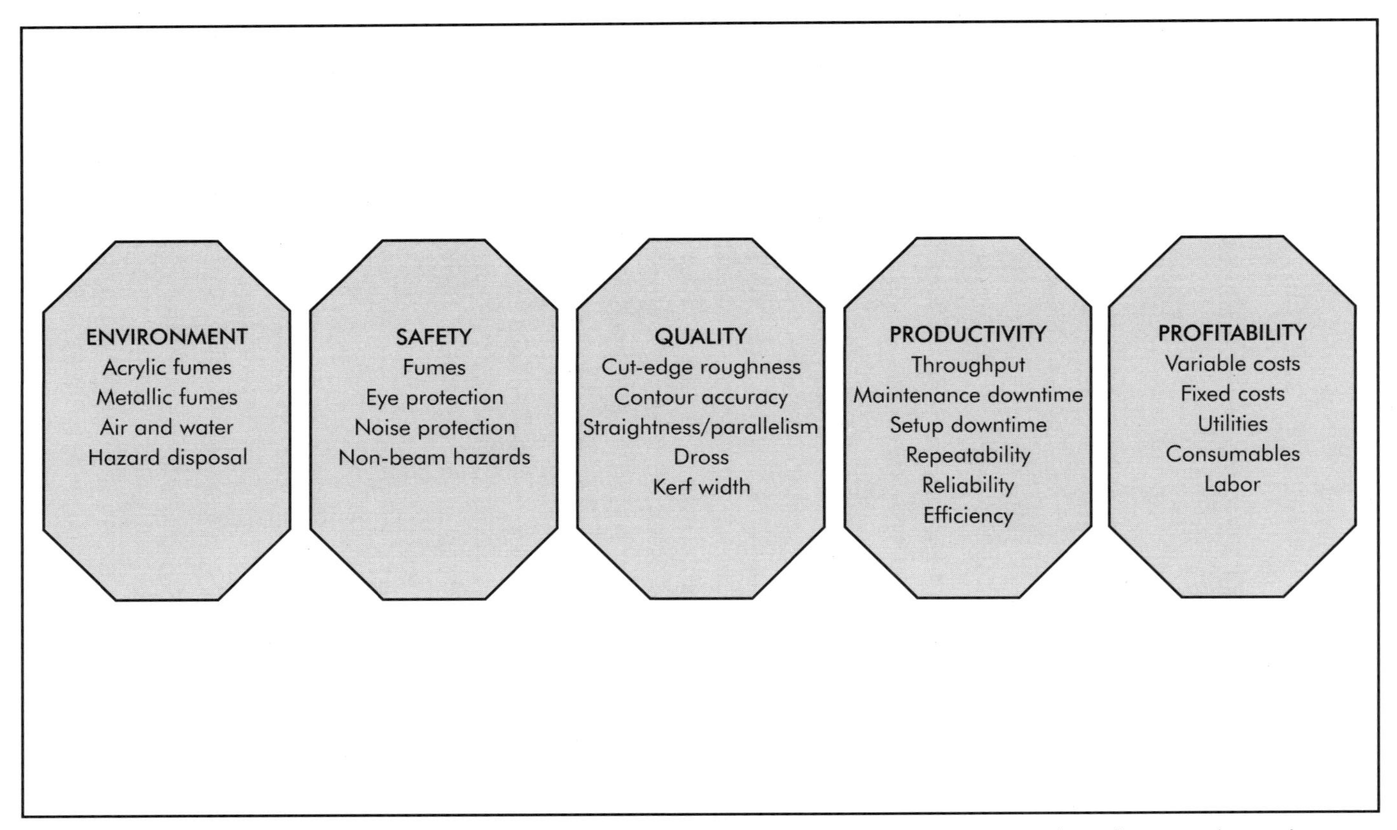

Figure 9-2. The importance ranking of key process-output variables remains customer and application dependent.

walls also could be considered to evaluate edge quality. Or, edge quality could be subjectively evaluated simply by the operator's educated "see, touch, and feel" test as is often the case in job shops.

- The process must have maximum-thickness cutting capability at a specified range of edge quality.
- The process must yield the same edge quality at different positions of the work envelope.
- The process must yield the same maximum-cutting-speed capability at different positions of the work envelope.
- The process must reproduce cutting performance without "tweaking" between preventive maintenance intervals.

Compromises could one day become influenced by the development of national or international standards. In the meantime, many reference the edge quality obtained from traditional processes such as plasma cutting, flame cutting, and mechanical saw, shear, or die cutting, or simply the edge-quality comparative scale offered by the laser-machine builder (when available).

Edge quality is most scrutinized at the engineering level. The quality of the cut edge impacts several aspects of manufacturing when fabricating and assembling sheet-metal components. It impacts the safety of operators or end-users that come in contact with sharp metal edges. Accelerated tool wear results from friction with hardened cut edges. Micro-cracks that develop along the cut edges can propagate into splits during forming or, even worse, when in use in the finished product. Recast layers in the HAZ greatly influence fatigue resistance, formability, and weldability.

Cut-edge-surface Roughness

Many plant operators evaluate cut-edge quality by visual means and touch-and-feel tests of an edge surface finish or smoothness. Smoothness evaluation of an edge is strongly operator dependent and subject to poor reproducibility and repeatability (R&R), despite the fact that operator training could reduce this variation. To reduce subjectivity and satisfy customers who require more rigorous quality monitoring, mechanical profilometer needle scans or noncontact optical surface scans are alternative ways to quantify cut-edge finish. With the exception of a few sensitive applications that require superior edge quality and demand monitoring with periodic rigorous checking during production, scientific roughness measurements are few and usually limited to research and development settings.

Figure 9-3 illustrates typical surface roughness patterns on a thick-plate's laser-cut edge. Always smoother at the top, roughness increases in the middle section and may end up so rough as to exhibit deeper and wider striations (gouges) at the bottom of the cut edge. When cutting metal with the workpiece's surface on a non-horizontal plane, the top part of the edge is defined as the one closest to the incident laser beam(s) and assist-gas when cutting with a single laser beam.

Figure 9-3. Typical surface roughness patterns on a thick plate's laser-cut edge. Always smoother at the top, roughness increases in the middle section and might end up with deeper and wider grooves (gouges).

At constant laser power, the thinner the metal, the smoother the edge's surface finish will appear. *Figure 9-4* illustrates a comparison of surface roughness profile measurements for top, bottom, and middle sections of a cut edge produced with two different laser powers. A higher peak power does not buy much speed; however, it yields less frequent gouging and shallower striations for an overall smoother edge.

The following explains what generates roughness of the cut edge in the first place. When cutting with a laser, hot liquid and vaporized metal are flushed away by assist-gas through the kerf. The

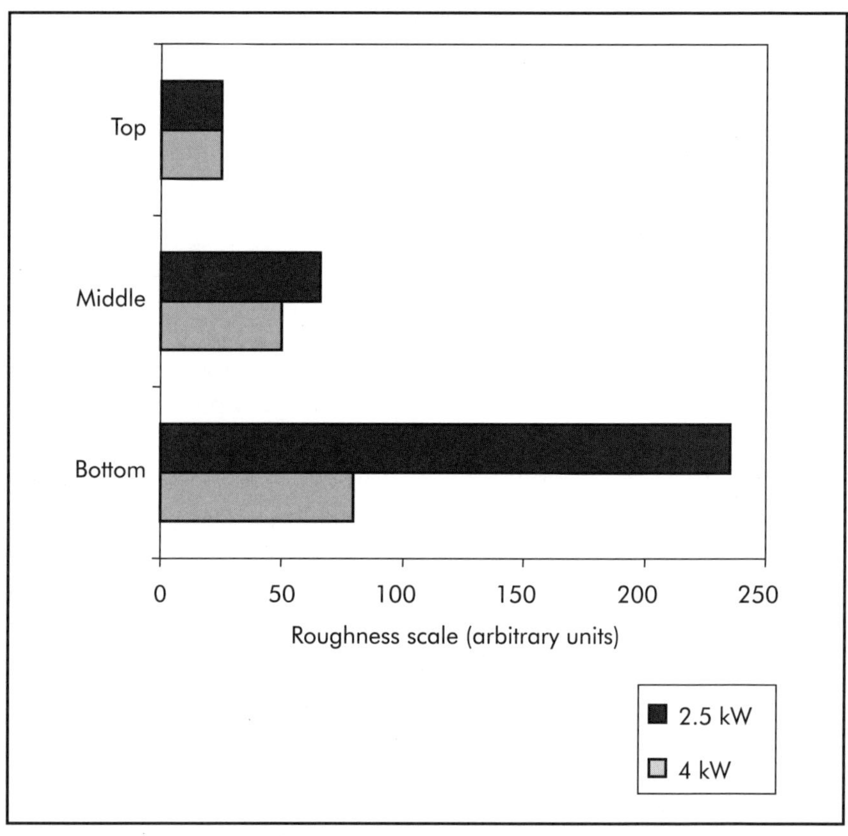

Figure 9-4. Cut-edge surface roughness comparison: 2.5- versus 4-kW CO_2 laser on 0.75-in. (19-mm) mild steel with O_2 assist-gas, 7.5-in. (191-mm) focal-length lens, and same speed of 30 in./min (0.75 m/min). Cuts achieved with the 2.5-kW laser yield more frequent and more severe gouging at the bottom of the kerf.

mixture of hot liquid and vaporized metal with the assist-gas represents two different viscous flows through a kerf of finite width. The flows interact with the laser beam, which is in some ways partially wave-guided by the side and front walls of the kerf, but is left free to disperse in the open-ended upstream part of the kerf. The flow of metal through the kerf's height cannot be perfectly laminar and uniform. Its resolidification occurs more or less rapidly depending on cutting speed and the metal's physical properties such as thermal conductivity and latent heat generated during solid-liquid transformation. The end result is a cut-edge surface with striation relief as a result of interaction with the laser beam before resolidification. The widening of the striations at the bottom of the kerf may relate to beam-diameter divergence and assist-gas-flow expansion through the open-ended upstream part of the kerf. Similar striation patterns can be observed with non-laser thermal cutting processes such as plasma cutting (Cook 2000).

When surface roughness breaks down severely, it exhibits deeper grooves or crevices called gouges on the edge's surface finish. Gouges are larger and deeper at the bottom part of the edge and sometimes develop all the way up toward the top of the edge. At the end of a closed-contour cut feature, gouges may be observed when the part finally detaches from the main plate and drops under the action of its own weight before the cut is completed at the bottom of the kerf. Part support may play an important role if such end-of-cut gouging cannot be tolerated.

Gouging is also observed when processing a corner-angle feature without appropriate adaptation of laser output as a function of motion feed rate, acceleration, and direction changes (Kanaoka, Murai, and Yuyama 1996). It can also occur when feed rate, power, duty, and focus-spot characteristics are not set properly for the alloy being cut or when these parameters have degraded significantly due to special or common causes.

Sources of Variation

Figure 9-5 highlights the 6M process-input variables with variations that can cause edge roughness. An itemized review of the variables follows for each of the 6M categories: material, man, method, measurement, machine, and Mother Nature.

Method Sources

Assist-gas pressure. Assist-gas pressure variations can result from an uncalibrated proportional valve system with an incorrect gas-pressure setting or setup. When cutting with-low pressure O_2,

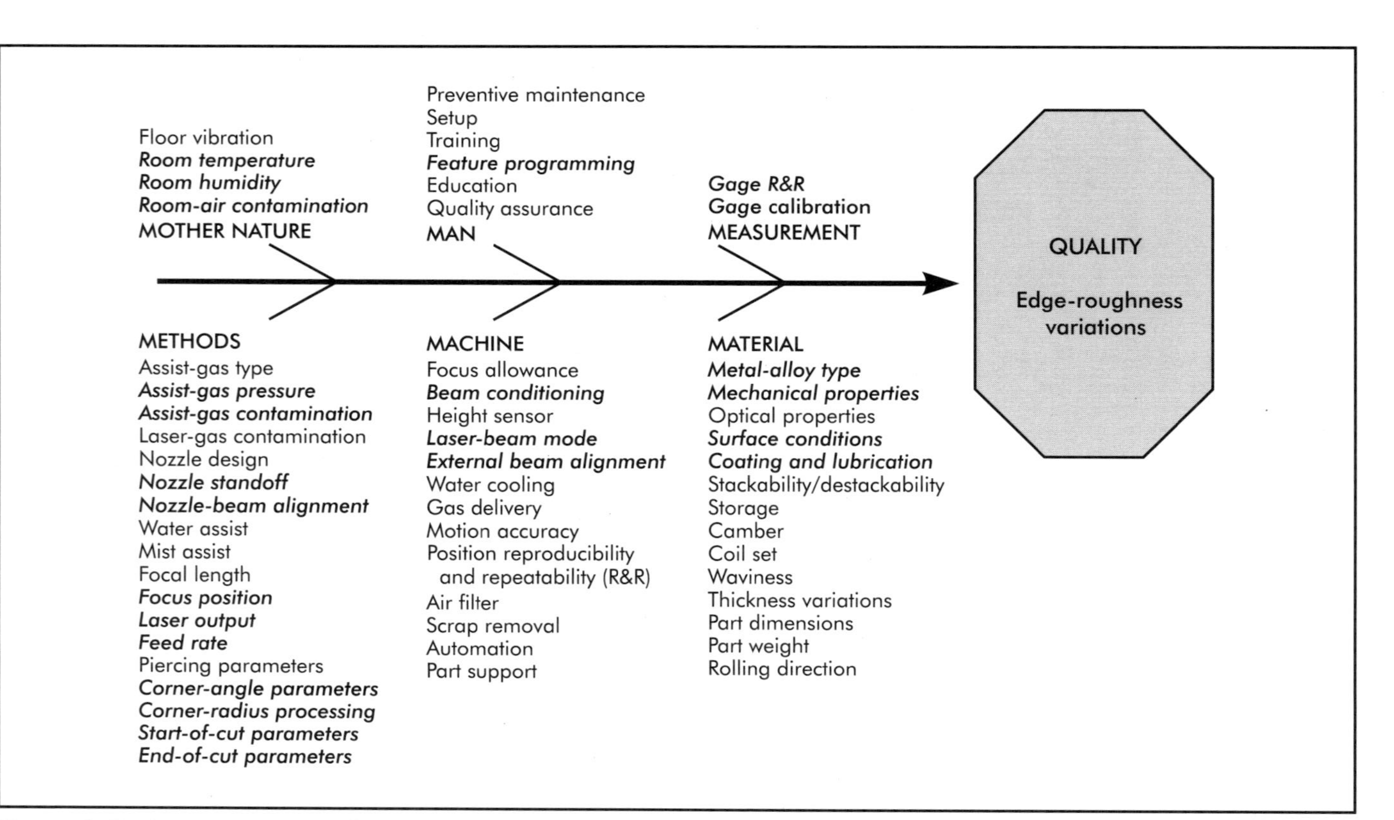

Figure 9-5. An increase in edge roughness results predominantly from variations in the highlighted (bold) input parameters.

it is common that too much or not enough pressure similarly impacts edge roughness when cutting plates thicker than about 0.125 in. (3.18 mm). Assist-gas pressure should be controlled to within less than ±1.000 psi (±0.07 bar) as established in Chapter 5. *Figure 9-6* illustrates the effect of too high of an O_2 pressure flowing through while cutting 1.00-in. (25.4-mm) mild steel. The increasing occurrence and severity of gouging can be seen at the bottom part of the cut edge as the flow of partially unburned O_2 bounces against the lagging part of the cut front in the kerf. The top part of the cut edge remains smooth.

Insufficient O_2 pressure limits the complementary energy brought by the metal's oxidation and exothermic reaction necessary to more efficiently melt and vaporize metal in the kerf. This results in a clear roughness increase to the point of gouging. In this case, the top part of the cut edge becomes rougher as well.

When cutting with high-pressure inert gas, such as N_2, shock waves developed under a supersonic flow regime can contribute to a noticeable increase in surface roughness. The shock waves

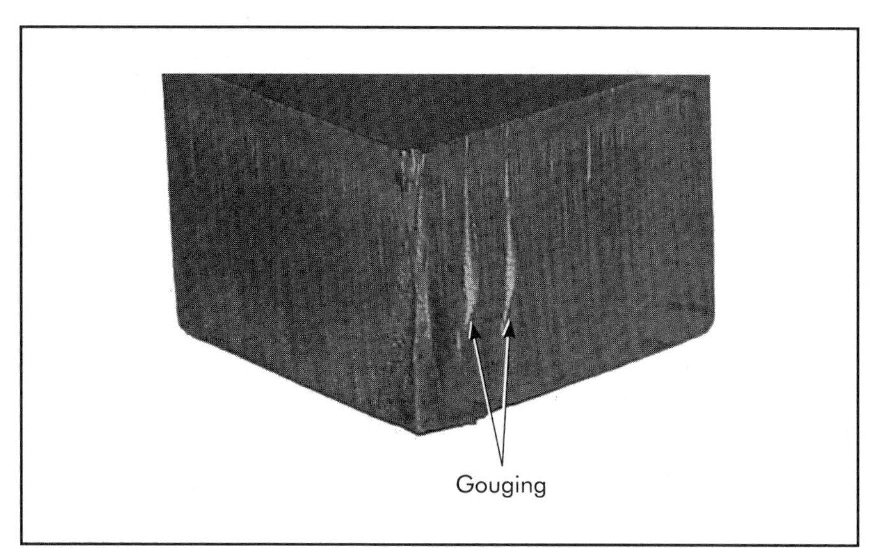

Figure 9-6. The flow of assist-gas, viscous hot metallic vapor, and liquid metal leaves an imprint of deepening and widening gouges. Sometimes gouges prevent proper through cut: the finished part does not drop out by its own weight and must be literally hammered out for collection.

bounce with sufficient strength against liquid metal in the kerf's walls and against the lagging part of the cut front to carve the cut-edge surface. Thicker metals yield deeper, grooved striations as seen in *Figure 9-7*. Gages thinner than about 0.25 in. (6.2 mm) can generally be cut with smooth edges using industrial CO_2 lasers of 1-kW average power or more.

Assist-gas contamination. Assist-gas contamination can have the same effect as insufficient or too much pressure. This contradiction takes place naturally in O_2-assisted, mild-steel laser cutting. Low-pressure O_2 contaminated with N_2 or Ar results in insufficient fuel for metal oxidation and exothermic reaction, which appears to the operator as a symptom of insufficient O_2 pressure. To remedy this effect, operators increase the assist-gas pressure without recognizing that significant contamination is taking place. This results in enough O_2 to exothermically oxidize the metal and assist in melting it. However, too much gas-flow pressure yields excessive gouging, particularly in thicker material.

Contamination of assist-gas occurs when leaks allow ambient air to diffuse into the assist-gas-delivery system. This diffusion can take place even when positive pressure flows through the gas-delivery system. Assist-gas lines must be flushed when the system has remained idle for a long period of time such as overnight or during weekend shutdown. Contamination also occurs by diffusion of ambient air in the gas flow during its travel between the nozzle exit and workpiece. The impact of assist-gas contamination on edge roughness is seen mostly in low-pressure O_2 assist and moderately in high-pressure, N_2-assist laser cutting.

Nozzle standoff distance. Nozzle standoff distance may vary under the control of a height sensor. If the height sensor is not calibrated properly or its response time becomes too slow, then nozzle standoff may vary from its nominal setup during cutting. A resulting change in the assist-gas flow dynamics and focus position yields unwanted variations in edge roughness. Many height-sensor devices are based on capacitive-sensor technology. Unfortunately, the signal from these sensors can be poisoned with electronic noise due to plasma radiation emerging from the kerf. The plasma-radiation-induced electronic noise becomes more intense with high peak power and slow feed rate. Edge roughness

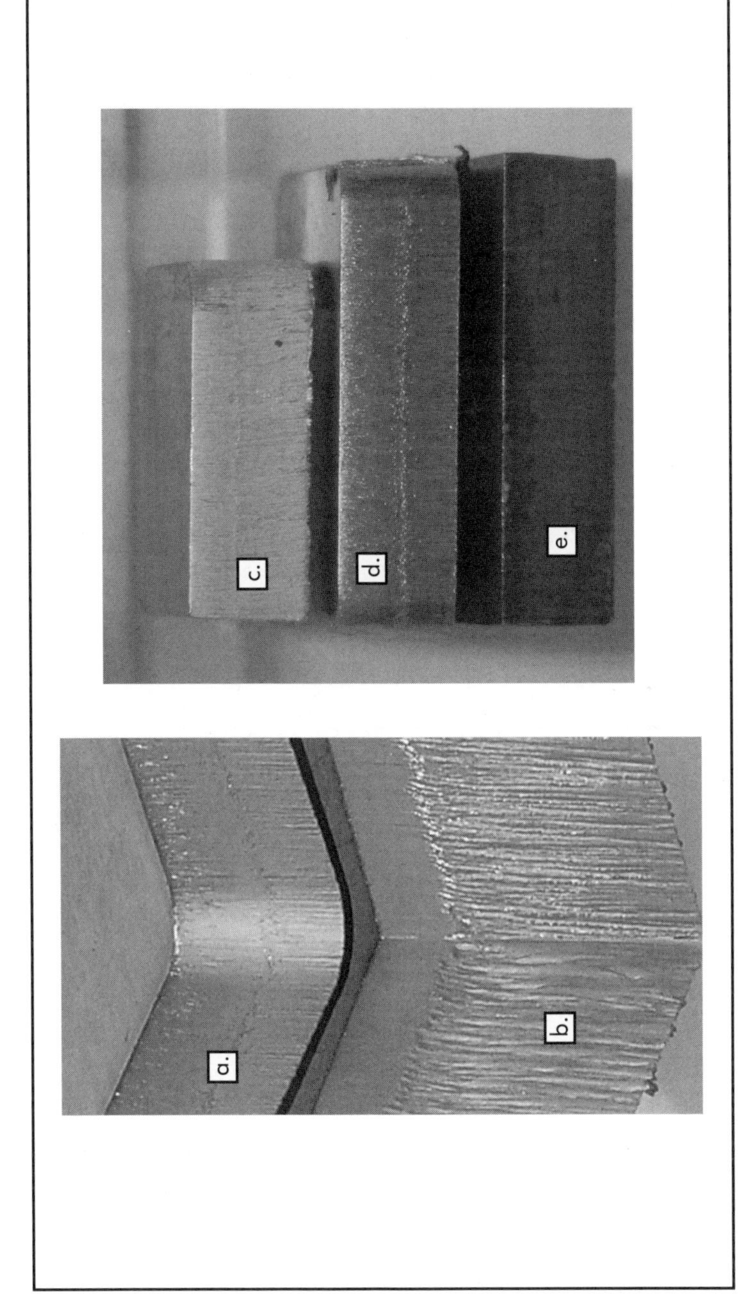

Figure 9-7. (a and d) Shown is 0.50-in. (12.7-mm) stainless steel cut with N_2 assist-gas; (b) 1.00-in. (25.4-mm) stainless steel cut with N_2 assist-gas; (c) 0.50-in. (12.7-mm) aluminum cut with air assist-gas; (e) 0.50-in. (12.7-mm) mild steel cut with O_2 assist-gas. Generally, stainless steel (a and d) yields rougher edges than mild steel (e); and aluminum (c) yields rougher edges than stainless steel (a and d).

increases to the point where cutting cannot be performed without significant reduction in feed rate.

Nozzle-beam alignment. Nozzle-beam alignment needs to be confirmed each time a nozzle tip or optics is displaced, removed, or replaced, and each time external beam alignment is performed. Misalignment typically yields cutting performance that varies with the direction of the cut progression relative to the misalignment with the nozzle center. *Figure 9-8* illustrates direction-dependent dross on stainless steel.

Focus position and laser output. Focus position and laser-output variations can be due to incorrect setup of cutting parameters, a miscalibrated height sensor, or a malfunction in the laser resonator or beam-delivery system.

Thermal lensing exemplifies malfunction in the beam-delivery system. When optics, and focusing lenses in particular, are subject to temperature gradients outside of specification, thermal lensing occurs. The optical properties change, resulting in noticeable impact on the focus size, position, and power-distribution pattern on the workpiece. *Thermal lensing* occurs when the surface of an optic becomes dirty. More laser-beam power is absorbed by the foreign contamination on the optic and less is available for good

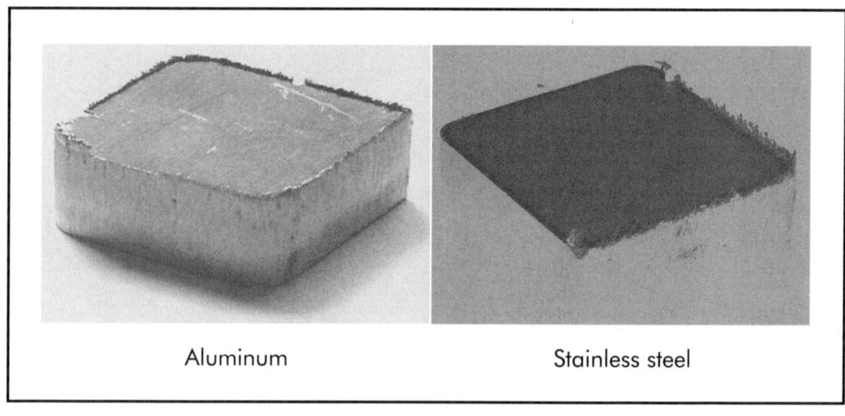

Figure 9-8. The amount of dross on these 0.50-in. (12.7-mm) aluminum and 0.50-in. (12.7-mm) stainless-steel samples appears to be dependent on the direction of the cut's progression. With aluminum, dross appears white and shiny and is relatively soft; on stainless steel, dross appears dark and is very hard.

quality cutting. This contamination, mostly non-uniformly applied, results in more heat absorption in certain locations, leading to localized temperature increases and non-axis-symmetric temperature gradient patterns. A laser beam impinging on an optic's surface will volatize most minerals and hydrocarbons present in ambient air from humidity or adjacent fabrication processes such as welding and painting. As a result, burn marks may accumulate on optics, alter their optical properties, and enhance absorption to a point of no return if cleaning action is not taken early enough.

Certain hydrocarbons, such as acrylic fumes, exhibit strong absorption of CO_2 laser radiation at 10.6 μm wavelength. If present in ambient air and in the beam-delivery system, their absorption adds to the optics' absorption, resulting in even further reduced actual peak power at the workpiece. Absorption of laser power by dust particles and fumes has another consequence—it creates temperature gradients in the air along the optical path inside the beam-delivery conduit. Temperature gradients, along with diffusion scattering of light by contaminants inside the beam-delivery conduit, result in alteration of the final focus-spot characteristics on the workpiece and its position relative to the workpiece's surface. Cutting performance, including worsening of edge roughness, will appear different than under nominal operating conditions.

Other laser-output characteristics that can trigger edge-roughness defects with direction dependency (see *Figure 9-8*) are asymmetry of the beam mode and polarization. The laser's resonator cavity must be tuned properly to yield an axis-symmetric mode at the rated power. A print of a mode can be easily obtained by shooting a raw laser beam onto acrylic block targets. Beam polarization should be preferably circular to yield direction-independent cutting performance. Failure to use proper polarization optics and properly align the beam's incidence on these optics can yield elliptical or linear polarization, both of which will yield direction-dependent performance.

Feed rate. Feed rate is one of the most reliably controlled cutting parameters. Well-mastered servo and numerical-control technologies precisely apply the desired linear cutting speed whether in 2-D for flat-bed cutting machines or 3-D shaped processing. Variations of feed rate do not generally occur without a special known and controlled cause. A feed rate set too high by error generally yields worse edge roughness. If edge-roughness worsening occurs for another reason, then smaller conservative feed rates generally make a laser-cutting process more tolerant to other input-parameter variations.

Start-of-cut parameters differ from rectilinear cutting parameters. Assuming that the workpiece is pierced through before the cut starts, motion accelerates from zero feed rate to the commanded feed rate. Laser-output parameters must start from minimum levels and increase progressively to commanded values. If the rate of increase of the laser power does not adequately follow the rate of increase of feed rate, then breakage gouging, as shown in *Figure 9-9,* may occur. It begins at the start of the cut and could continue to the point where cutting is not performed all the way through the material's thickness.

End-of-cut parameters also differ from rectilinear cutting parameters. Motion goes from the commanded feed rate down to zero. Laser-output parameters should adequately vary from commanded values down to zero power to avoid burning. Particularly for thicker plates, dwell time at the end of the cut may be necessary to enable the lagging part of the kerf front to catch up with the laser-beam position and complete the through-cut before turning off the power completely. If workpiece support is not adequate, the cut part or the skeleton may drop out under its own weight shortly before the cut is completed. This yields a recognizable breaking gouge at the end of a cut. *Figure 9-9* illustrates start-of-cut gouging and end-of-cut breakage gouging.

Material Sources

The metal-alloy type and its mechanical properties and surface condition variations make noticeable differences in cut-edge roughness when the cutting conditions are close to the maximum thickness and/or maximum feed-rate capabilities of the machine. For example, aluminum 6xxx and 5xxx series alloys have such significant differences in physical properties (see *Table 3-1*) that at equal laser power and feed rate, noticeable cutting performance differences are expected, particularly when processing materials thicker than about 0.12 in. (3.0 mm). The 6xxx series

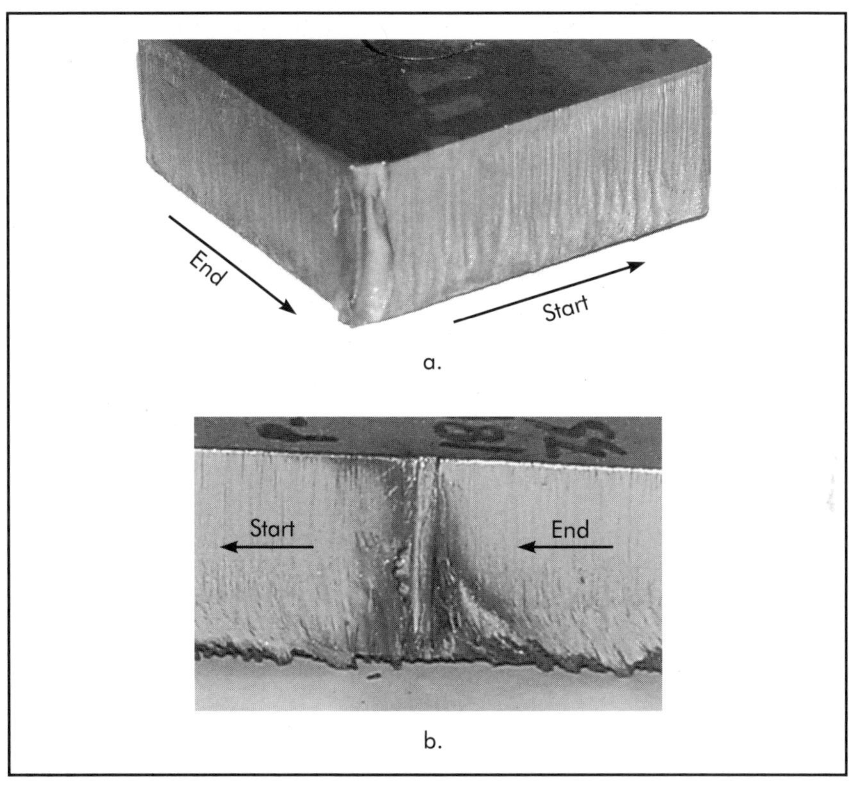

Figure 9-9. Breakage defects occur often at the start and end of cutting on thick plates. Such defects can be avoided by carefully adjusting the laser output as a function of feed-rate variations at the start and end of cut. Examples: (a) 0.75-in. (19-mm) mild steel cut at 30 in./min (762 mm/min) with a 3-kW CO_2 laser in pulsed mode and O_2 assist-gas; (b) 0.375-in. (9.53-mm) stainless steel cut at 30 in./min (762 mm/min) with a 3-kW CO_2 laser in pulsed mode and N_2 assist-gas.

yields potentially rougher cut edges due to its higher thermal conductivity.

Several independent studies by steel mills such as Bethlehem Steel in the U.S., Rautaruuki Raahe Steel in Europe, and Chubu Steel in Japan, have confirmed the strong influence of surface conditions on edge roughness. Scales and rust promote rougher cut surfaces to the point of gouging. If a scale- and rust-free material surface is not possible, a reduction in feed rate may bring a modest to satisfactory improvement in productivity.

Coating and lubrication variations generally do not affect laser-cut-edge roughness except for coatings that change the optical properties of the metal's surface. Such is the case with anodized aluminum, which consists of a thicker than usual coating of aluminum oxide (Al_2O_3) applied electrolytically to the metal surface. This oxide layer is extremely hard and has a matte white or in some cases black appearance, which depends on the chemistry of the electrolyte solution. The oxide layer enhances the absorption of infrared (IR) radiation, such as the 10.6-μm wavelength of a CO_2 laser beam, and results in a less rough cut-edge surface.

Machine Sources

Beam-conditioning variations are rare because most beam-conditioning systems are designed with stationary mirrors or such that the only moving optics are flat mirrors with no focusing properties. However, users must be aware of some exceptions. An adaptive optics system consists of at least one mirror with a radius of curvature that can be mechanically altered on the fly. Also, some original dynamic collimators have moving non-flat mirrors and lenses. In these exceptions, variations of the focusing properties may drift out of control, thereby changing cutting parameters, and thus requiring a change in setup to avoid a rougher cut edge.

Laser-beam-mode variations are unavoidable and affect cutting performance in general and edge roughness in particular. The effect on edge roughness is more noticeable when processing close to the maximum capability of a laser-cutting system, that is, at either maximum thickness or maximum feed rate per set thickness.

Laser-beam-mode variation results from the aging of consumables and non-repairable items, such as optics or glassware in CO_2 lasers, and flash lamps and water-cooling channels in YAG lasers. Due to aging, both power and mode degrade. Power can be compensated for with larger excitation from the power-supply unit (PSU) of the pumping mechanism. However, beam-mode quality cannot be compensated for with more input power from the PSU.

Since most of the power distribution on a beam cross-section is concentrated close to the center of cavity mirrors, contamination has a higher probability to make a burn mark in this spot. Operating with dirty optics is less efficient since more power is needed from the PSU to achieve the same commanded output power as with clean optics. At the same time, it promotes higher-order modes, that is, larger M^2 values. The best response to this problem is cleaning or replacing the dirty optics per a preventive maintenance (PM) schedule and realigning the cavity mirrors for nominal beam mode and power per the laser manufacturer's specifications and procedures. The effect of a larger M^2 value is a larger focus spot at a shifted focus position relative to the workpiece's surface, which potentially results in cut-edge roughness variation.

External beam alignment plays a large part in a machine's ability to laser cut at a specified rate and quality. This alignment can vary due to change or replacement of an optic in the beam-delivery system or in the laser cavity. If the task is improperly performed, astigmatism may be enhanced, yielding different focus characteristics at different focus positions across the work envelope. There is also a higher probability of beam clipping inside the beam-delivery system. All potentially result in a rougher cut-edge surface.

Mother Nature Sources

Room temperature, humidity, and pollution variations naturally affect cutting performance. Operation in high-humidity conditions and air pollution with some hydrocarbon compounds, such as acrylic fumes and other compounds from welding and spray-painting applications, require precautions (for example, using a dry-air purge system) to protect the beam-delivery system optics and conduits. Pollutants absorb infrared laser radiation and increase beam dispersion by diffusion scattering. Humidity condensation exposes optical surfaces to particles such as natural minerals or hydrocarbons. These contaminants will be burned progressively on the surface of the optics, negatively affecting the operation in general, starting with cut-edge roughness. Setting the temperature of the cooling water above dew point to prevent humidity condensation on optics is recommended. Practically, the cooling-water temperature can be set at least 2° F (1° C) above room temperature.

Some laser-cutting installations are literally exposed to the elements in environments such as metal fabrication shops that operate with open overhead doors to permit truck and train traffic. Operating on a February morning versus an August afternoon can mean a difference in temperature of 100° F (38° C). Such severe environmental changes can noticeably alter the dynamics of assist-gas flow and the geometry of mechanical components by shear thermal expansion or contraction. Mirrors and their mounts in the beam-delivery system and laser, as well as the copper assist-gas nozzle's exit diameter, are subject to these changes, which raise the risk of a roughness increase. An adjustment in cutting parameters and alignment may be needed if excessive temperature and humidity variations occur within a short time span.

Man Sources

Feature programming must be selected carefully by the operator and designed judiciously by an experienced part-program writer. Start and end of cut, corner radius, and angle features may require on-the-fly adaptation of input parameters such as feed rate, laser output, assist-gas output, and focus adjustment.

Experienced operators recognize that when the time approaches for preventive maintenance on external or cavity optics, neither the beam-mode characteristics and focus spot nor the peak power at the workpiece may resemble what they were 500–2,000 hours of operation earlier. A conservative choice of cutting parameters helps avoid the need for tweaking to compensate for this difficult-to-eliminate drift of beam-delivery performance.

Measurement Sources

Gage reproducibility and repeatability (R&R) and calibration always play a dual role depending on the gage in question. In most cases, cut-edge roughness is qualitatively and subjectively measured by look and feel. The gage is the operator's eyes or thumb. The absence of standards, and sometimes the absence of edge-roughness specifications, makes this measurement somewhat arbitrary. However, roughness itself is not affected by the low reliability of the human gage. On the other hand, gages such as assist-gas proportional valves and laser-power probes may directly impact edge-roughness quality if improperly calibrated and incapable of measuring with repeatability variation smaller than the tolerances specified for the cutting process.

CONTOUR ACCURACY

Contour accuracy is mainly a function of motion-system accuracy and repeatability. However, in some instances that demand a superior level of accuracy, cutting parameters can play a dynamic role. The vast majority of laser-cutting machines are computer numerically controlled. A few with rudimentary one- or two-axis motion requirements can be found with programmable-logic-controlled motion. In all cases, the human/machine interaction brings user-friendliness to an operation and facilitates the automatic translation of computer-aided design (CAD) drawings into industrial laser-cutting part-program code.

Sources of Variation

Contour accuracy is strongly machine dependent, but also man and method dependent since it involves intelligent software programming to overcome the shortcomings of the thermal cutting process. The fishbone diagram of *Figure 9-10* highlights KPIV variations that influence contour accuracy.

Method Sources

An example of feed-rate variation occurs due to a large gantry inertia, which does not enable a machine to respond instantaneously and perfectly to direction changes sent by the machine's controller, yielding contour inaccuracy. *Figure 9-11* illustrates how each direction change is actually a large number of discrete actions taken by the controller at small incremental steps during each interpolation loop of a few milliseconds. Consequently, when magnified under a microscope, a programmed continuous curved

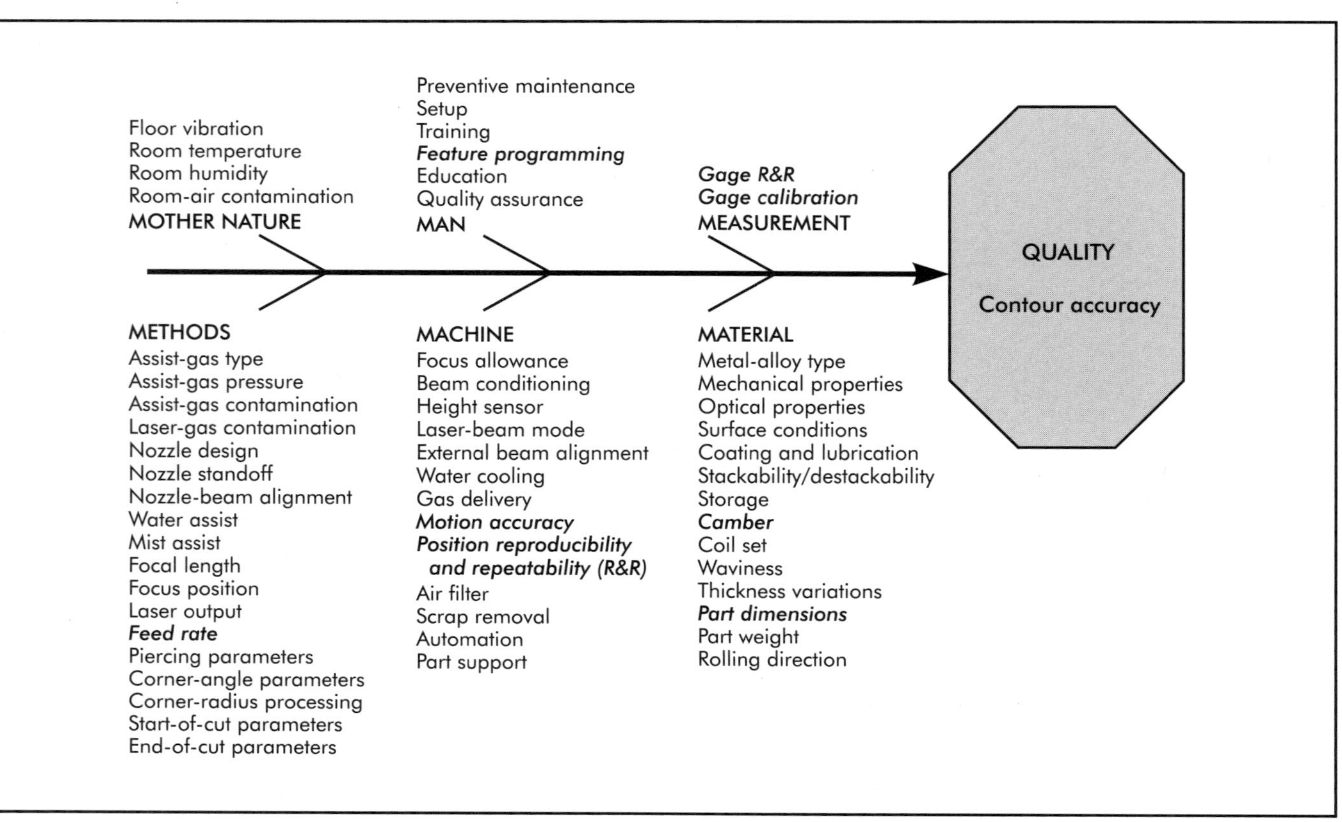

Figure 9-10. Contour accuracy error results predominantly from variations in the highlighted (bold) input parameters.

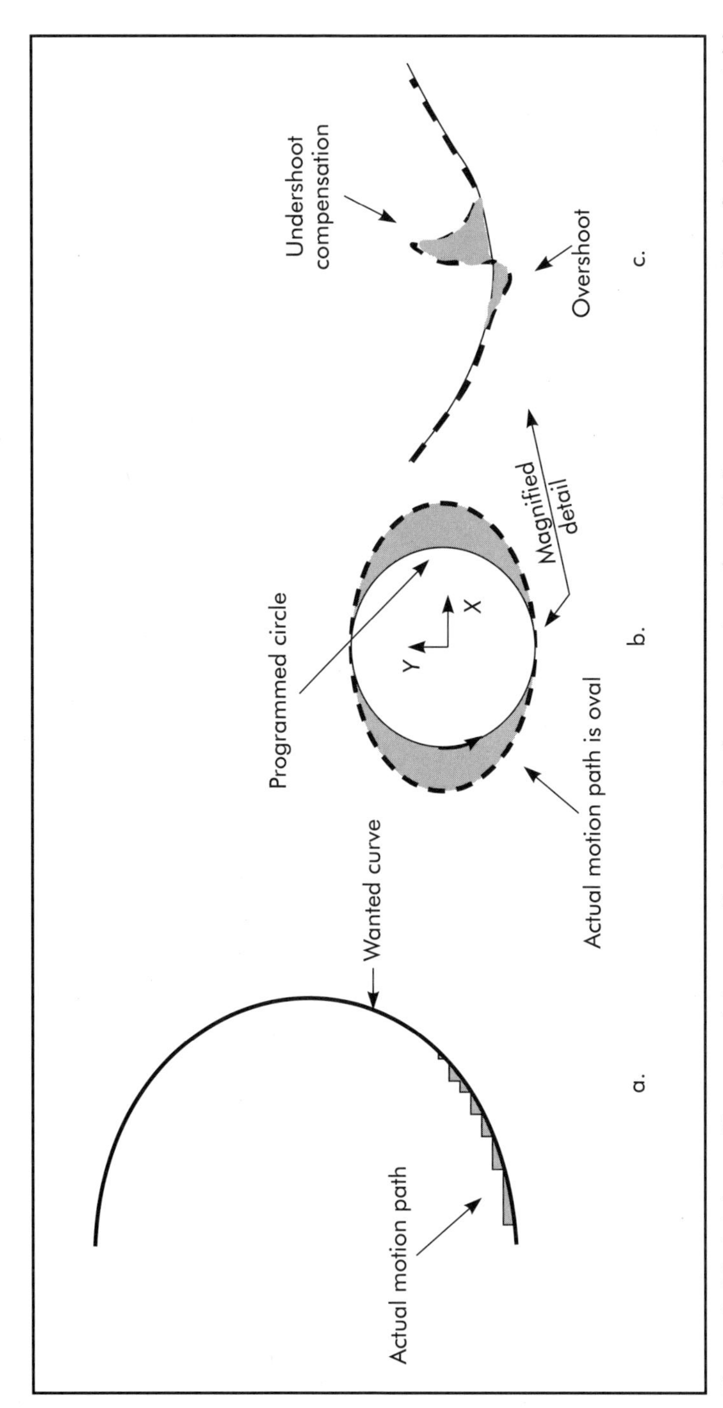

Figure 9-11. (a) A curvilinear path is actually the result of a succession of small discrete segments. Slow feed rates yield continuous curves with little contour accuracy error (shaded area). (b) At speeds higher than the machine's mechanical motion design can handle, circles may end up cut like jagged-edge ovals due to the difference in inertia in the X and Y directions. (c) A magnified view of the cut edge shows an overshoot quickly followed by a compensating undershoot where one axis motion changes its acceleration direction.

feature is in actuality a succession of small linear steps. At high speed, a number of linear steps might be made in error before response to a direction change sent by the controller takes effect. Circles programmed at increasing speed result in oval-shaped cuts due to the difference in inertia between the *X* and *Y* axis, and the speed of the processor in the controller unit. In many cases, the computer numerical control (CNC) automatically reduces the actual feed rate to maintain the contour accuracy of specific features. This should be done in conjunction with adequate laser-output adaptation.

Machine Sources

Position R&R at a given feed rate determines contour precision and accuracy. Most machine motions are powered by a servo-controlled motor, which is linked to machine frames by ball-screw transmission gears and sometimes belt transmission gears. Absolute encoders mounted on the motor can give an exact reading of the number of revolutions of the servo, which computes into an absolute position value. Mechanical backlash of the ball-screw transmission mechanism appears as one source of positioning error. It can be compensated for with the proper motion code in the program. However, mechanical backlash cannot be totally eliminated.

Motion accuracy varies with a gantry's rigidity. The same is true for robot-arm rigidity. Under strong acceleration, a *Y*-axis gantry frame can bend sufficiently enough to yield noticeable variations in *X*-axis position for each point along the *Y*-axis gantry. The nodes of this bending strain are at each end of the gantry on either the ball-screw gear or the guiding rail. Bending strain results in contour inaccuracy and, if resonance-frequency vibration of the mechanical machine apparatus is approached, mechanical fatigue failure of the equipment.

For the best contour accuracy, an ideal machine would have the fastest processor in the controller, a gantry with maximum rigidity and minimal mass for low inertia, and linear motors with absolute scales/encoders measuring axis position rather than servo revolutions. Even with an imperfect machine, motion accuracy can be optimized by intelligently limiting motion acceleration based on machine design and inertia. Today's CNC machines automatically restrict the acceleration to a value dependent on the radius of curvature of a programmed feature. This means a reduction in feed rate proportional to the square root of a feature's curvature radius; tighter radii command lower accelerations and feed rates. *Figure 9-11* illustrates how at high speed, a programmed circular path may yield an oval cut. The magnified view of the circle shows overshoot and undershoot errors occurring at the point where the velocity of the vector direction changes.

When cutting thick plates at low-to-medium speed, good contour accuracy can be expected on the top part of the workpiece. However, at the bottom of a workpiece net contours are deformed, possibly due to heat distortions and asymmetry of the laser's focus-spot characteristics or nozzle misalignment. These discrepancies in contour accuracy between the top and bottom side of a thick plate (see *Figure 9-12)* are difficult to circumvent and might have to be accounted for as a specification limit of the thermal cutting process.

Material Sources

Material camber and incoming part dimensional accuracy can become impediments to final cut-contour accuracy when positioning and crowding mechanisms cannot correct their variations or repeat the same sheet/plate position and orientation reference before the start of the cut. Springback and other stress released in the material due to heat input during laser cutting makes a perfectly straight cut path turn into a curved cut line. To minimize such thermal distortion, tension-leveled sheet material may be specified. For 3-D part processing, tooling fixtures can correct material springback deviations and serve as positioning reference locators. Contour accuracy consequently becomes solely machine dependent. Five-axis gantry machines generally exhibit better positioning R&R than articulated robots.

Man Sources

Feature programming can improve contour accuracy by taking kerf width into account. Some controller software has built-in part-

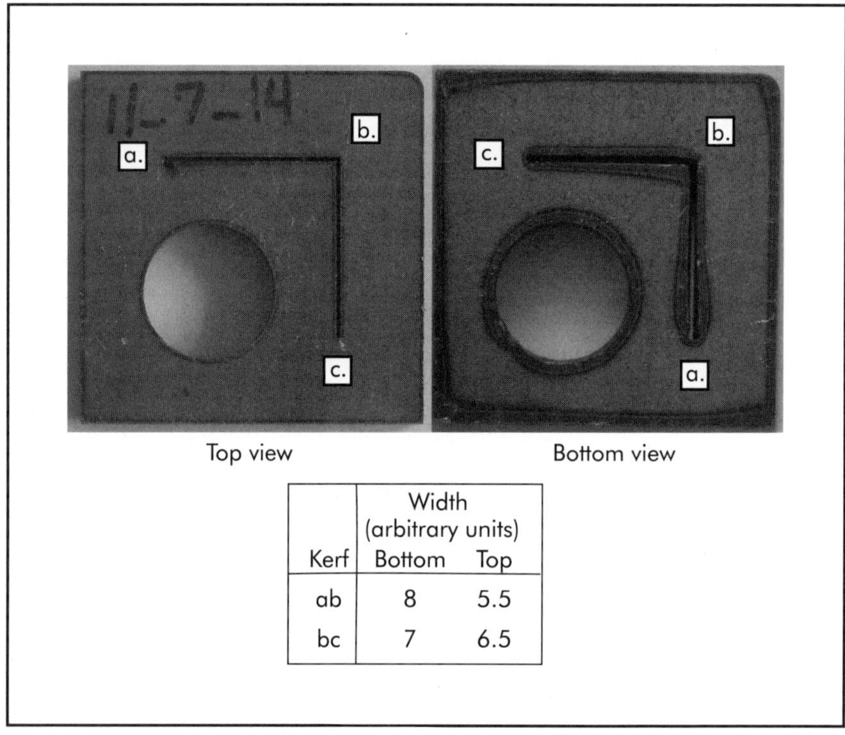

Kerf	Width (arbitrary units) Bottom	Top
ab	8	5.5
bc	7	6.5

Figure 9-12. Top and bottom views of the kerf and of a circular hole in 0.50-in. (12.7-mm) mild steel. While the top part of the hole appears perfectly circular, the bottom appears oval to the naked eye. Kerf width differences can be measured with filler gage, or by simple image magnification. Measurement confirms that the cutting process was slightly direction-dependent, resulting in kerf walls that are not parallel, but tapered.

programming codes that compensate for kerf width automatically to yield a more accurate final-cut contour. Operators must judiciously use such existing control features or write similar custom part-program macros.

Servo tuning is crucial to machine setup. When well performed, it can optimize the maximum permissible mechanical acceleration sustainable by a motion system to yield contour accuracy within specified tolerances. Maintenance engineers need to be well trained in servo tuning and educated in basic physics to understand the dynamics of torque, mass, inertia, velocity, momentum, force, and acceleration.

DROSS

Mechanical cutting methods, such as sawing, shearing, and die blanking, generate burrs. The equivalent for thermal cutting processes is dross formation at the bottom of the kerf. *Dross* is mostly resolidified core metal coated with a harder metal-oxide layer that sticks to the kerf's edge. The harder metal oxide generally melts at a higher melting temperature than the core metal. So, when oxidation of the external surface of molten droplets exposed to ambient O_2 occurs, the external surface quickly turns into a solid layer around the core metal droplet, which is still in liquid form while being expulsed through the kerf by assist-gas flushing action. With metals having high thermal conductivity, these droplets cool even faster by conduction loss in the core workpiece. By the time the laser beam's focus spot passes and the elongated droplet (elongated by the action of flushing assist-gas and gravity) cools to a solid state, dross has developed like a stalactite.

Assist-gas pressure, contamination, and focus position variations negatively affect dross generation the same way they affect edge-roughness quality.

Sources of Variation

Dross formation occurs mainly from the material and method variations highlighted in the fishbone diagram of *Figure 9-13*.

Method Sources

To reduce dross, cutting can be performed in an inert gas environment that prevents oxidation. Achieving a totally inert gas environment, such as with argon (Ar) assist-gas, is expensive. The use of a neutral assist-gas, such as N_2, is the next best choice. However, ambient atmospheric oxygen may still find its way in the hot liquid bath of the kerf zone after passage of the laser beam. The assist-gas delivery system and nozzle geometry can prevent oxygen contamination of the neutral assist-gas. A larger nozzle diameter or a concentric double-nozzle system isolates the kerf

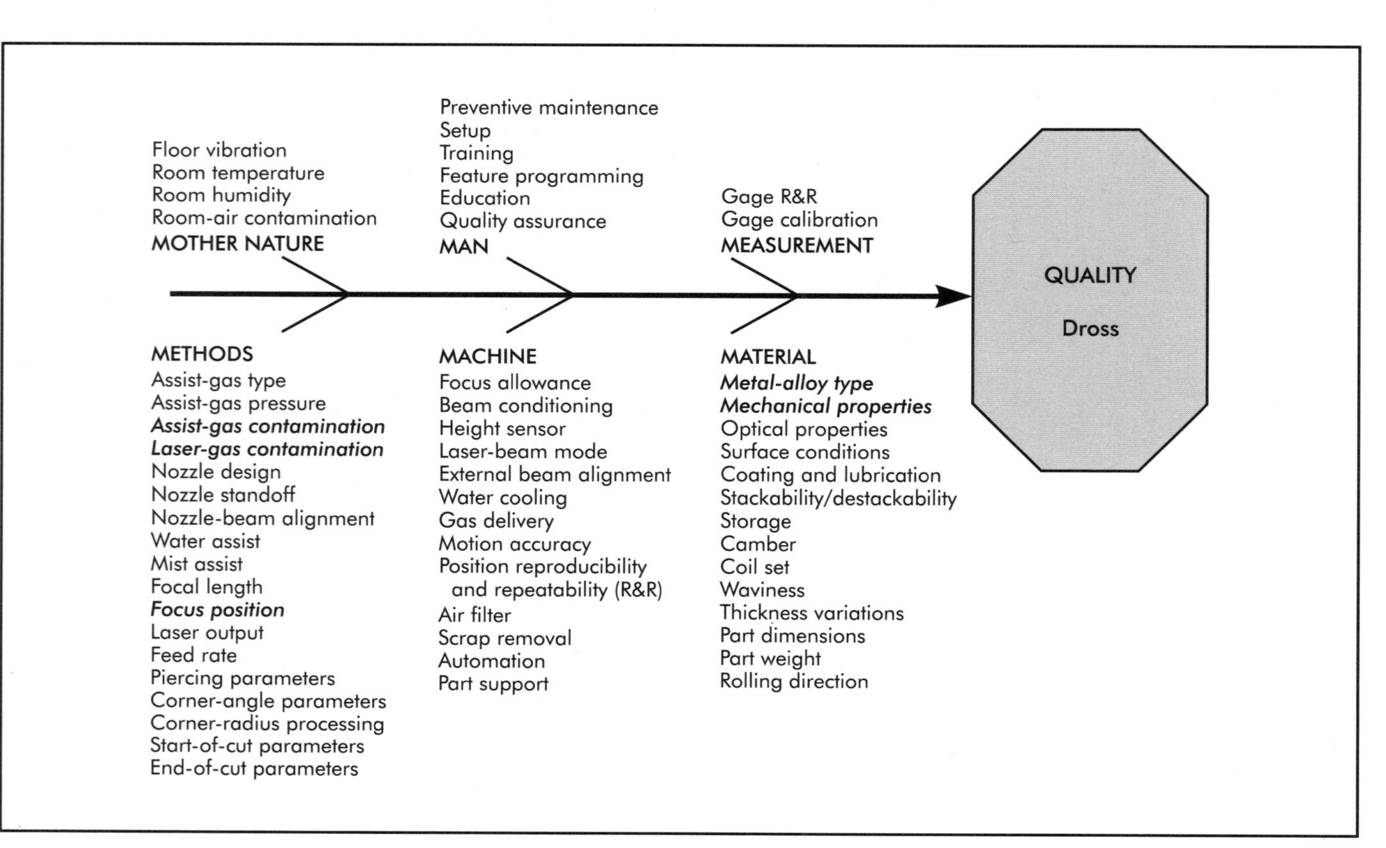

Figure 9-13. Hanging dross results predominantly from variations in the highlighted (bold) input parameters.

zone from atmospheric oxygen and prevents its diffusion into the inert assist-gas stream.

Thicker plates make it extremely difficult to totally eliminate dross. The power density at the bottom edge is also a key factor, so the focus position needs to be optimized to minimize or eliminate dross. The optimum focus position is found by trial and error in the field. However, in general, high heat intensity at the bottom of the kerf helps.

Material Sources

Dross is mostly observed with metals exhibiting high conductivity, low viscosity of the hot liquid phase, and oxidation that is self-limiting. Mild-steel cutting with oxygen or nitrogen does not usually exhibit noticeable dross. With metals such as stainless steel and aluminum, dross is a common occurrence. It becomes more invasive when material thickness increases. *Figure 9-8* shows photographs of dross on the cut edges of stainless steel and aluminum.

Metal-alloy types and their mechanical properties exhibit different dross behaviors. At constant laser-output power, dross formation increases with material thickness. Thin sheets of steel, stainless steel, and aluminum up to about 0.125-in. (3.18-mm) thick can be laser cut virtually dross-free with most industrial laser-cutting systems. Mild steels can be laser cut dross-free even with workpieces as thick as 1.00 in. (25.4 mm). Dross is difficult to eliminate with aluminum or stainless steel thicker than about 0.375 in. (9.53 mm).

EDGE STRAIGHTNESS

Motion systems must deliver accurate motion to attain accurate cut contours. When commanding a straight-line cut, some tolerance ranges on straightness can be as low as 0.003 in. (0.08 mm) over an entire length of cut as long as 72 in. (183 cm). Contemporary laser-cutting machines are capable of delivering motion accuracy of ±0.001 in. (±0.03 mm) over a 6 × 12 ft (1.8 × 3.7 m) work envelope. Other variables are considered to yield a straight cut. For example, any thermal cutting process releases internal stresses originating from coil set, coil camber, and coil waviness, even when the sheet or plate is clamped during cutting. What was a perfectly straight-line path per a commanded accurate motion system springs back into a curvilinear cut line (see *Figure 5-10*). A solution is to relieve tension from the sheet metal before processing by making sure the coil it originated from passes through a tension leveler before the sheets are cut out of it.

Machine design also has an impact on the straightness of a cut, particularly at high speed and acceleration. If the *Y*-axis gantry possesses low rigidity, then different points along the *Y* axis will have varying *X* positions under high-acceleration motion. High acceleration can bend the *Y* gantry beyond the position-accuracy tolerance requirement. Therefore, straight cuts processed at excessive accelerations in the *X* direction can exhibit out-of-specification straightness variations with their *Y* position. A laser-cutting machine should be designed with a high rigidity over mass ratio of the *Y*-axis gantry and acceleration clamped by radius to prevent cuts with straightness outside tolerance specifications.

EDGE PARALLELISM

A cross-section of a cut edge can show tapered, rather than perfectly vertical, kerf walls. Although such taper is generally within specifications and always significantly less than the taper experienced with, for example, plasma cutting processes, in a few applications it requires special attention and control. *Figure 9-14* shows some evidence of a tapered angle by comparing kerf widths at the bottom and top surfaces of a workpiece. Even in these extreme cases and for most applications, the taper remains negligible at a few milliradians. A tapered angle can be measured by introducing a filler gage through the kerf or by photomicrograph.

Some applications specify a minimum taper for the cut edge. Intentionally changing the angle of incidence of the laser beam and the co-axial assist-gas from normal to beveled incidence produces a slanted cut edge by design.

When moving across a work envelope, the optical-path length of the laser beam varies significantly unless special precautions

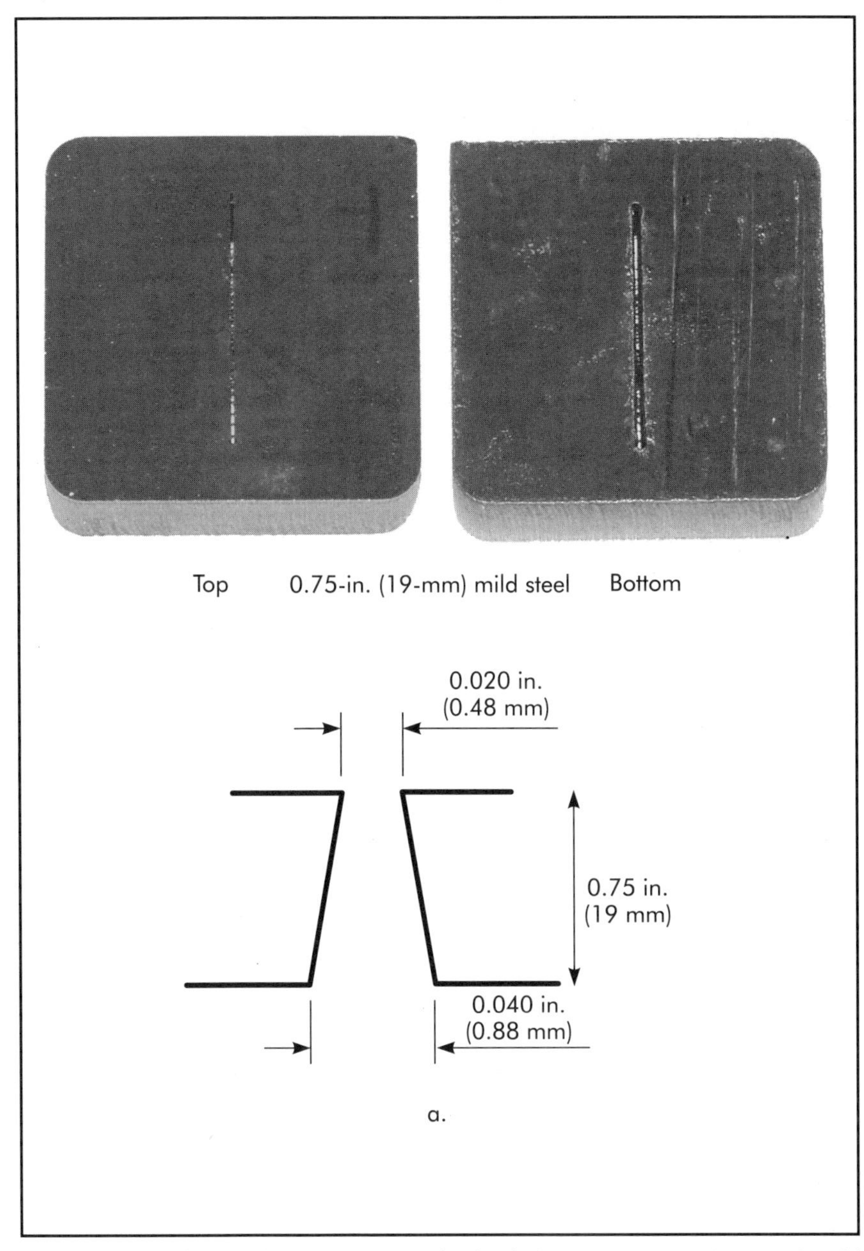

Figure 9-14. Top and bottom views of a kerf slit: (a) 0.75-in. (19-mm) mild steel cut with a 3-kW CO_2 laser has evidence of edges with a tapered angle of about 10 mrad; (b) 0.125-in. (3.18-mm) aluminum cut with a 2-kW CO_2 laser has evidence of edges with a tapered angle of about 12 mrad.

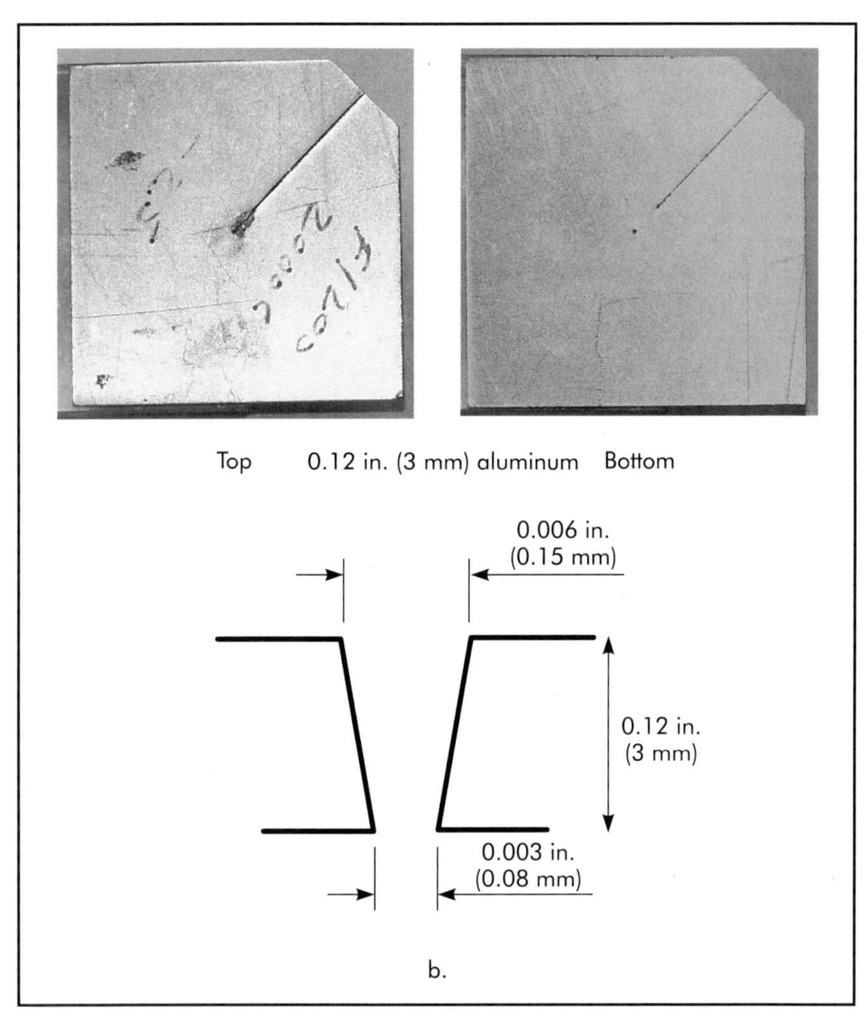

Figure 9-14. continued.

are taken. On a 6 × 12 ft (1.8 × 3.7 m) table, the optical-path-length change is at least 18 ft (5.5 m) from the near field to the far field. If the laser beam is left to naturally propagate with its inherent divergence, then the focusing characteristics will yield significant kerf changes and, therefore, alter edge parallelism and taper. Action such as a reduction in feed rate can still make cutting feasible, but different kerf-width characteristics change edge parallelism. A feed-rate reduction increases heat input and distortions on edge parallelism once the workpiece cools down. This can be avoided by designing a beam-delivery system to reduce or eliminate the variation of beam characteristics across the work envelope. Collimators, constant beam-path systems, and adaptive optics are some design tools that can be used for this endeavor.

KERF WIDTH

Kerf width is a function of more than just focus-beam spot position and size. The kerf width is also determined by the material's metallurgical, mechanical, and thermal properties, and the workpiece's surface conditions. In general, with higher heat-conduction-coefficient material and lower latent heat, wider kerfs can be expected. With constant material properties, kerf width is altered by focus position and diameter, as well as feed rate, commanded peak power, commanded duty, commanded frequency, focal length, and f-number. The presence of dust or organic gas contamination along the optical-path length has noise influences on the focusing properties and, therefore, on kerf-width variations.

The kerf-width target for a cutting process needs to be well chosen to alleviate concerns over repeatability and reliability of the process. For example, a kerf that is too narrow indicates a process on the brink of breakdown. The cut part cannot easily separate from the workpiece skeleton. When cutting thicker-gage materials, the best beam focusability works against obtaining a minimum kerf width and forces hefty defocusing to achieve cutting. On the other hand, a wide kerf is indicative of excessive heat input into the metal—a product of a low efficiency and low productivity process. Low efficiency may be due to any combination of too slow of a feed rate and too large of a focus-spot diameter.

A typical kerf in mild steel 0.50 in. (12.7 mm) and thicker is 0.020 in. (0.51 mm) with ±0.002 in. (±0.05 mm) variation allowed to account for measurement precision and process-input variations, such as material type, metallurgy, and thickness, from one workpiece to the next. Variations due to measurement alone account for at least ±0.0005 in. (±0.013 mm) error when using a filler gage to measure a kerf.

BURNING

Cutting quality is extremely sensitive to one parameter in particular: feed rate. With most CNC motion systems, the motion's acceleration and speed is automatically optimized on the fly to produce the feature contour based on the mechanical properties and capabilities of the machine. Speed changes result from deceleration and acceleration, since the commanded feed rate is the highest speed observable during cutting of straight-line features.

If the laser power incident on the workpiece remains constant while the feed rate varies, then the heat input per linear length unit of the workpiece fluctuates as well, potentially resulting in uneven cut quality. A visual indicator of the mismatch between the motion's speed and laser output is a burning effect, recognizable by an increase in the width of a discolored heat-affected zone.

Cutting at slow speed and low average power avoids variations in heat input per linear length unit of the workpiece. It eliminates the need for significant deceleration and acceleration at small radii of curvatures or corner angles. This solution, however, does not totally eliminate burning and reduces productivity significantly. When small radii features act as "thermal fins," cooling by conduction through the body of the workpiece is reduced and convection alone is not sufficient to evacuate heat from the fin, so heat builds and burning occurs. A better approach for higher productivity is to control the laser output (peak power, pulse duty, and pulse frequency) as a function of linear feed rate. Dependent on the speed of the controller's processor and the speed of its communication with servomotors and the laser, the laser-output adaptation lags more or less as the linear speed changes. *Figure 9-15* shows heat build up and burning at heat fins.

REFERENCES

Cook, David. 2000. "Implementing a PAC Operator Training Program." Fabtech International, Session 204, Cleveland, OH, November. Dearborn, MI: Society of Manufacturing Engineers.

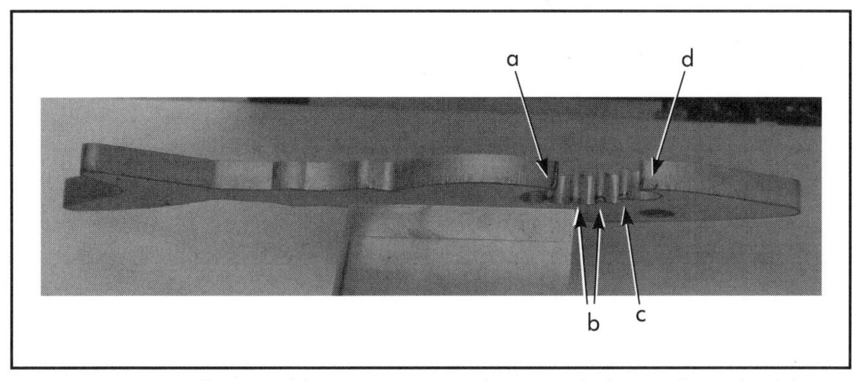

Figure 9-15. Evidence of burning in stainless steel due to heat buildup in heat fins. The heat buildup and burning would have yielded even worse cut quality if the laser output had not been adapted to feed-rate changes. (a) Sharp corner-angle feature turned outward on the body of the workpiece acts as a heat fin. There is burning of the edge from top to bottom. (b and d) A small-radius feature turned outward from the body of the workpiece acts as a heat fin. There is burning of the bottom edge. (c) A small-radius feature turned inward on the body of the workpiece does not act as a heat fin. Cooling by conduction with the body of the workpiece helps avoid burning.

Kanaoka, M., Murai, T., and Yuyama, T. 1996. "Automatic Condition Setting of Materials Processing CO_2 Laser." International Congress on Applications of Lasers and Electro-Optics (ICALEO), Section C pp. 1-9. Orlando, FL: Laser Institute of America.

Productivity

"The more haste, ever the worst speed."

—Charles Churchill

INTRODUCTION

As one cell among many in an entire manufacturing plan, the laser-cutting process generally attracts attention commensurate to its cost and to the *Star Wars* mystique still surrounding it. As most manufacturing managers have learned, sometimes a missing one-cent bolt can slow or halt a multi-million dollar installation designed to run super-high-speed production. A comprehensive approach to productivity helps avoid traditional pitfalls that can lead to costly management choices in procurement of equipment and costly operator choices in cutting-parameter setup.

Productivity encompasses more than just processing speed. Setup, maintenance, and repair account for a substantial part of actual cycle time. Just-in-time (JIT) production and lean manufacturing with a minimum inventory of raw material, work-in-process, and finished goods have changed the strategy from high-speed operations with dedicated tooling to highly flexible operations with minimal waste. In the past, the manufacturing community was obsessed with speed for high-volume production of the same engineered product. Most companies soon realized that the focus on speed must be tempered with flexibility. The requirement of flexibility is a direct consequence of increased competition and globalization.

New products and more "flavors" per product line must be constantly generated to appeal to customers. Aggressive customer-centric marketing translates into a larger variety of part numbers to satisfy market needs. More product variety requires more engineering variations, which require fast turnaround and flexibility. A manufacturing enterprise must be prepared for shorter product cycles and the multitude of varieties within a product line. This forces an emphasis on JIT delivery, lower inventory, and lean manufacturing with fully integrated cells. When optimized, lean-manufacturing cell integration invariably leads to less waste and more compatible cycle times between cells. The flexibility of a laser-cutting system makes it suitable to small batches and high diversity of part numbers.

THROUGHPUT

Productivity must be measured for laser cutting as integrated within a manufacturing enterprise. It must take into account setup and maintenance and repair influences on actual throughput. Throughput is often too simplistically equated with processing speed. This mistake often leads to the wrong choice of equipment, laser power, automation level, and openness.

More than just processing time, actual resultant cycle time should be a common denominator of throughput. Actual resultant cycle time represents the average period of time to output one specific part taking into account preventive maintenance cycles and mean-time-between-failure periods for a certain operation. Time to output does not generally equal time to manufacture. Resultant cycle time is greatly influenced by material feed time, processing time, finished-part unload time, scrap- and waste-removal time, setup downtime, preventive-maintenance downtime, spare parts availability, and field serviceability. Of all these factors, only processing time is a value-adding activity. Processing consists of laser piercing and laser cutting. Value-adding activities must be the limiting factors for reduction of cycle time. Time for all other non-value-adding processes or waste should be reduced to a minimum, with the interval between downtimes being extended to a maximum period.

Cycle Time versus Processing Time

Cutting time, piercing time, destacking/stacking time, feed time, and setup time integrate into an ideal cycle time. Actual cycle time should also consider other productivity factors, such as preventive maintenance (PM) and repair and plant organizational deficiencies. These deficiencies may include various situations such as a forklift truck not being available on time for material handling, material identification errors, a complex procedure for downloading part programs to the machine's numerical controller, or damaged material rejected upon arrival.

Figure 10-1 drafts actual cycle time in a simple example. In this example, T_1 can be referred to as an ideal cycle time in which the impact of preventive maintenance, repair, setup, plant inefficiencies, and other special causes of downtime are neglected. Among several methods that can be used to account for downtimes in the resultant cycle time estimation, the average method below seems simple and realistic.

$$C_T = P_T \times \frac{1}{\frac{T_1 - DT_1}{T_1}} \times \frac{1}{\frac{T_2 - DT_2}{T_2}} \times \ldots \times \frac{1}{\frac{T_n - DT_n}{T_n}} \qquad (10\text{-}1)$$

where:

C_T = resultant actual cycle time, min
P_T = processing time, sec
D_1 = event 1 downtime for part loading/unloading every T_1 period, sec
D_2 = event 2 downtime for setup change occurring on average every period, T_2, min
T_n = interval between production downtime due to event n, min
D_n = event n downtime during which processing cannot be done, min

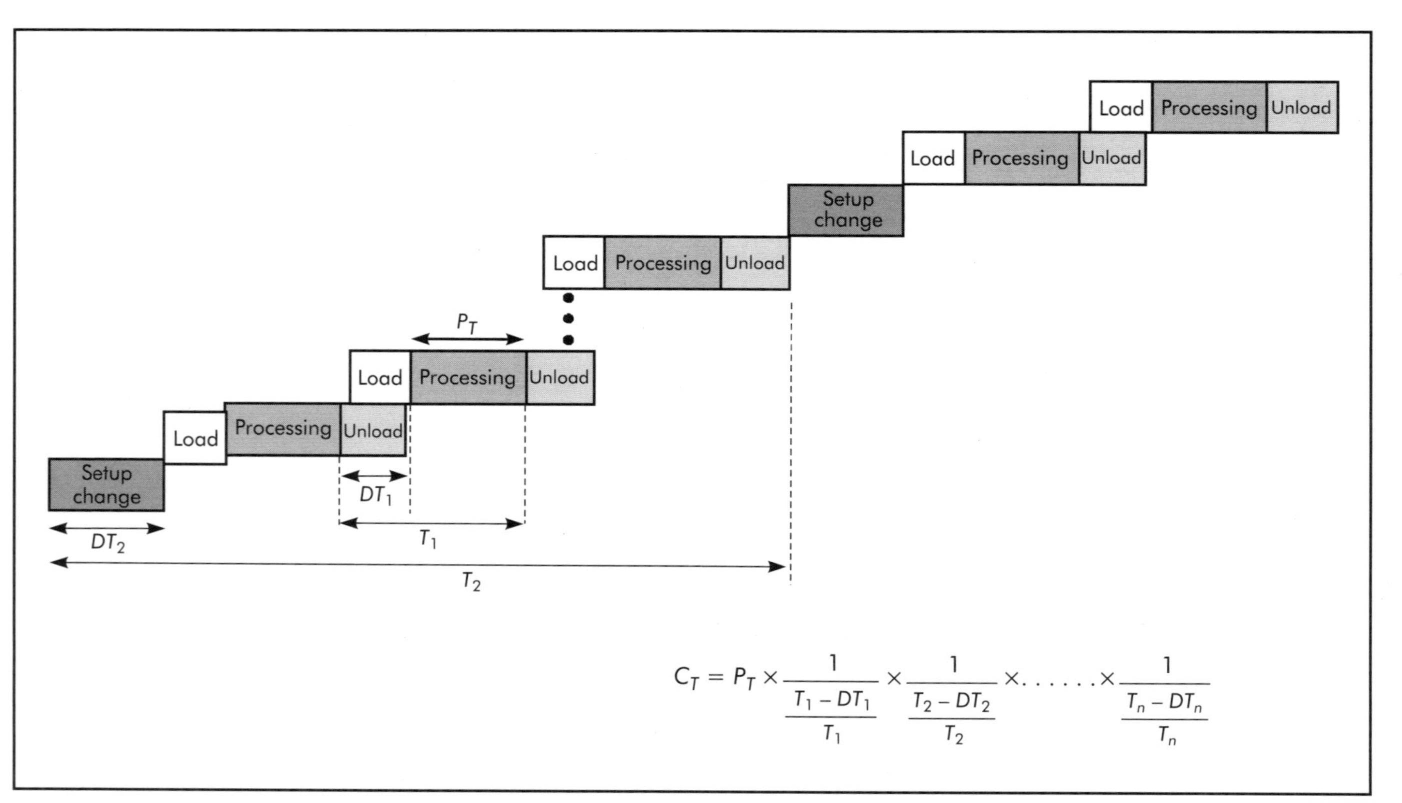

Figure 10-1. Example of a sequence of operation with event one, loading/unloading, and event two, setup change; both increase resultant cycle time, C_T.

So,

$$\frac{T_n - DT_n}{T_n}$$

represents a productivity factor for event n. A productivity factor is a positive number between 0 and 1. Events with small productivity factors increase the effective cycle time, C_T, more than events with large productivity factors. In other words, for productivity factors, larger is better. T_n and DT_n depend on the level of expertise of the operation and maintenance crew, operation methods and environment, workpiece material, and quality of the equipment design. For example, a facility that uses a sophisticated assist-gas purge system and clean gas-delivery system is expected to increase the period between downtime, making C_T that much closer to P_T. T_n could represent mean time between failure (MTBF) with DT_n corresponding to an estimate of a typical or average downtime for repair. Machine manufacturers and independent market intelligence are obvious sources of information on numerical values for DT_n and T_n based on field data.

Case Example

In the following example, a laser-cutting system running two shifts of 10 hours per day/250 days per year (5,000 hr/year) claims a contour-cutting feed rate of 236 in./min (6 m/min), with setup downtime of 12 minutes every 3 hours. The shift changes account for 30 minutes of production downtime per day. The part being cut has 335 in. (850 mm) of contour length, with material-handling time for loading and unloading of 7 seconds each. Loading and unloading each part is done partly during processing time, resulting in the addition of only 2 seconds of downtime per part-processing cycle. The scrap conveyor and dumpster must be emptied every 4 hours during a 5-minute shutdown for dumpster exchange. PM is to be performed every 1,000 hours with an average downtime of 5.5 hours (4 of which are during scheduled daily shutdown). Occasional equipment failure computed from previous years' data shows an average MTBF of 12 months with average cumulative downtime of 6 production days per repair. Occasional production interruptions due to miscellaneous plant inefficiencies compute to an average cumulative downtime of 20 minutes per shift.

The actual cycle time for this case example is computed in *Table 10-1*. Load/unload time accounts for the largest contribution to the total of 47% waste. The purchase of a more powerful laser enabling a faster cutting feed rate would be useless if it yields a cutting time shorter than the 7 seconds necessary for material-handling sequences. Beyond this performance, material-handling cycle time becomes the limiting factor and faster cutting speed becomes a just-in-case capital expenditure.

In the observation of many laser-cutting operations throughout the U.S. and Canada, some job shops have manually operated installations with an average actual cutting and piercing processing time contributing to as low as 35% of actual cycle time. Others with material-handling automation, computer-numerical-control automation of part setup, supervisory control, CAD/CAM digitization, and networking capabilities can cut actual cycle time per part in half. In these cases, the average cutting and piercing time

Table 10-1. Case example cycle-time calculation

	Productivity Factor, %	*T*	*DT*	Comment
Load/unload	81.0	10.5	2.00	$T = 8.5 + 2$
Scrap removal	97.9	4	0.08	$DT = 5/60$ hr
PM	99.9	1,000	1.50	$DT = 5.5 - 4$
MTBF	97.6	5,000	120.00	$DT = 6$ days × 20 hr/day
Shift change	97.9	24	0.50	
Setup	93.3	3	0.20	
Miscellaneous	96.7	10	0.33	$DT = 20/60$ hr

P_T = cutting time = 8.5 sec

C_T = 12.46 sec

Resultant productivity factor = 8.5/12.46 = 68.2%

$C_T - P_T$ = 3.96 sec or 47% increase

Cutting speed = 236 in./min (6 m/min) = 39 in. sec (100 mm/sec)
8.5 sec cutting time > 7 sec material-handling time, so cutting time is the limiting factor
1 + 1 = 2 sec of load/unload downtime occurs every 8.5 + 2 = 10.5 sec

contributes to as much as 68% or more of resultant cycle time per part as illustrated in *Figure 10-2*. Full automation would bring in complete CAD/CAM capability with automatic part-program generation and download to the machine's numerical controller. With material-handling automation, destack/stack and setup times could be cut four-fold. The relative contributions of non-value-adding steps to resultant part-cycle time can typically be reduced by half with automation.

Threshold Point for Laser Cutting Justification

Comparing a laser-cutting operation and a traditional punch-press cutting operation for sheet metal, such as that used extensively in the electronics industry, reveals the tool-less setup downtime advantage of laser cutting. In fabricating plants it is not unusual to observe press and die setup time lasting over 20 minutes, whereas setup time with a fully automated, computer-

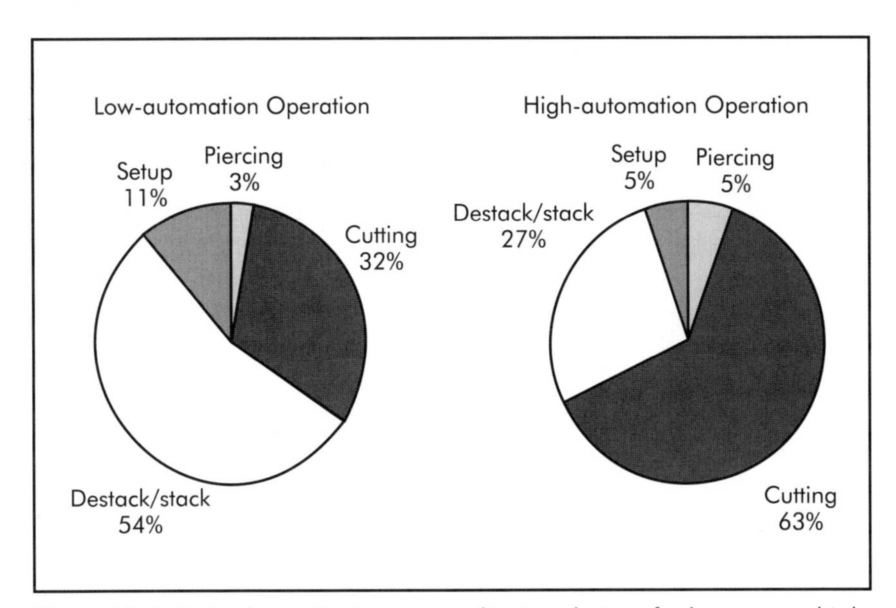

Figure 10-2. Typical contributions to resultant cycle time for low- versus high-automation operations. High automation includes material handling as well as supervisory control automation and generally results in lower overall cycle time and waste.

controlled laser-cutting machine is shortened by at least 75%. Even though punching-press speeds are still significantly faster than laser-cutting speeds, the shorter setup time required for laser operations makes it favorable for low-volume batch applications. The threshold volume per batch at which total press production time becomes shorter than total laser production time depends on the laser-cutting cycle time. *Figure 10-3* compares the productivity of laser cutting versus punch-press die cutting for batch volumes of two parts. One part is laser cut in 12 seconds. Laser-cutting can actually result in shorter actual resultant cycle time in production than punch-press cutting, as long as the volume required per setup remains less than 230 per batch. For a part with fewer features and a laser-cutting time of 3 seconds, this threshold jumps to 450 parts per batch.

A similar analysis can be conducted between laser blanking and press die-blanking operations such as the ones used extensively in the automotive and appliance industries. In these industries, progressive-die operation using more than one blanking tool can be compared to laser-blanking operations with multiple laser-cutting stations. The laser-cutting stations can be in a progressive configuration (such as illustrated in *Figure 2-10*), in parallel configuration, or any combination of alternative configurations. Volume thresholds should be analyzed on a case by case basis. Without material handling and machine and control automation, laser-cutting productivity struggles to measure up (outside of prototype production) to the large throughput capability and speed of traditional cutting with presses and blanking dies. With complete automation, the gap in processing speed makes less and less of a difference, particularly due to the advances in laser-processing speed at increasing laser powers.

MAINTENANCE DOWNTIME

The most productive manufacturing operations have long periods between maintenance times and short maintenance downtimes. This becomes more crucial for large-volume production such as in the automotive and appliance industries where cycle times are measured in seconds with precision of two digits after the deci-

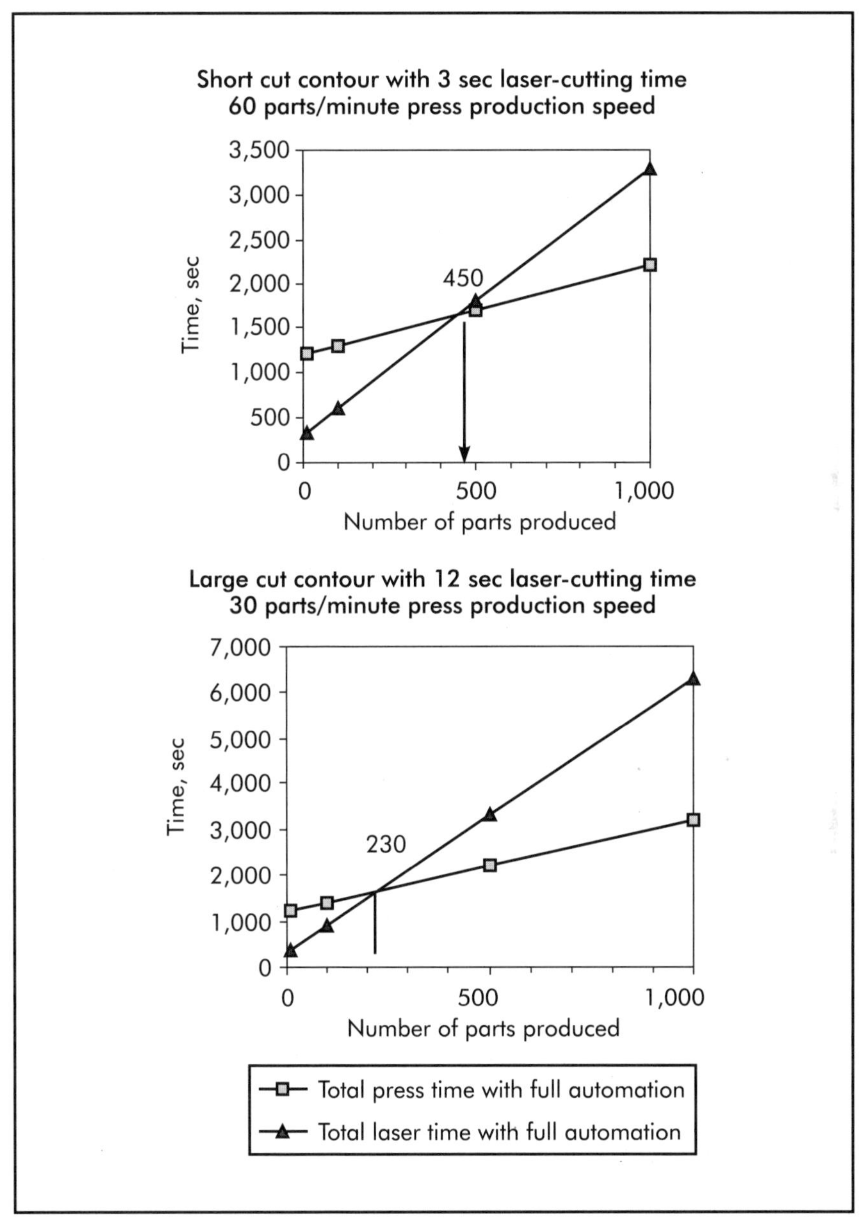

Figure 10-3. Laser cutting versus punch-press die cutting: setup downtime makes a difference in the time to manufacture. A comprehensive analysis of actual cycle time determines the threshold volume below which the production order can be produced faster with laser cutting.

mal point. At these high throughputs, downtime can be measured in terms of loss of sales—from several $100 per hour for an upstream fabricator supplier to several $100,000 per hour for a downstream assembly manufacturer. Maintenance downtime cannot be neglected.

A complete laser-cutting system can be broken into modules—laser resonator, beam-delivery system, laser-gas delivery system, assist-gas delivery system, gas-filter system, water chiller and water delivery system, control system, power-motion system, waste-removal system, and material-handling system. Each module needs a well-timed sequence for preventive maintenance (PM) and replacement of consumables. *Table 10-2* lists potential maintenance items and examples of typical maintenance periods and downtimes for a CO_2 laser-cutting operation.

Lean-manufacturing techniques demonstrate that it is far more productive to follow PM recommendations and have total control of schedules and duration of downtimes than to skip it and face out-of-control and unexpected downtimes. Accelerated performance degradation and more frequent equipment failure are too often and easily blamed on alleged equipment-design deficiencies. The PM recommendations of the original equipment manufacturer should never be neglected. They can be optimized by each end-user based on experience.

Table 10-2 illustrates how following PM schedules increases cycle time by 7.25% (0.928 resultant PM productivity factor) for a 2.5-kW CO_2 laser-cutting operation versus a 13.5% increase (0.881 resultant PM productivity factor) for a 5-kW CO_2 laser-cutting operation. Adding the normal estimated repair downtimes might yield a total of 11.3% increase in cycle time (PM and repair productivity factor of 0.898) with a 2.5-kW laser versus an 18.8% increase (PM and repair productivity factory of 0.842) with a 5-kW laser. If even a single PM task is neglected, the resultant PM productivity factor might slightly improve, showing less increase in overall cycle time. However, neglecting a PM task may also disproportionately increase the overall cycle time if the occurrence of abnormal equipment failures raises the frequency and mean duration of repair downtimes. Unlike PM downtime, repair downtime is highly unpredictable, which is particularly risky to just-in-time, lean-manufacturing enterprises.

Table 10-2. Typical PM and repair downtimes for CO_2 laser cutting

PM Task	Estimated Downtime, hr	Period, hr	2.6-kW Laser Productivity Factor, %	5-kW Laser Productivity Factor, %
Capacitive sensor calibration	0.25	500	1.000	0.999
Cooling water exchange	1.00	1,000	0.999	0.999
Cutting nozzle change	0.25	20	0.988	0.975
Resonator O-rings	4.00	5,000	0.999	0.999
External mirrors cleaning/change	4.00	500	0.992	0.984
Focusing lens cleaning/change	0.25	20	0.988	0.975
Laser calibration testing	0.25	20	0.988	0.975
Laser mirrors cleaning/change	20	1,000	0.980	0.975
Motion-system lubrication	0.5	500	0.999	0.999
Replace optical-path air filters	0.5	2,500	1.000	1.000
Oil and filter change	0.25	1,500	1.000	1.000
Machine overhaul	96	20,000	0.995	0.995
Resultant productivity factor			0.928	0.881
Repair Task	**Estimated Downtime, hr**	**MTBF, hr**		
Cutting head	48	6,000	0.992	0.989
Water chiller	48	12,000	0.996	0.995
Motion system	72	125,000	0.999	0.999
Glassware change	72	10,000	0.993	0.990
Blower	72	20,000	0.996	0.993
Power supply	48	7,500	0.994	0.991
Vacuum pump	72	20,000	0.996	0.996
Resultant productivity factor			0.967	0.955
Resultant PM and repair productivity factor			0.898	0.842

Laser-cutting Machines

Laser manufacturers' PM recommendations vary with model types and technologies. Laser resonators are just one of the components of a laser-cutting machine and can be categorized in just a few common design configurations with common components (see Chapter 4). The following sections review downtime expectations for the various components of laser-cutting machines.

Laser Control Unit

A control unit for laser operation, maintenance, and diagnostics can range from a stand-alone rudimentary and totally open programmable control with its own display to a unit completely integrated with the numerical control of the machine. In all cases, it is generally a repairable component with a MTBF of several years, requiring little or no maintenance downtime.

Laser Cavity Optics

A standard laser cavity is composed of folding mirrors, a rear mirror, and an output-coupler (OC) mirror. Intra-cavity mirrors are considered consumables and, depending on the model, output power, and method of operation of the laser, they have a typical life between cleaning of 500–2,000 hours. Life between replacement of cavity mirrors varies between 2,000–6,000 hours for the same model of laser used at different locations with different applications and different operators. Most vulnerable, the outside surface of an OC mirror may be exposed to room temperature, room humidity, room dusts, and ambient air contaminants. Operations that are maintenance conscious protect the outside surface of an OC mirror from environmental variations, including during weekend and holiday shutdowns.

Folding mirrors. Most industrial lasers have one OC mirror and one rear mirror. Higher laser power generally requires an increased number of components such as glassware, power supplies, and folding mirrors. The latter is justified because of the benefit of saving floor space. CO_2 laser designers enclose large lasers with a long optical path length (OPL) within a small floor space by folding the OPL into several segments with a clever arrangement of folding mirrors. For example, a 4-kW CO_2 laser may have an optical path length of 26.2 ft (8 m) between the OC and rear mirror. This all fits in several folded segments within a cabinet of the same footprint size as a 2-kW CO_2 laser with only 13.1 ft (4 m) OPL (*Figure 10-4*) or an 8-kW laser with 52.5 ft (16 m) OPL. However, the increase in the number of mirrors adds complexity and sensitivity to cavity tuning procedures. Similarly, higher-power YAG lasers come with an increased number of folding mirrors and YAG crystals in the cavity.

Back reflection. Back reflections reduce the life of cavity optics. When cutting highly reflective material such as aluminum, a percentage of the laser beam incident on the workpiece is reflected off the surface. Some of these reflections find their way back inside the laser resonator cavity, thus the name "back reflection." Back-reflection rays penetrating the laser cavity produce highly efficient pumping energy that adds to the energy delivered by the laser's power supplies. This back-reflection pumping energy is amplified accordingly in the laser cavity. The resultant intra-cavity peak laser power reaches extremely high levels that approach or may exceed the threshold for coating breakdown on cavity mirrors. This can significantly shorten the life of cavity mirrors and other components such as O-rings and glassware. Optics life reduction of 50% is not unheard of for multi-kilowatt-output-power lasers cutting and etching aluminum surfaces with 10.6-μm wavelength beams. Downtime for cleaning or replacing a cavity optic can range from half a day to a day if all spare parts are readily available.

The large majority of reflections off a workpiece's surface can be composed of mono-directional specular reflections; less than a few percent are isotropic nonspecular reflections. Processing with the focused laser-beam axis at slightly less than perfect normal incidence on the workpiece can change the direction of back reflections and consequently limit them to only nonspecular reflections. So long as the deviation from normal incidence reaches no more than a few milliradians, processing performance is not significantly affected.

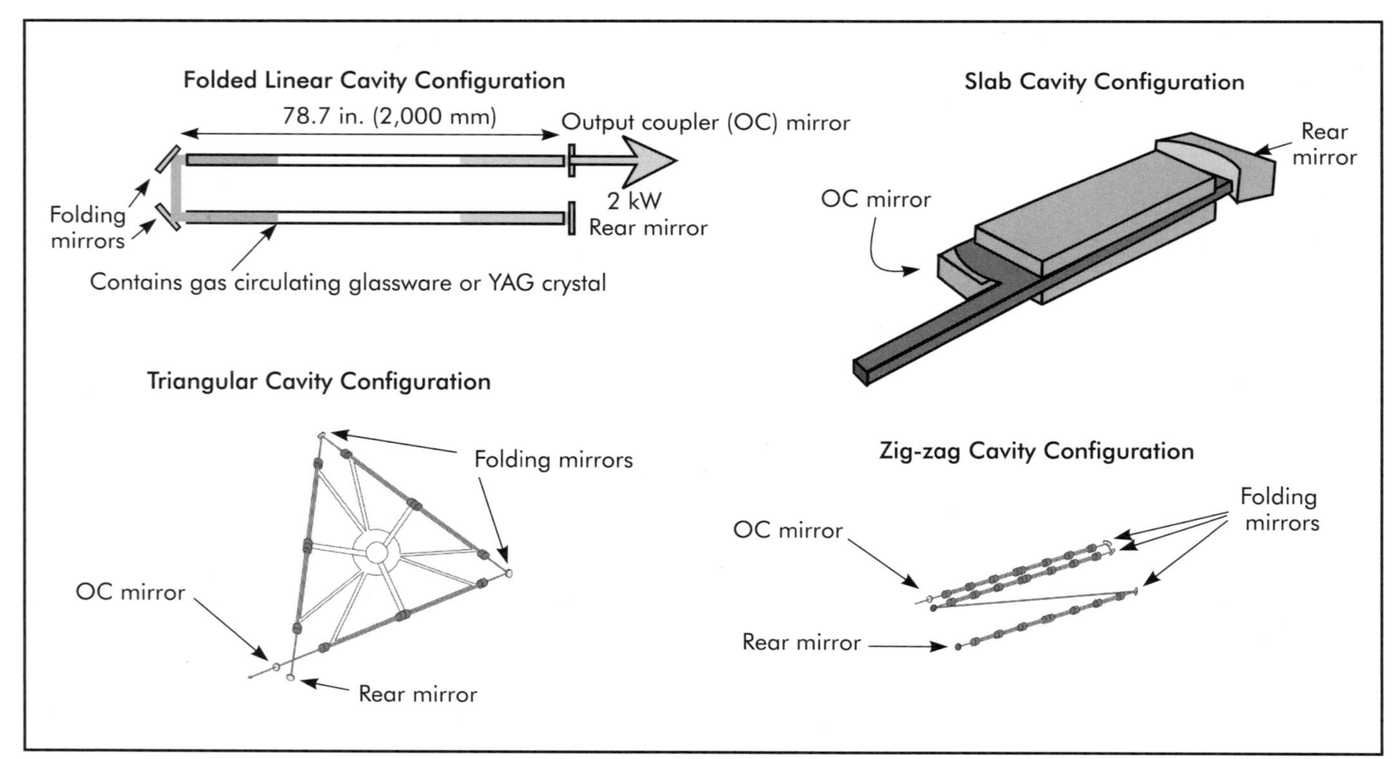

Figure 10-4. Small-footprint configurations for multi-kilowatt lasers show folded intra-cavity optical paths. The slab laser's output-beam cross-section is rectangular and requires beam-shaping optics to make it circular and axis-symmetric. Its M^2 *number is the closest to 1 of all the other commercially available configurations.* (Courtesy Rofin-Sinar)

Consider the example of an external OPL of 16.4 ft (5 m) between the OC mirror and the workpiece, a laser resonator with an intra-cavity OPL of 16.4 ft (5 m) between the OC and rear mirror, and a cavity aperture of 0.8 in. (20 mm). The cavity aperture is usually represented by a characteristic dimension(s), such as the diameter of the laser beam exiting the cavity. Deflection of 1 milliradian from normal incidence should eliminate back reflections due to specular reflections of the laser beam on the workpiece. A rule of thumb is formulated by:

$$2 \times D_{ni} \times (E_{OPL} + C_{OPL}) > A_C \qquad (10\text{-}2)$$

where:

D_{ni} = deviation from normal incidence, radian
E_{OPL} = external optical path length, ft (m)
C_{OPL} = cavity optical path length, ft (m)
A_C = cavity aperture, ft (m)

In practice, rare are the cases where the beam-to-workpiece incidence angle is controlled to within less than ±2.5 milliradians. This indicates that specular reflections do not systematically result in harmful back reflections.

Back reflections due to nonspecular reflections are most difficult to eliminate, particularly when processing material that is highly reflective to the wavelength of the laser beam.

Focusing lens. Clearly, along the external OPL, the focusing lens is generally the optic with the shortest life as it is closest to the workpiece and exposed to room atmosphere and sparks of hot metallic particles recoiled upward from the kerf. Since it is in most cases a transmissive optic, uniform cooling of the lens is not as efficient as with reflective mirrors, leading to the strong possibility of temperature gradients across the lens diameter. These gradients yield thermal lensing that can degrade cutting performance and contribute to early lens failure. In both cases, the impact on productivity is manifested through more downtime to troubleshoot cutting performance degradation and clean or replace the lens.

The focusing lens life between cleaning can be 3–5 times shorter than for other optics along the OPL. Most machine builders implement a design allowing easy access, removal, installation, and alignment of the focusing lens. Often, a precisely machined sliding drawer serves as a focusing lens mount to ease access to it. Water cooling of the focusing lens is achieved by conduction with the periphery flange of the lens. High laser power calls for a thick focusing lens edge to enable more efficient cooling and reduce the temperature gradient across the lens diameter.

PM productivity. Overall, it seems self-evident that a larger number of components, coupled with higher energy input and output power management within a common base engineering design, makes maintenance downtime longer for higher-power lasers than that experienced with lower-power lasers. A typical comparison between productivity factors for a 2.6-kW laser and a 5-kW laser is illustrated in *Table 10-2*. Different frequencies of occurrence and different average maintenance downtimes per occurrence between these two laser powers are expected. Rather than focus solely on the resonator's output power differences, it must also be considered that the entire cutting system, including the beam-delivery system and processing head, is subjected to:

- different average power levels;
- different power gradients along the entire optical path length and incident on all optics; and
- different material interaction dynamics with the workpiece.

It can be observed in the field that a 5–10% decrease in PM and repair productivity occurs when doubling the laser power. In terms of the "touch and feel" gage, a plant operator accustomed to operating a 2.6-kW laser may perceive this 5–10% decrease as abnormal when transitioning to a 5-kW laser based on the standards set with the lower-power laser. This can be accentuated if the 5-kW laser is used at the boundary of its capability such as when processing more challenging or thicker material at higher speed. Manufacturers must strengthen the design of all system components in new higher-power laser-cutting machine models.

Cleaning and replacing external optics. A larger number of optics in the beam-delivery system means more downtime associated with cleaning, replacing, and realignment. A typical flying optics machine can have at least two moving mirrors, and at least one stationary mirror in the beam-delivery system. This does not include mirrors used for optional beam collimation or adaptive optics with an optional constant beam-path feature. The beam-delivery optics and optical path need protection from particles, humidity, and pollutant contamination. The entire optical path of a beam-delivery system will remain generally isolated from the plant's ambient atmosphere with the use of solid enclosures, flexible "bellow" covers, and compressed dry air for pressurizing. Optics along the path length should be water cooled. To avoid harmful condensation on the surface of the optics, the temperature of the cooling water should be set above dew point, which is generally at least 2° F (1° C) above room temperature.

One cause of shortened mirror life is improper cleaning procedures. Most external optics are copper or silicone surfaces with gold-based coatings. They can be cleaned using acetone or isopropyl alcohol and optical cleaning tissue. Acetone evaporates within a few seconds at room temperature. It is corrosive to most O-ring rubber material and care must be taken to allow its complete evaporation before mounting the mirror in contact with O-rings. Once chemically attacked, O-ring material residues contaminate mirror surfaces and accelerate their degradation. More powerful cleaners, such as acetic acid or other commercial compounds, can be used to remove tough stains from mirror surfaces. These solutions are not harmful to the mirror coating at low temperature, but can speed mirror-surface degradation when exposed to laser-gas mix at high temperature. It is essential that special optics-cleaning solution be restricted to use by well-trained maintenance personnel. Before re-installing the mirror in the cavity, the mirror surface must be thoroughly cleaned with harmless alcohol, such as isopropyl, to remove all traces of cleaning solution.

Gas-delivery Systems

Laser cutting takes place with assist-gas such as air, pure oxygen, pure nitrogen, pure argon, or a special mix of inert and non-inert gas. Purity of assist-gas is usually specified around 99.5% or above. In contrast, laser gas generally requires a higher global purity of about 99.995% for use in the resonator cavity to maximize performance and reliability. For CO_2 lasers, mixtures of gas generally composed of nitrogen, carbon dioxide, and helium are delivered in specially treated cylinders. As detailed in Chapter 4, a gas-delivery system should preferably be made of rigid stainless-steel tubing or flexible polyethylene tubing. It is important that the system be essentially free of contamination.

When using rigid tubing, such as copper, flux filler should not be used for joining as it has a tendency to degas slowly and thus contaminates gas delivery for a long period of time. For any tubing that has been warehoused without end plugs, care must be taken to flush out the dirt, dust, and oil-mist contaminants residing inside. Acetone can be used as a flushing compound as it vaporizes quickly after dissolving most contaminants.

When assembling cylinders to manifolds and regulators, care must be taken to eliminate leaks. A method of testing for external leaks consists of sealing the gas-delivery system after having pressurized it to approximately twice the atmospheric pressure. A gas-pressure indicator is then used to measure the pressure drop rate after about 15 minutes. If the rate surpasses about 5 torr (7 mbar) per hour, the leak should be located and fixed. Leaks are more likely to occur at fittings and manifolds. Some sophisticated helium-detection equipment can be used to locate a leak. It requires that the system be pressurized with helium. Sources of leakage can then be pinpointed with great accuracy by a helium-detector probe.

When replacing empty lasing-gas cylinders with new ones, at least some part of the gas-delivery system must be open and exposed to ambient air. It is essential that this ambient air be flushed from the system before entering the resonator and before the laser is used for cutting. Gas-delivery systems should incorporate appropriate valves that can isolate the majority of the gas-delivery system from ambient air during cylinder changeover. Valve-controlled outlets enable flushing the contaminant ambient air with the new cylinder gas content before opening to the system.

If not purged before reaching the laser cavity, contaminants will wear intra-cavity components during operation. For example, some mirror surfaces might degrade by adsorbing these contaminants. Power-supply units and pumping mechanisms might have to work beyond nominal conditions to compensate for the combined effect of contaminated laser gas being used and the cavity mirrors' reflectivity being reduced. Although minor laser-gas contamination by itself might not often lead to immediate component failure, it contributes to a cumulative effect that shortens mean life between cleaning or replacement of components, such as mirrors, glassware, O-rings, electrodes, or even power supplies.

During operation shutdown, such as overnight or during the weekend, it is a good practice to pressurize the gas-delivery system above twice the ambient atmospheric pressure. This has the effect of limiting contamination by diffusion of ambient air in the gas-delivery system. For lasing-gas-line flushing and pressurization, the length of tubing and piping should be kept as short as possible.

Also, when switching from one assist-gas to another, the entire assist-gas-delivery system down to the cutting nozzle must be flushed with the new assist-gas prior to resuming with cutting or piercing. This flushing exercise can take just a few seconds if the section of the beam-delivery system common to different types of assist-gas is minimized in volume.

Laser Excitation Mechanism

The pumping mechanism used to energize an active medium can be discharge electrodes for CO_2 laser-gas mix, or flash and arc lamps and diode lasers for a YAG crystal. Whereas electrodes in high-frequency excited CO_2 lasers are considered neither consumables nor repairable, for older types of direct current (DC) -excited lasers, electrodes require frequent cleaning. For YAG lasers, lamps are considered consumables with life varying from 300–1,000 hours for continuous-wave units and 5–200 million pulses for pulsed units (Kugler 2001). The low efficiency and reliability of flash lamps have encouraged the development of alternative pumping mechanisms such as those in diode-laser-pumped YAG lasers. The reliability of pumping diodes, such as the GaAlAs type, measured in terms of MTBF, is reported to be ten times that of flash lamps (Zediker 2000).

Gas Blowers

Some models of CO_2 lasers, such as a sealed diffusion-cooled CO_2 laser (see *Figure 4-4*), use technology-enabling stationary gas and no turbo blower. This presents the advantage of having no mechanically moving lubricated parts and consequently less maintenance and repair-related downtime. Such lasers have challenged designers' ingenuity for heat dissipation management and control in the laser-gas chamber when laser output is being constantly cycled, such as during laser cutting of metals.

Most industrial high-power CO_2 lasers have turbo blowers for laser-gas recirculation. Some turbo blowers operate at several tens of thousands of revolutions per minute (RPM) and generally use special-grade oil to lubricate the ball bearing and cap their temperature. Some of this oil may contaminate the laser gas unless appropriate design and maintenance precautions are followed. Use of oil can contribute to a shorter time between cleaning/replacement of optics, O-rings, power supplies, and other components of the resonator. In practice, these blowers have a time between replacement of 10,000–20,000 hours, and thus have a modest negative impact on productivity (see *Table 10-2*).

Alternative magnetic bearing technologies enable oil-free turboblower operation, which eliminates oil contamination of intra-cavity components. The expected increase in mean time between maintenance should lead to an increased total PM productivity factor. Magnetic bearing technology is still new and difficult to control at high RPM. Once sufficient field reliability data are collected, this technology will reveal true improvement of mean time between maintenance, mean time between failure, and overall productivity.

Beam-delivery System Alignment

YAG lasers do not use gas. The trade-off is periodic cleaning and replacement of YAG crystals, flash lamps, or the diode lasers of the pumping mechanism, and replacement of water-cooling distribution channels. These actions often call for a realignment of the external beam-delivery system. Most YAG laser-cutting systems use flexible optical fiber instead of mirrors as a beam-delivery system. These fibers, depending on their design (step index versus graded index) and diameter, laser power, and bending radii along the OPL, have varying MTBF supplied by the manufacturers. MTBF is better confirmed by experience.

Each time a cavity optic or YAG crystal bar is cleaned or replaced, the output laser beam's entry in the fiberglass must be realigned to optimize its efficient capture through the fiberoptic entrance. Once this realignment is completed, no further alignment is necessary because the fiberoptic automatically guides the laser beam to its final destination, the processing head. Each replacement of a processing head calls for realignment of the collecting optic with the output of the fiberoptic. The fiberoptic properties of a waveguide limit downtime considerably for external beam alignment.

For CO_2 laser systems, the beam-delivery system is composed of a sequence of mirrors and lenses. The mirrors may be flat or curved. Some mirrors have adjustable radius of curvature such as for adaptive optics. Adjustment of the radius of curvature is made either by fluid pressure, such as water-based fluid, or actuated using piezzo-electric crystals forced to bend the mirror.

Most mirrors of the beam-delivery system are either stationary or mounted on the X, Y, and Z axes of the machine. They can be finely adjusted for beam alignment purposes about a horizontal A and vertical B tilting axis as shown in *Figure 10-5*. External beam alignment is needed each time an optic is removed from its mount for cleaning or replacement. External beam alignment consists of adjusting the A and B tilting axes for each optic downstream of the one that has been cleaned or replaced. Two guidelines for external beam alignment can be followed:

1. An incident beam needs to be preferably centered on each optic's surface.
2. A reflected beam must be parallel to the motion axis relative to which it is propagating.

The most popular method for external beam alignment consists of using a crosshair target as seen in *Figure 10-5*. For a few milliseconds, a laser beam is shot at a cardboard target placed immediately behind the crosshair. The center of the crosshair indicates the center of the mirror. The burned imprint of the beam against the cardboard allows measurement of a deviation distance between the center of the imprint and the center of the crosshair's image projection on the cardboard. The mirror upstream of this target can then be adjusted by tilting it appropriately in both horizontal

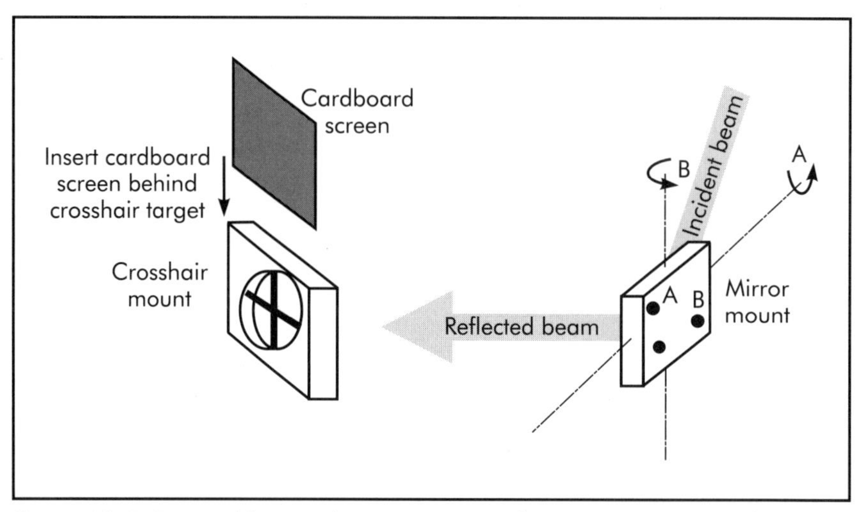

Figure 10-5. External beam alignment: a crosshair target is mounted in place of the downstream mirror. The upstream mirror can be tilted or rotated about the A and B axes. The reflected beam can then be aligned to impinge the center of the crosshair at every position along the optical path of the beam-delivery system.

and vertical directions to reduce the deviation distance to zero. If the crosshair target is mounted on a moving axis, then the tilt adjustment of the upstream mirror must lead to zero deviation distances at both ends of the moving axis. Once external beam alignment is completed, it should remain stable until one of the optics is removed and replaced along the path, or until the laser resonator's output-beam pointing direction has noticeably changed. Most optical mounts along the OPLs of industrial systems are of rugged, heavy-duty mechanical construction and stable.

After powering up a laser, it takes at least a couple of minutes for all of the resonator's mechanical and optical components to heat from room temperature (cold mode) to nominal operating temperature (hot mode). By burning acrylic blocks, such as those shown in *Figure 10-6*, differences between cold and hot mode are distinguishable with the naked eye. The cold- and hot-mode shots exhibit slightly different geometric features and pointing directions. Mode tuning to the manufacturer's specifications will set the machine for minimum difference between hot and cold modes.

Even the best-quality resonator designs exhibit these differences. However, they are well controlled within known limits. The difference between hot- and cold-mode burn even varies with distance along the external OPL, and tolerances to such variations vary from machine to machine and application to application. Machines with short OPLs are less sensitive to the differences than flying optics machines with long OPLs. Conditions such as cutting at maximum permissible feed rate for a certain thickness and material and cutting the maximum permissible thickness for a certain laser-output power are also more sensitive to hot and cold differences. For such situations, a simple 2–3-minute warm-up "dry run" may be sufficient to insure operation in hot mode. External optics must be efficiently cooled to avoid similar cold- versus hot-mode temperature drift, particularly for optics such as collimator mirrors, adaptive optics, and focusing lenses.

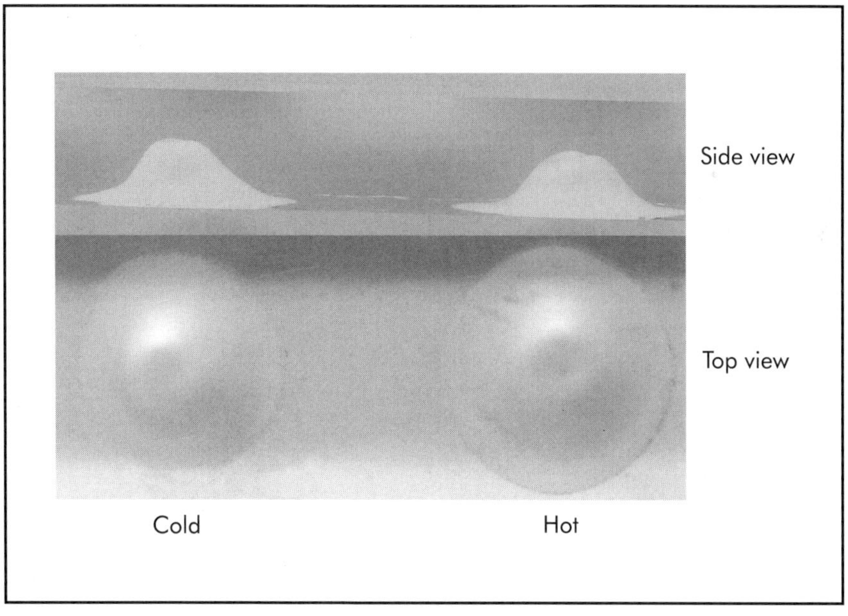

Figure 10-6. Mode burns are generated by shooting a CO_2 laser beam for a specified number of seconds on an acrylic block. When the cavity is properly tuned, the difference between cold and hot mode is minor, although visible with the naked eye.

The laser-beam output direction can change for differing reasons. One is poor design, in which the output-beam direction changes substantially with operating conditions. Another is floor vibration that moves the orientation of the laser relative to the machine base. In other cases, mode tuning of the laser invariably leads to output-beam direction change significant enough to warrant external beam alignment. With external OPLs typically of 19.7–49.2 ft (6–15 m), 1 milliradian deviation in pointing direction justifies external beam-alignment downtime.

PROCESS AUTOMATION

With computer numerical controls (CNC) and computer automation, part programs and cutting-parameter libraries can be instantly downloaded and rapidly set or modified on- and off-line anywhere within an information-system network. Parameter libraries stored in local or remote personal computer (PC) memories can be accessed automatically for each job. Cutting parameters include focus position, assist-gas pressure and type selection, laser output-power characteristics, and even production tracking identifiers from computerized supervisory control.

In a very competitive market environment, it is essential to use productivity tools such as computer-aided design/computer-automated manufacturing (CAD/CAM) and nesting software, along with electronic communication networking to transfer, process, analyze, and archive data. The goal is to accelerate and keep under control request-to-order and order-to-delivery process cycles. Electronic communication capability allows remote access to the machine by troubleshooting experts, thus potentially cutting response time, warranty costs, and expense associated with the physical dispatch of a specialized maintenance engineer along with replacement parts on site. It enables diagnostics within minutes of an incident rather than within a day to dispatch. Remote accessibility also enables supervisory control of status and events, thus calling alarm to out-of-control trends, so corrective action can be scheduled before failure occurs. All of these factory automation tools contributed to the immense productivity boost experienced by manufacturing toward the end of the 20th century.

Material Handling

In the queue of operation steps, non-value-added material handling appears to be the weakest link for high productivity gains. The manipulation of thick heavy plates or large-sized thin sheets requires personnel and heavy-duty loading, unloading, and crowding equipment. Material-handling automation has many advantages.

- It can free up manual labor.
- It reduces destacking/stacking and crowding times.
- It minimizes the probability of damage to material such as denting or bending oversized panels.
- It lowers the probability of injury due to handling heavy or oversized panels.
- It increases repeatability and reproducibility.

Material-handling automation is highly recommended in high-volume production environments. However, for job-shop type operations, generally with low volume per batch and an increasing number of different batches, the price of automation to suit many product varieties and raw sheets and plate material of various shapes and sizes is becoming prohibitive if not impossible to justify. For job shops, it is preferable to put effort into setup downtime reduction with partial automation.

SETUP DOWNTIME

Many operations have a single operator simultaneously running several machine cells. To reduce downtime, setups requiring high-level technical skills and time-consuming tasks must be limited.

Replacing a nozzle tip or a focusing lens requires nozzle-centering downtime. Nozzle centering is often done manually by the "shoot and adjust" method described in Chapter 5. It is important to perform the nozzle-centering procedure after the laser resonator and the beam-delivery system have transitioned to hot mode. The pointing direction difference between hot and cold mode is largest at the nozzle exit, and generally in the far field, with a few exceptions. With the most advanced designs, nozzle-centering downtime is eliminated when specially machined nozzle tips have their flange seat against the focus-head assembly to maintain the same nozzle-center position whenever a new nozzle tip is installed.

Special machine features can significantly cut setup downtime and are generally offered as options. Among them, an auto-focus head, illustrated in *Figure 10-7a*, is a popular feature that auto-

a.

Figure 10-7. (a) Auto-focus heads enable automatic servo-controlled focus positioning without altering nozzle standoff. Positioning can be done on the fly without stopping production. (b) Break-away heads prevent destruction of the focusing head during collisions. (Courtesy Cincinnati, Inc.)

mates focus positioning with a servo axis and an absolute encoder. The focus position is adjusted without changing the nozzle standoff. A break-away feature, shown in *Figure 10-7b*, prevents catastrophic damage during a collision by detaching the head from the gantry, thereby triggering a safety switch that stops motion. The head can be reinstalled quickly and production restarted without the need for realignment downtime.

REPEATABILITY AND RELIABILITY

Even with full automation, repeatability remains a struggle for laser-cutting processes in many job-shop operations. Too often, operators waste valuable time fine-adjusting setup parameters in an attempt to reproduce cutting feed rates and edge quality achieved 1,000 hours of operation earlier with different material and different contour features. It is essential to adopt cutting parameters that can tolerate a drift in optics cleanliness between

Laser head in operating position   Break-away head after interference

b.

Figure 10-7. continued.

PM times and variation of material surface conditions. There is a yet-to-be-developed reliable method to adapt cutting parameters on the fly to these known variations. Such a method might result from a compromise between establishing tolerances in specifications for material, conservative feed rates, cut-edge-quality standards, and setting adequate time intervals for preventive maintenance.

Reliability is mainly a function of machinery design and the establishment and implementation of operation and maintenance procedures. Machine builders spend much design effort to protect a machine's reliability from operator mistakes and misuse. End-users must understand how critical proper operation and maintenance procedures are to reliability as it severely impacts productivity.

IMPACTS OF PROCESS INPUTS

The fishbone diagrams in *Figures 10-8* through *10-12* highlight the potential process inputs that influence productivity outputs. The following sections discuss these influences and how to control them.

Impact of Material

One of the most frequent causes of downtime is related to incoming material. There are many metal-alloy types with varying properties and quality, and differing surface conditions and optical properties. Quality variations, such as surface rust and scales, add to the difficulty in processing the purchased material. In an ideal world, the machine design would make laser cutting tolerant to all material variations. However, the reality is that laser-material interaction strongly depends on material characteristics such as surface condition.

To store and have available a known reference "good material" is a smart practice. At a minimum, it can be cut for troubleshooting purposes to identify or exonerate a new unknown material as the source for a cutting defect or productivity deficiency. Most

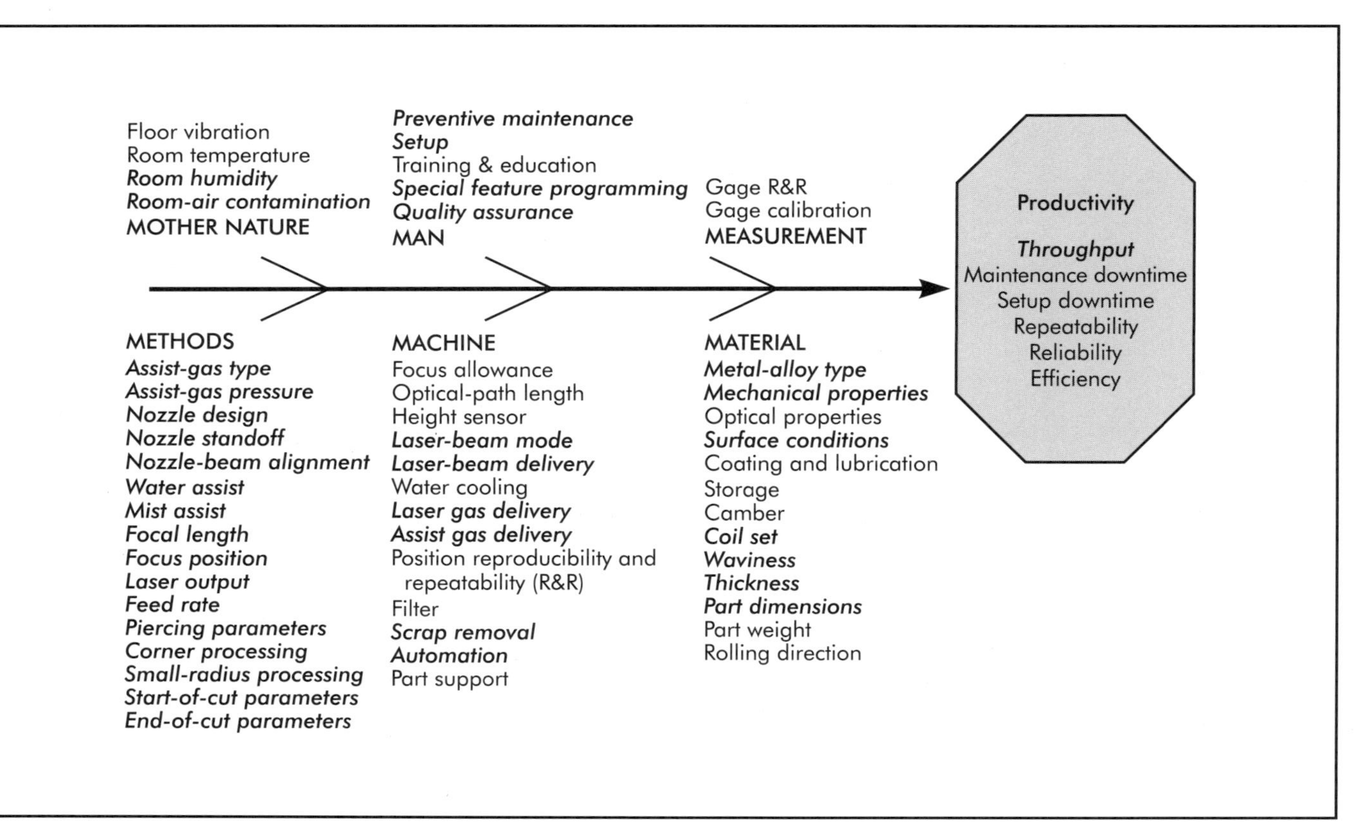

Figure 10-8. This fishbone diagram highlights in bold the main process inputs that influence throughput.

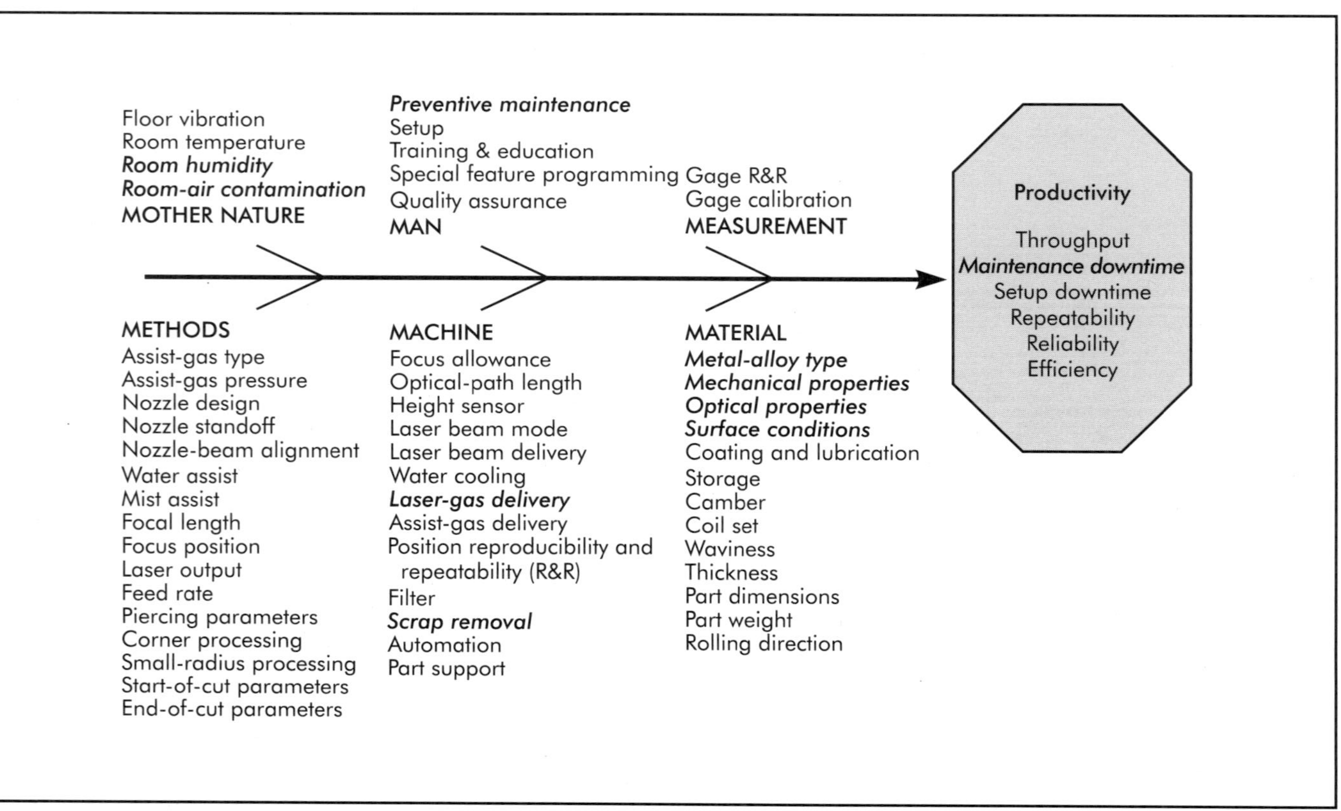

Figure 10-9. This fishbone diagram highlights in bold the main process inputs that influence maintenance downtime.

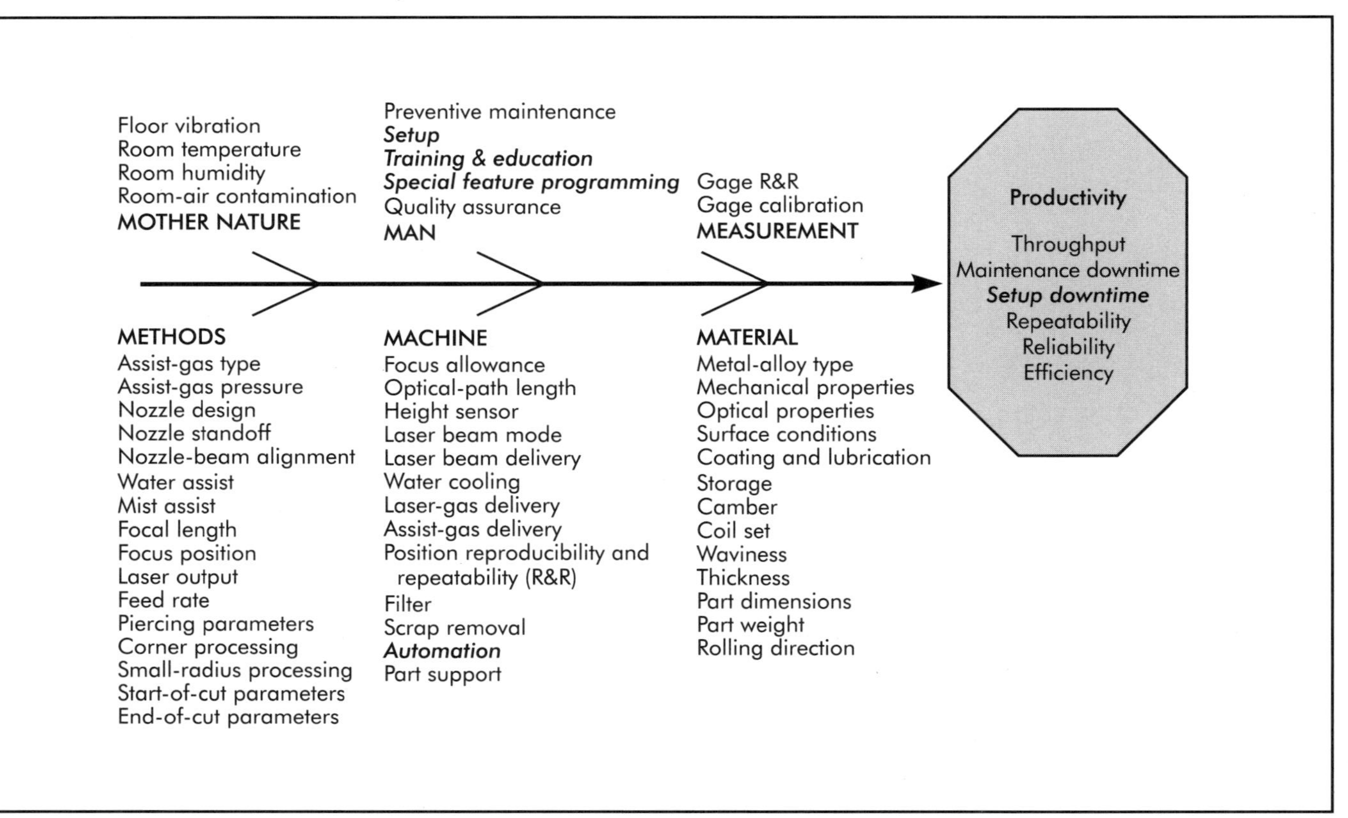

Figure 10-10. This fishbone diagram highlights in bold the main process inputs that influence setup downtime.

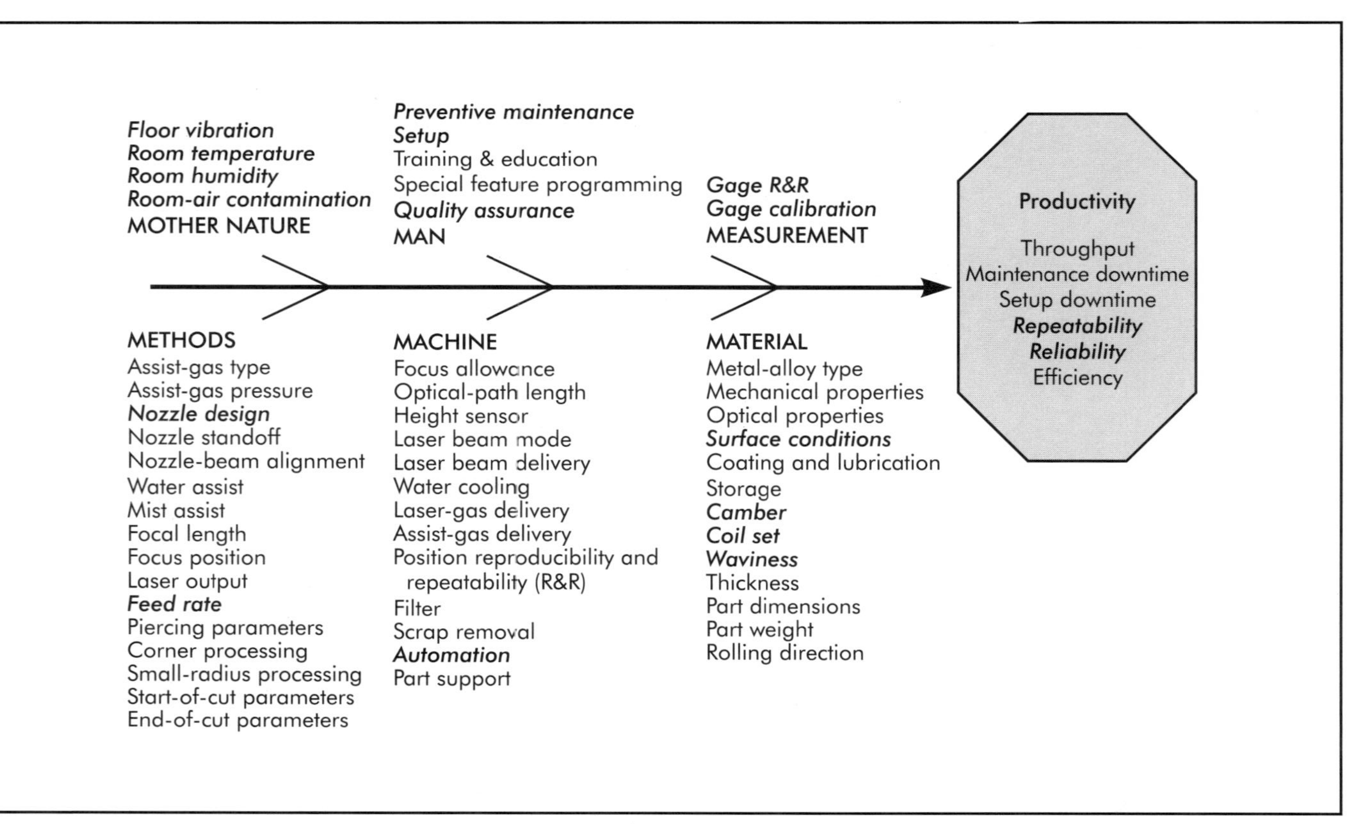

Figure 10-11. This fishbone diagram highlights in bold the main process inputs that influence repeatability and reliability.

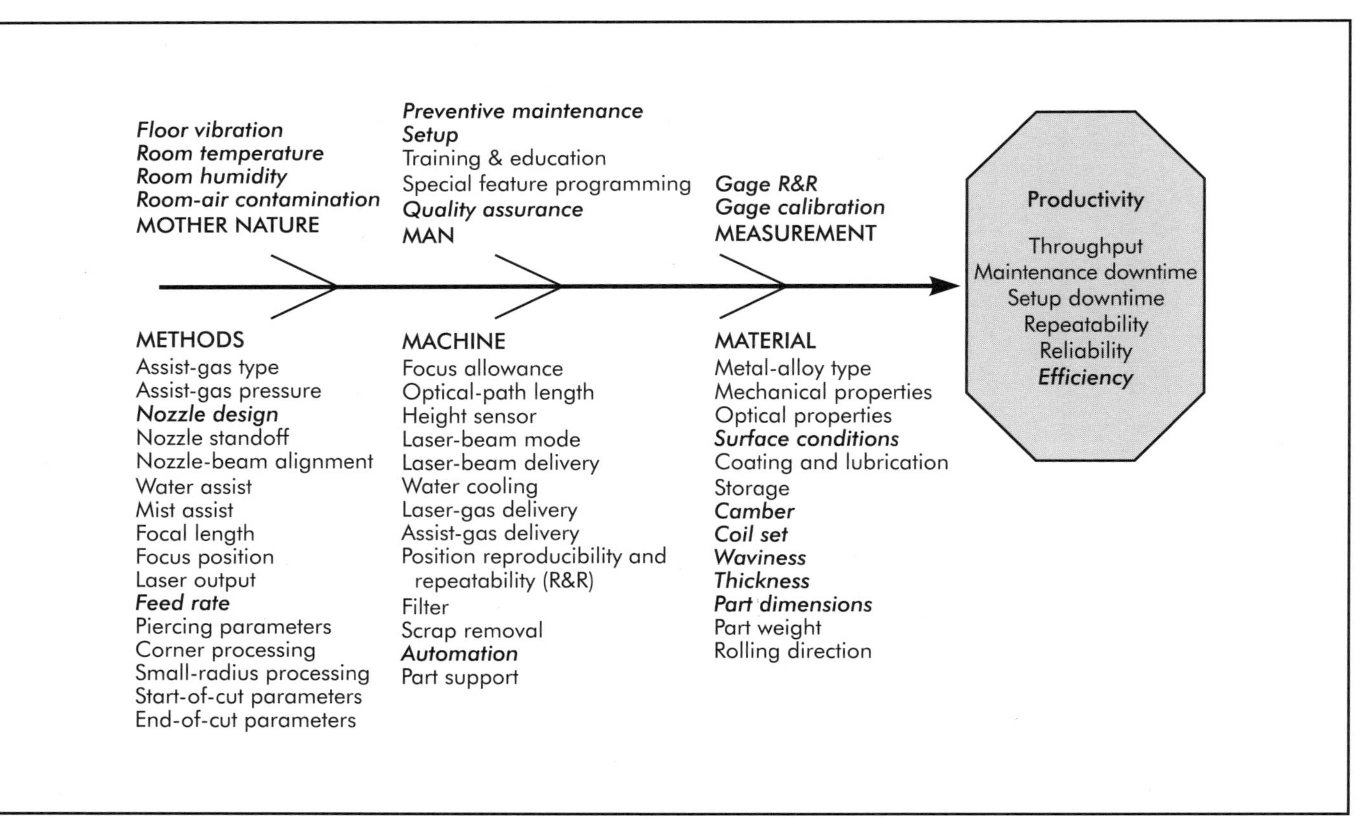

Figure 10-12. This fishbone diagram highlights in bold the main process inputs that influence efficiency.

metal alloys come with a multitude of minute alloying variations that can be responsible for significant mechanical and metallurgical properties. They also may have different coatings and degrees of surface rust and scale. Coil set, waviness, and thickness variations upset cutting quality and cutting speed, resulting in downtime needed to finely adjust setup parameters. To avoid downtime for these adjustments, it is recommended to process known "laser-friendly material" and train receiving agents and operators to recognize early enough whether a specific material quality is within specification.

A direct consequence of downtime can be a decrease in average throughput over a cycle. This becomes particularly problematic when downtime occurs under the time constraints of JIT delivery requirements.

Material waviness, coil set, and camber hinder good repeatability of setup, particularly with thin-gage material. When coil set and waviness can be altered by a springback reaction to high-pressure assist-gas, the ensuing vibration imparted locally to the workpiece cannot always be faithfully followed by the height-sensor mechanism. Such a problem can be reduced by intelligent part support such as templates shaped to each part feature. Templates impose a surface reference against which a sheet can be pressed or clamped. They hold the disadvantage of needing a different dedicated template for each part number. Feed rates also can be chosen conservatively to increase tolerance to flatness variations as illustrated in *Figure 10-13*, resulting in nozzle-workpiece standoff variations and reduction of throughput (Mombo Caristan 1999).

Camber may yield finished products that are out of dimensional specification and must go to scrap. To increase tolerance to camber with an adapted nesting solution, larger engineering offal may have to be accepted. A less costly alternative is to design a positioning mechanism and procedures that can correct camber shifts, or reduce camber to insignificant proportions with proper tension leveling, slitting, and annealing equipment.

The reflective properties of materials can shorten the life of optics if reflections from surfaces find their way back to the laser cavity. If well aligned with the optical axis of the cavity, these back-reflection rays increase the laser-output peak power, in some cases by 100% or more when compared to the commanded value. The

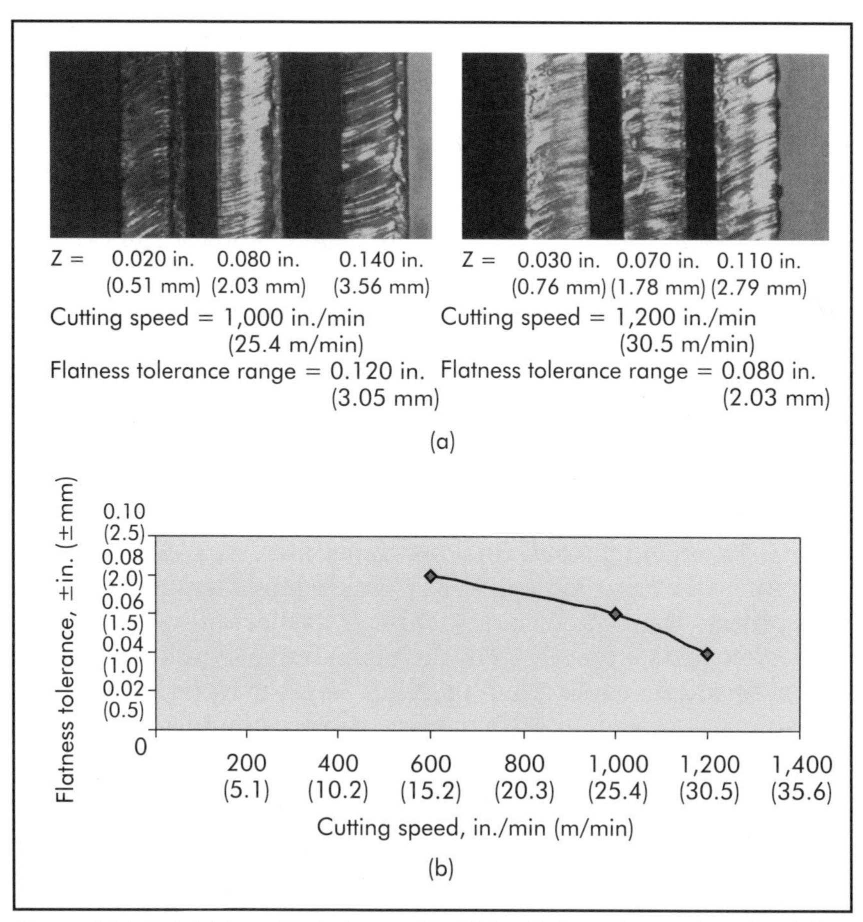

Figure 10-13. (a) Magnified views of 0.04-in. (1.0-mm) cut edges for different values of nozzle standoff Z. The angle of the striations was used to comparatively scale cut-edge quality. (b) Flatness tolerance of the laser-cutting process on 0.04-in. (1.0-mm) thick, galvanized steel as a function of cutting speed. A continuous-wave, 6-kW laser power, 5-in. (127-mm) focusing lens, and nitrogen assist were used (Mombo Caristan 1999).

actual intra-cavity peak power is so high that it accelerates the degeneration of cavity optic coatings, which are not designed for such out-of-specification thermal shock and gradients in pulse mode. Increased output peak power above optical specifications may also damage external optics prematurely. As a consequence of the increase in output peak power, operators may become satisfied with the improved cutting performance and increased feed rate. Little do they realize that it will be short-lived. Field-service data reveal that optics life between replacements can be reduced by as much as 50% due to back reflections.

A method to diagnose back reflection is to generate a test-cut feature program that allows the laser-beam focus spot to travel uninterrupted on the workpiece surface for longer than the response time of the power sensors in the laser resonator. Such response time is typically 2–3 seconds for pyroelectric devices. If the average laser power measured and read on the control display becomes abnormally higher than the product of duty × commanded peak power, then it may indicate the presence of back reflections and an alarm might be triggered.

The thickness and dimensions of materials have a direct impact on productivity as well. Laser-cutting speed decreases substantially when material thickness increases. As a consequence, piercing and cutting time increase, making for a less-efficient cutting process than when cutting thinner gage. However, this paradoxically yields an increase in the percentage of cycle time taken by value-adding cutting and piercing steps, thus making cutting thick gages more productive in a strict lean manufacturing sense.

Very thin materials and oversized parts require handling care to reduce surface scratches and bending and denting risks. This requirement slows down handling and feeding sequences. In other words, coupled with a reduction in cutting and piercing time per part at higher speeds, it increases the percentage of cycle time taken by non-value-added handling steps. From a strict lean manufacturing perspective, it seems like a less-productive process unless adequate material-handling automation can alleviate the aforementioned conditions.

Impact of Machine

Automation

Automation of setup is a sure way to reduce operator errors and mistakes that increase downtime and waste. In many instances, automation optimizes productivity only to the extent that the human behind it allows. For example, when cutting thick metals, most automation software creates part-program nesting with repeated piercing steps. The software should consider avoiding piercing time that is longer than the time to cut through workpiece offal skeleton to traverse from one feature to the next. These types of traverse cuts are processed at much slower speed than rapid traverse, but can be processed at faster than nominal feed rate because the cut-edge quality is of no importance. Traverse-cut feed rate can outpace nominal feed rate by as much as 50% in thick-gage cutting and 100% in thin-gage cutting.

Some of the largest sources of waste are downtime spent for scrap removal and material searching, handling, and positioning. The high cost of material-handling automation forces many operators to manually handle material. Ingenious equipment designs, such as the common dual worktables, enable processing on one table while unloading, loading, and positioning on the second one.

Special Feature Programming

For scrap removal, a dilemma exists between wasting time up front to laser-cut offal skeleton to smaller sizes to enable its automatic drop through and collection by a scrap conveyor, or wasting time later to manually remove large pieces of offal skeleton that clog the worktable. Good nesting software should consider cutting patterns that yield small-dimension offal pieces rather than an oversized skeleton. Incidentally, scrap metal can have a higher selling price when reduced to smaller pieces.

Beam-delivery System

By the sheer fact that optics in the beam-delivery system wear out progressively as dust, spatters, and other foreign agents contaminate their reflective or transmissive surfaces, it becomes difficult to achieve 100% repeatability in all cases at all times. Clean industrial mirror surfaces absorb at most 1% of laser power per mirror; whereas dirty mirrors can easily absorb at least twice as much, and do not focus the beam with the same efficiency as clean optics. With at least four optical elements in a CO_2 laser's beam-delivery system, the total absorption changes from 4–8% within less than 2,000 hours of cutting, which at 5,000-W rated output power amounts to a significant 200–400 W loss. Therefore, using cutting feed rates recommended by a machine builder with premium material and clean optics can be risky if these data were established at the fringe of the machine or process capability. It is more productive to cut at 90% of published optimum feed rate with 0% downtime due to cutting condition deterioration than to cut at an aggressive feed rate with constant tweaking interruptions needed to achieve acceptable cut quality. Smart organizations should record maximum new feed rates achieved after each PM and old feed rates achieved just before that PM. The median feed rate between new and old should be adopted as the new feed rate.

Laser-beam Mode

The surface reflectivity of cavity mirrors degrades with time as they are under chemical attack by laser gas mixtures in CO_2 lasers or atmospheric moisture and pollutants in YAG lasers. To compensate for reflectivity degradation in mirrors, more pumping energy is discharged into the cavity (radio frequency [RF] or DC excitation for CO_2 lasers and flash lamp or diode-laser-light power for YAG lasers). This compensation is adequate to achieve rated output power. However, it does not necessarily compensate for beam-quality deterioration because the optics are still dirty and the resonating laser beam has a slightly different mode structure than it did 2,000 hours of operation earlier. The laser-beam mode may lose some of its axis-symmetry and energy-distribution features. When this occurs, beam focusability and cutting results are altered and productivity suffers.

Impact of Methods

Feed Rate

Adopting conservative feed rates and using large-aperture nozzle design with long, straight sections increases tolerance to variations in incoming material types, properties, surface conditions, and waviness. Conservative feed rates avert downtime due to tweaking and fine adjustments of cutting parameters when consumables age and degrade before scheduled PM. The resulting repeatability increases confidence in the JIT capability of an operation.

Assist-gas Variation

Using O_2 as assist-gas when cutting thick plates results in higher feed rates due to the exothermic oxidation of metals. However, its use is at the expense of quality as oxide scales and dross have a tendency to develop on cut edges. To reduce or eliminate dross, non-chemically reacting gas, such as N_2 and inert gas such as Ar, perform satisfactorily at the expense of slower speed. The contamination of assist-gas by air through leaks or venturi-effect diffusion should be prevented to avoid out-of-specification cut-edge quality and a cutting speed that forces downtime for troubleshooting.

Focal Length

Focal lengths of 5 in. (127 mm) and shorter enable faster cutting feed rates for metal sheets thinner than 0.25 in. (6.4 mm) of mild steel and 0.187 in. (4.7 mm) of aluminum and stainless steel. For thicker gages, focal lengths of 7.50 in. (190.5 mm) and longer deliver better cut-edge quality than shorter focal lengths, without a significant feed-rate sacrifice, particularly when operating in pulse mode. Longer focal lengths result in focusing lenses positioned farther away from a kerf and less exposed to hot metallic particles recoiled from it. The choice of long focal lens is now common in industry for productivity gains. For some lasers with superior beam quality, that is an M^2 value of less than 2 for CO_2 lasers and less than 20 for YAG lasers, a 7.50 in. (190.5 mm) or higher lens can be used on thin to thick gages.

Impact of Man

Training and education enable operators to produce with minimum downtime. Knowledge specific to the laser-cutting process allows them to make the right decisions and understand and troubleshoot problems quicker. Ideally, identification of optimal setup parameters should be limited to calls to the right parameter library.

Quality assurance often relies on an operator's assessment of what a "good" acceptable cut is and is not. Training and experience are essential for this assessment, but not sufficient. Subjectivity implies poor reliability and repeatability because of personal judgment and evaluation. Quality-conscious organizations should develop references and clear guidelines to reduce the dependency on human sight, touch, hearing, and qualitative memory.

In many instances, edge-quality requirement changes depend on the application. These changes are not always conveyed to operators. So, operators may apply unnecessarily stringent quality specifications and thus unnecessarily slow overall productivity. With some challenging material, certain quality specifications may not be achievable unless special expensive measures are applied.

Scheduled preventive maintenance should be performed even when it seems that it may not be needed for a few more days or weeks. A short-term gain from skipping or delaying scheduled PM based on the absence of visible symptoms often results in longer and more expensive unscheduled repair downtime.

Impact of Mother Nature

High room humidity and hydrocarbon pollution can be harmful to the optics of the beam-delivery system, particularly in the sense that it traps minerals and hydrocarbons by condensing on the surfaces. Water used for cooling should be above room temperature to prevent condensation. Certain hydrocarbons absorb laser-beam energy and even diffuse the beam-energy distribution and propagation along the optical path, resulting in cutting-performance degradation. Ideally, the laser-cutting machine should be installed in an air-conditioned facility to avert an increase in downtime induced by atmospheric humidity and pollution. When this is not possible, precautions such as dry purging the enclosed beam-delivery system are helpful.

TOTAL PRODUCTIVE MAINTENANCE

Total productive maintenance (TPM) is a discipline geared toward maximizing manufacturing effectiveness. The aim is to maximize the synergies between operations and maintenance for an overall increase in productivity and profitability, by reducing waste and increasing capacity utilization. Maintenance costs represent between 15–40% of the total cost of typical manufactured goods, of which one third is wasted (Wireman 1991). The following are examples of waste.

- Poor documentation and communication lead to equipment under warranty getting repaired without claiming the cost from the equipment vendor.
- Poor process and programming knowledge does not spur optimization of a product design for a particular application. Piercing sequences in laser-cutting of thick plates are a prime example where piercing time can often be significantly reduced if better nesting capabilities are utilized.
- Poorly maintained equipment is more prone to unexpected failure and associated downtime, and increased utility cost. Dirty cavity mirrors, miscalibrated cavity-pressure gages, and inadequate cavity tuning force the power supplies of most industrial lasers operating in closed-loop control to increase the pumping mechanism power to output the commanded peak power. This means lesser overall efficiency of the laser-cutting machine.

Equipment Effectiveness

The performance of production equipment can be measured in terms of capacity utilization or, in TPM jargon, equipment effectiveness (E_E). E_E is the product of three efficiency-rate quantities.

$$E_E = A_R \times P_R \times Q_R \qquad (10\text{-}3)$$

where:

A_R = availability rate
P_R = performance rate
Q_R = quality rate

Any equipment can theoretically produce 100% defect-free parts during 100% of the total day, seven days a week, at 100% of the intended throughput rate. Such a condition would yield 100% E_E. The reality is, of course, slightly different as illustrated in *Figure 10-14*. World-class organizations should target at least 85% E_E.

Availability Rate

Starting from the total time in a given period and subtracting scheduled downtimes, a net available time (N_{AT}) can be obtained.

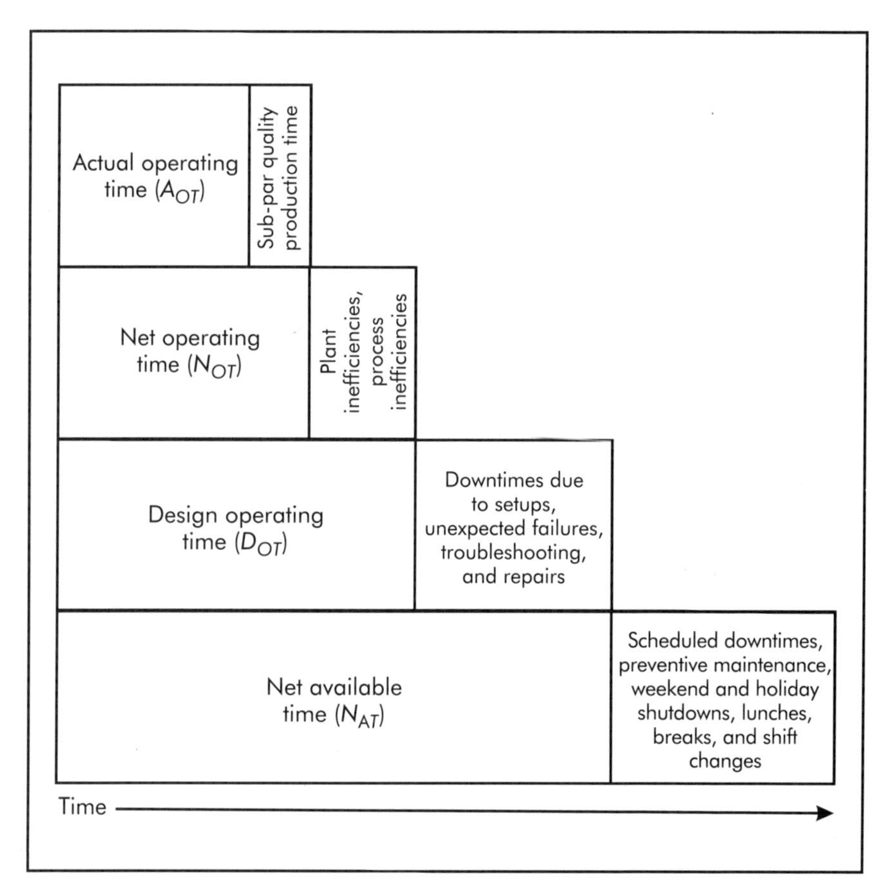

Figure 10-14. TPM measures equipment effectiveness: E_E ($E_E = (D_{OT}/N_{AT}) \times (N_{OT}/D_{OT}) \times A_{OT}/N_{OT}) = A_{OT}/N_{AT}$).

Scheduled downtimes occur during planned preventive maintenance, weekend and holiday shutdowns, lunches, breaks, and shift changes. From N_{AT}, downtimes due to setups, unexpected failures, troubleshooting, and repairs can be subtracted to obtain the design operating time (D_{OT}).

$$A_R = \frac{D_{OT}}{N_{AT}} \tag{10-4}$$

A world-class operation should target at least 90% availability.

Performance Rate

Machine manufacturers supply capability data in terms of processing speed and ideal cycle time (I_{CT}). Let the volume of input (V_{OI}) represent the number of parts run. The net operating time (N_{OT}) is a result of subtracting downtime due to plant inefficiencies (idling time, for example) and process inefficiencies (reduction in cutting speed, for example) from D_{OT}. The performance rate is defined by:

$$P_R = \frac{I_{CT} \times V_{OI}}{D_{OT}} = \frac{N_{OT}}{D_{OT}} \tag{10-5}$$

A world-class operation should target at least a 95% performance rate.

Quality Rate

The volume of output from a process can be obtained simply by subtracting the volume produced at sub-par quality standard (S_{QS}) from the V_{OI}. For example, a sheet that can produce ten parts due to optimized nesting, produces seven good parts, one sub-par quality part, and two defective parts. The customer will accept the seven good parts and the one sub-par quality part as all eight are still within specification. The customer will reject the two defective parts because they are out of specification. In this example, V_{OI} = 10 and S_{QS} = 3. The actual operating time (A_{OT}) is a result of subtracting the time to produce sub-par quality parts from N_{OT}. Q_R is defined by:

$$Q_R = \frac{V_{OI} - S_{QS}}{V_{OI}} = \frac{A_{OT}}{N_{OT}} \tag{10-6}$$

A world-class operation should target at least a 99% quality rate, and according to Equation 10-3, an E_E of at least 90% × 95% × 99% = 85%. If the quality rate, performance rate, and availability rate are measured in terms of sigma as will be elaborated on in Chapter 13, then a six-sigma target would mean that each of these rates would be at 99.9997%. This would yield a longer-term target of E_E = 99.9997% × 99.9997% × 99.9997% = 99.9991%.

TPM is important to adopt for laser cutting as it emphasizes the need for synergy between operation and maintenance. It also removes maintenance from isolation as a necessary and costly evil and integrates it within an overall discipline aimed at reducing waste and increasing productivity and profitability.

REFERENCES

Kugler, Thomas R. 2001. "Nd:YAG Lasers." *LIA Handbook of Laser Material Processing*, pp. 37-44. John F. Ready and Dave Farson, eds. Orlando, FL: Laser Institute of America.

Mombo Caristan, J. C., Penn, Wayne, Mudiam, Sai, and Karube, N. 1999. "High-speed High-power Laser-blank Cutting and Welding." International Congress on Applications of Lasers and Electro-Optics (ICALEO), San Diego, CA. Orlando, FL: Laser Institute of America.

Wireman, Terry. 1991. *Total Productive Maintenance: An American Approach*. New York: Industrial Press.

Zediker, M.S., Haake, M., and Cook, C. M. 2000. "Laser-diode Material-processing System." International Congress on Applications of Lasers and Electro-Optics (ICALEO), pp. D1-8. Orlando, FL: Laser Institute of America.

eleven

Profitability

"What we need to do is learn to work in the system, by which I mean that everybody, every team, every platform, every division, every component is there not for individual competitive profit or recognition, but for contribution to the system as a whole on a win-win basis."

—W. Edwards Deming

INTRODUCTION

For end-users, profitability is driven by sales and hinges on the bottom-line cost of operations, including investments in equipment, facilities, supplies, utilities, material, labor, preventive maintenance, and repair. The following sections attempt to break down and itemize principal cost considerations in the profitability equation. These considerations can be used, regardless of the company, as a basis to build a business case or identify areas for improvement. Business cases differ specifically from company to company due to differences in accounting methods and labor structure, levels of automation, environmental laws, and tax laws. Several operating costs analysis examples can be found in the literature (Bell 2000; Julian 2002).

Despite its centerpiece status, a laser resonator is only about 15–40% of the total price of an industrial system for laser cutting of metals, depending on the level of automation. The rest of the price is distributed among a beam-delivery system, gas-delivery system, motion system, main machine-base frame, numerical controller, electrical cabinets, gas filter, scrap conveyor system, material-handling and positioning system, software development, design, engineering, and installation. For a complete return estimation, add complementary capital expenses such as a foundation, electrical main and secondary distribution, floor space for equipment and storage of raw material, and work-in-process and finished product packaging and shipment.

This chapter will focus only on equipment procurement, maintenance and repair cost, and utility costs for electricity, gas, water, compressed air, telecommunications, and scrap and waste costs.

FEASIBILITY AND DEVELOPMENT

Before deciding on a substantial investment in a laser-cutting machine, it is important to have an indication of how different equipment performs with the majority of the materials to be cut. In that regard, rather than chasing the elusive machine that can do it all, the 80/20 rule can be applied. Among an array of potential cutting applications, identify the top 20% of applications that contribute to 80% of either revenues or profit margin. Feasibility and development efforts for the top 20% of applications should yield the best engineering, manufacturing, and marketing criteria for the procurement specification.

In most cases, feasibility is addressed by checking cutting quality against arbitrary standards based on a comparison with conventional cutting methods or those set by a machine builder. However, this is mostly done in laboratory settings, by expert applications engineers, with beam-delivery designs, materials, and environmental conditions that may not necessarily represent the intended application. Preferably, each machine builder or supplier under consideration will demonstrate cutting performance with customer-supplied material on a "real world" machine or in conditions emulating a real-world machine and its environment. The beam-delivery system and optical-path length should be similar to that of the application. The following test can be performed:

1. Cut at the rated maximum thickness of mild steel with O_2 assist-gas, stainless steel with N_2 assist-gas, and aluminum with N_2 or air assist-gas on the machine. Feed rate becomes a second-priority, critical-to-quality parameter.
2. Cut at rated feed rate for 0.04-in. (1.0-mm) thick mild steel, stainless steel, and aluminum with N_2 assist-gas. Generally, cut-edge quality becomes a second priority to maximum cutting-speed capability.

A test cutting profile should exhibit certain features that can reveal the capabilities and limitations of machine performance. For example, a kerf cut may be used to reference kerf-width measurement and piercing time. Round circles can be chosen to verify the accuracy of the diameter, contour, pitch, and number of holes-per-minute cutting-speed capability. Small circles (diameter smaller than material thickness) represent benchmarking tests to rank small-feature cutting capability, particularly for thick gages. Corner angles, including acute angles smaller than 45°, must be included to confirm processing capability for sharp corner-angle features. *Figure 11-1* displays an example of a cut sample exhibiting 10 different test features.

Chapter 3 details how surface conditions, such as rust and scaling, have a strong impact on cut quality. Processing capabilities can vary with alloying compounds such as carbon, magnesium, silicon, manganese, and others. It is advisable to not only process the optimum material used by a machine builder, but to also confirm capability on the typical material quality processed at the end-user's site.

In some cases, an end-user may want short-run production to evaluate C_{pk} capability and overall machine behavior over entire shifts. A test of machine flexibility over a range of material with various setups should also be part of the evaluation process.

PROCUREMENT

Machine distributors or machine builders will quote systems itemizing different features. It is incumbent upon the buyer to sort through the items from different quotes and establish comparison

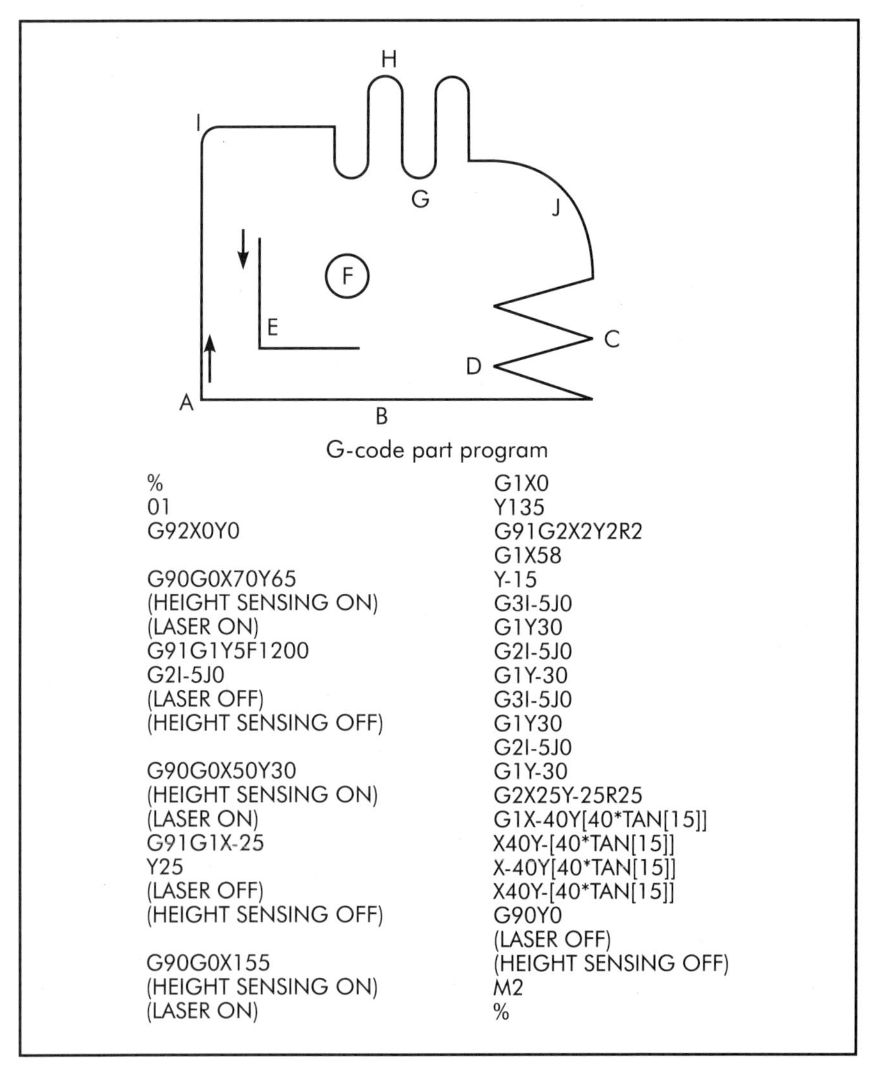

Figure 11-1. Test cutting sample: (A) 90° corner angle; (B) periphery segments of about 5.9 in. (150 mm) in length; (C) acute angle fin of 15° or less; (D) acute angle of 15° or less on internal periphery; (E) piercing and kerf in two directions; (F) small circle with radius of 0.2 in. (5 mm) or less; (G) small radius of 0.2 in. (5 mm) or less on internal periphery; (H) small radius fin of 0.2 in. (5 mm) or less; (I) small radius corner of 0.08 in. (2.0 mm) or less; (J) large radius corner of 1 in. (25 mm) or less. The practical envelope dimensions and values of small radii and acute angles can vary with material thickness. The thinner the sheet, the smaller the allowable radii, angles, and envelope dimensions.

criteria to help navigate through the maze of features and advantages versus disadvantages. Specifications can be established for floor space, ruggedness to sustain material-handling collisions with heavy-duty machinery, material weight and envelope, scrap-removal rate and mechanism with/without shredder, and the operator control station's design and position.

The first step is to establish the package with the highest value. Value can be measured by an index ratio of the customer's critical-to-quality (CTQ) ranking over price. Establish comparative scales for a list of ranked CTQ items, such as total initial price, financing availability, operation cost estimates (utilities, consumables, maintenance and repair, and training), prerequisites, accessories costs, preventive-maintenance downtime estimates, service response time, net floor space, weight, field serviceability, IT communication capability, and safety.

In a second step, bids are collected per the comparative scales for each CTQ item from the vendor's information and benchmarking intelligence. A third step consists of analyzing the bids and establishing vendor or quotation ranking based on the weight factor for each CTQ item. Methods for overall ranking vary from simple total compilation to more sophisticated average and spread analysis.

COST OF OWNERSHIP

Development Costs

The end-user's financial responsibility is reduced to the cost to supply specific material for testing and the corresponding freight charges, as well as travel and lodging expenses associated with purchasing and engineering functions. Whenever possible, cutting tests should be conducted on a machine similar to the one to be purchased.

Capital Expenses

The initial expenditure is for the laser-cutting equipment and its accessories such as a water chiller, gas-delivery system, and an air filter. Other fixed expenses include facility requirements such as main and secondary distribution for electrical power, gas, water, information systems and telecommunications; foundation work; air conditioning when specified; floor-space expansion; accessories; storage of raw material, work-in-process, and finished goods; and receiving, packaging, and shipping stations.

Some manufacturers may choose to depreciate equipment and facility assets over several years. In such accounting methods, leveraged expense-based costs, overhead, and general and administrative labor costs are considered for pricing purposes only, and are usually not rolled into hourly running costs. Typically, in the United States in the year 2000, laser-cutting subcontracted work could be priced between $150–250/hour depending on the volume of the order and technical specifics.

Operating Costs

Besides the variable cost of labor, operating costs include consumables and maintenance and repair costs. These costs can be categorized into cutting consumables and non-cutting consumables.

Non-cutting consumables describe all hardware and utilities necessary to enable the equipment and accessories to function properly and on command. They include utilities such as lasing gas, electricity, water, and maintenance items such as the laser resonator's internal optics, O-rings, machine-drive lubrication, compressed air, oil and air filters, and the workpiece support fixture. Higher laser powers generally yield higher hourly operating costs of non-cutting consumables.

Cutting consumables describe hardware and utilities necessary to perform laser-cutting processing. They include all optics of the beam-delivery system downstream of the output-coupler mirror, from the phase-retarder polarization mirror to the focusing lens and optional windows, cutting-nozzle tips, utilities such as assist-gas and mist/water, and electrical power at rated output during processing. Optic surfaces can be cleaned of some spatters, contaminants, and burns and reused several times until they are deemed unworthy of further cleaning and discarded. The life of a ZnSe focusing lens, for example, can vary across a large span of time, typically between 300–1,000 hours, depending on the material being processed, the skills of the operators and maintenance crew, the laser power, and the machine's design. Nozzle tips can last up to 300 hours. Cavity-mirror life span typically extends from 500 hours in the worst applications and operating conditions to 3,000 hours in nominal operation conditions. *Figure 11-2* compares the typical cost per hour for cutting and non-cutting consumables at two different power levels and for four different applications. Cutting consumable costs seem to be overwhelmingly under the influence of assist-gas cost. A doubling of laser power increases the cost per hour by 30–40% to counterbalance the increase in throughput and cut quality.

Figures 11-3 to *11-6* confirm the predominance of assist-gas cost. They provide a revealing breakdown of relative operating cost per component for the four applications of *Figure 11-2*. Although

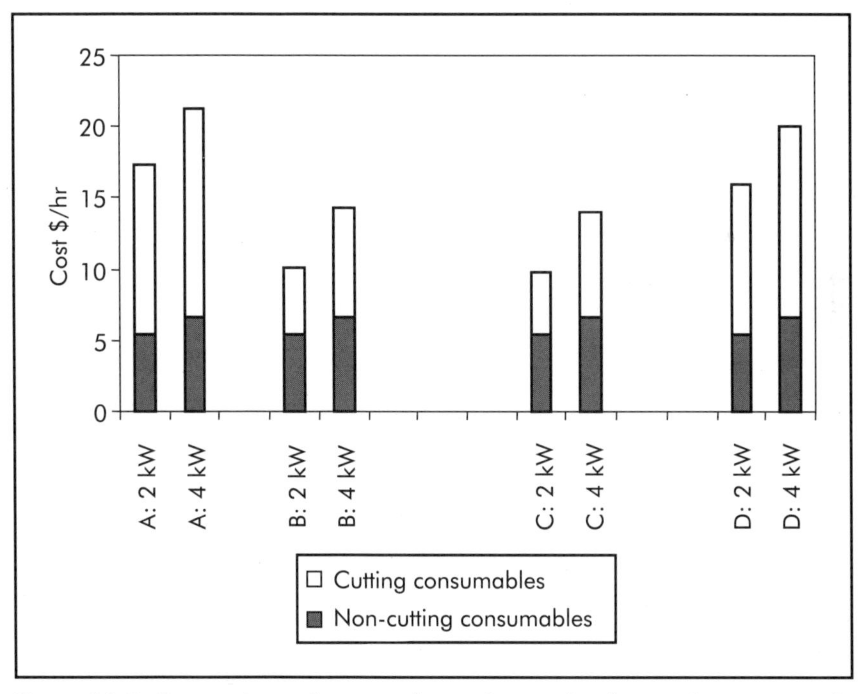

Figure 11-2. Comparison of cost per hour of operation for two laser powers in four different applications: (A) 0.04-in. (1.0-mm) mild steel with 147 psi (10 bar) N_2 assist-gas; (B) 0.50-in. (12.5-mm) mild steel with 7.5 psi (0.5 bar) O_2 assist-gas; (C) 0.250-in. (6.35-mm) aluminum with 118 psi (8 bar) air assist-gas; (D) 0.250-in. (6.35-mm) stainless steel with 118 psi (8 bar) N_2 assist-gas.

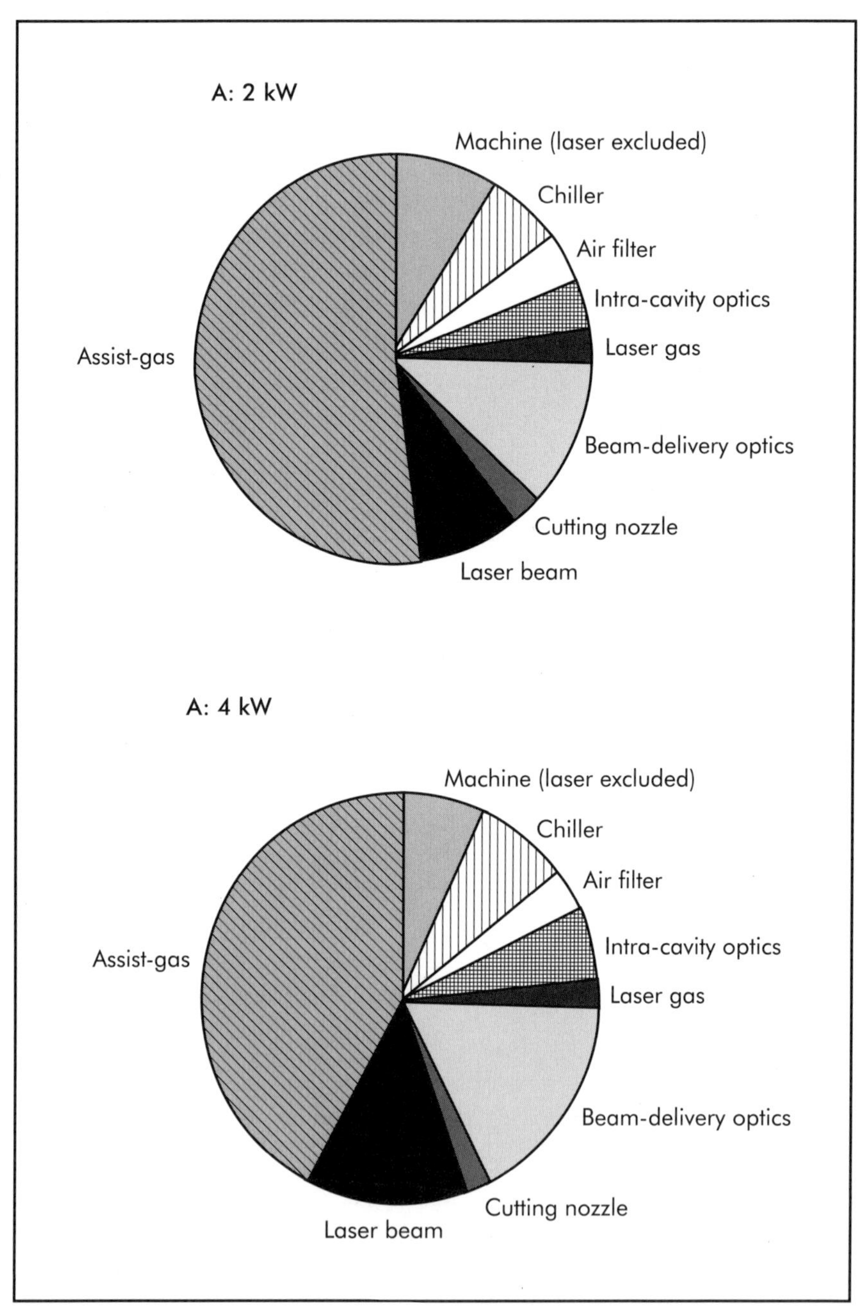

Figure 11-3. Relative cost distribution for laser cutting 0.04-in. (1.0-mm) mild steel with 147 psi (10 bar) of N_2 assist-gas.

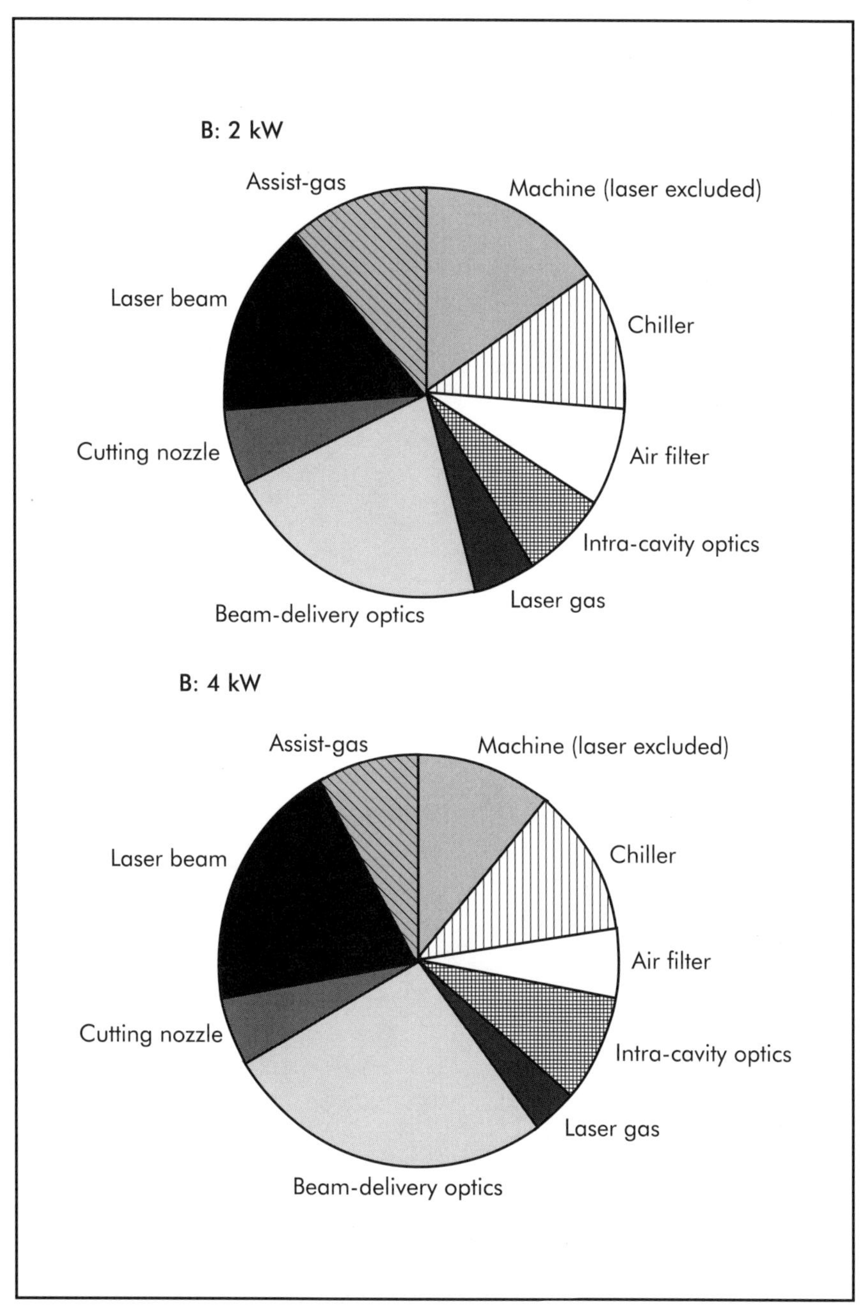

Figure 11-4. Relative cost distribution for laser cutting 0.49-in. (12.5-mm) mild steel with 7.5 psi (0.5 bar) O_2 assist-gas.

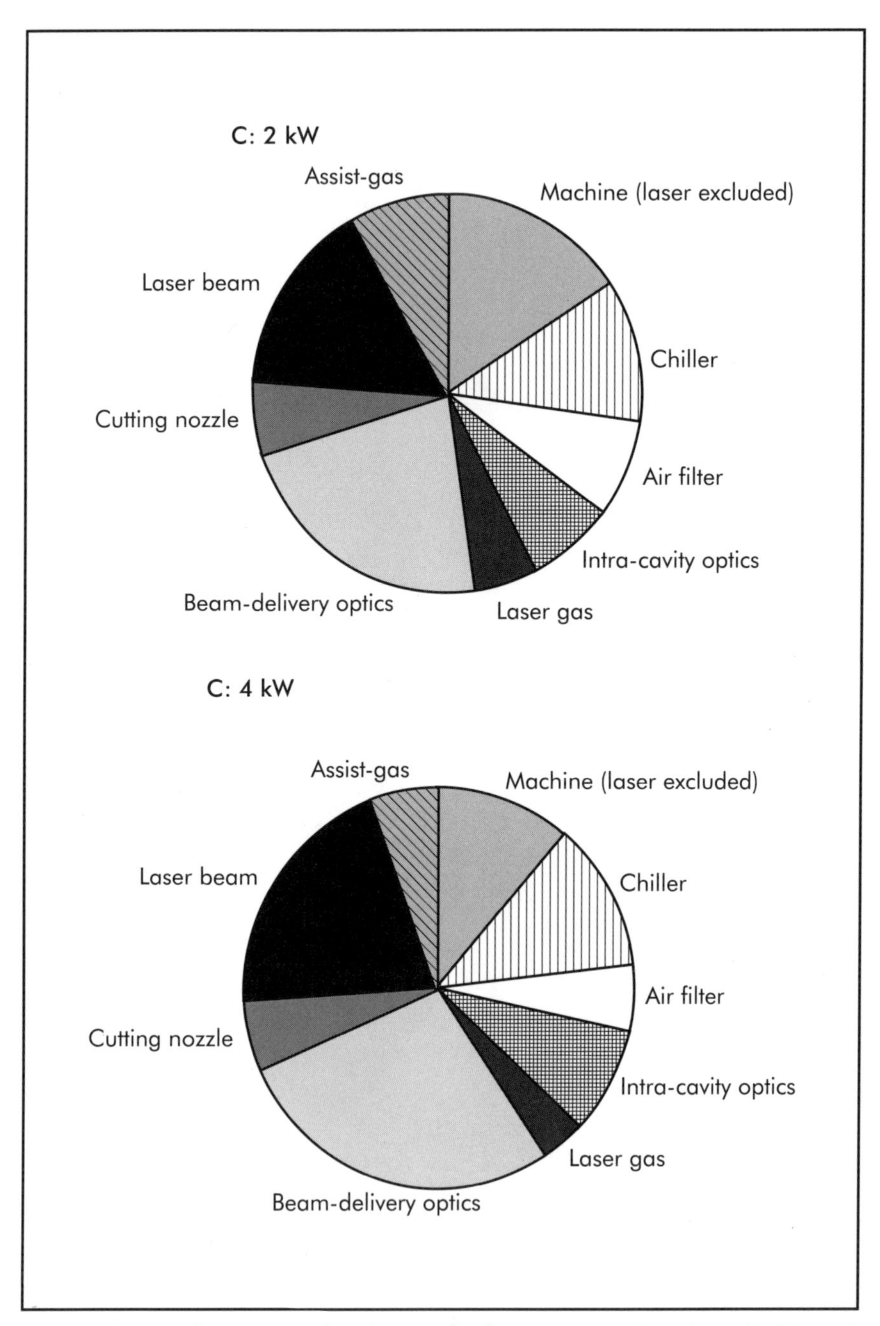

Figure 11-5. Relative cost distribution for laser cutting 0.250-in. (6.35-mm) aluminum with 118 psi (8 bar) air assist-gas.

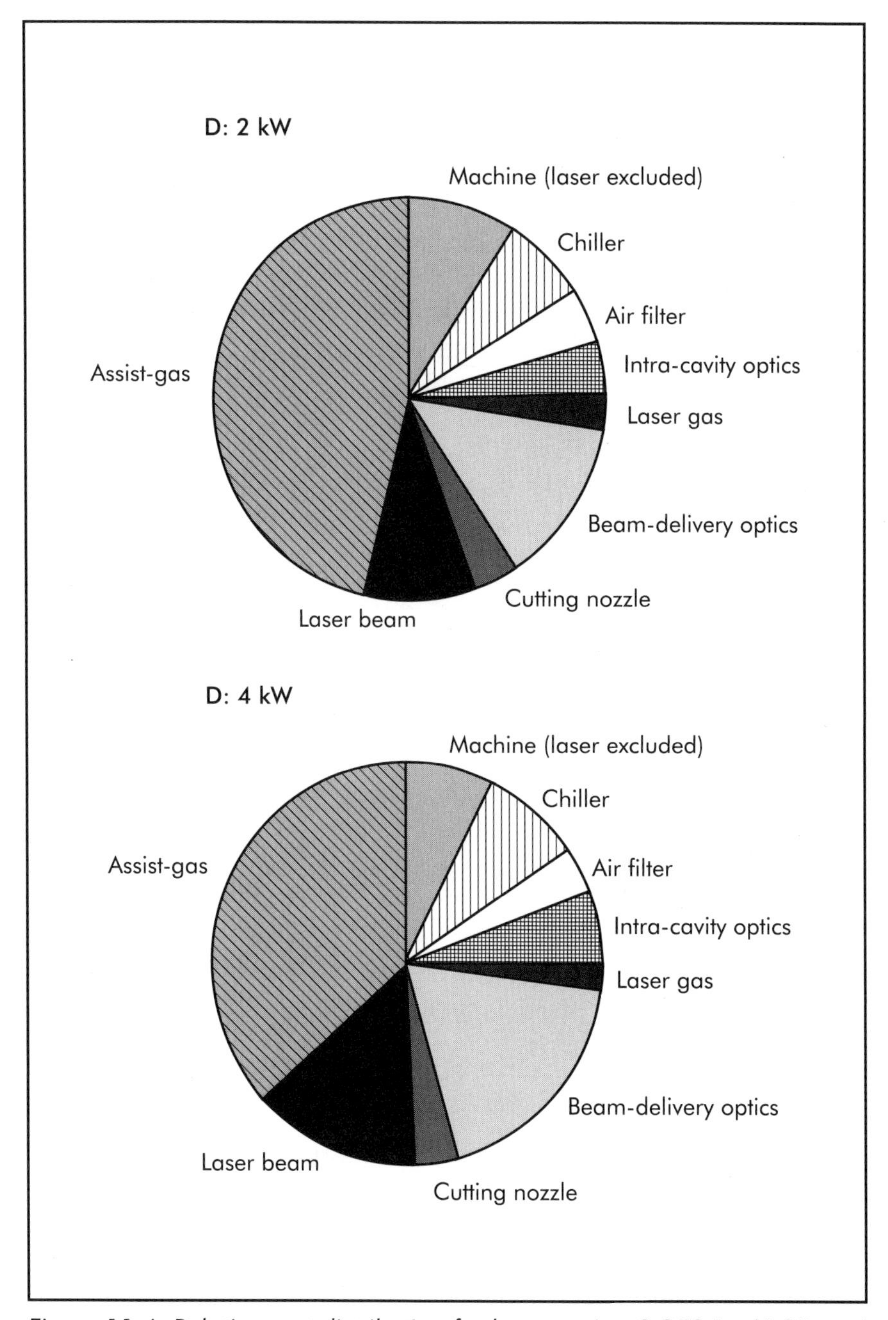

Figure 11-6. Relative cost distribution for laser cutting 0.250-in. (6.35-mm) stainless steel with 118 psi (8 bar) N_2 assist-gas.

non-cutting consumables do not generally change with the application, there are some exceptions. For example, cutting of highly reflective material, such as aluminum, can increase cavity optics consumables' cost by shortening their life.

The cost of a laser-cutting system increases with rated output power and so does the cost/hour to run the operation. The increase in operation cost per hour is not directly proportional to the increase in power. While a 4-kW laser offers twice as much heat as a 2-kW laser, cost per hour increases only 20–40%, depending on the application. High-pressure N_2 cutting will result in significantly higher consumable cost than low-pressure O_2 assist-gas or air assist-gas cutting. With high-pressure N_2 cutting, assist-gas cost approaches 50% of the total operation costs (labor not included). Assuming beam ON time of 75%, cutting consumables account for 50% of operating costs when processing with O_2 or air versus close to 70% when processing with high-pressure nitrogen.

Beam-delivery optics and intra-cavity optics consumables appear to be the second and third highest-cost consumables, respectively. When cutting thin gage with high pressure N_2, the cutting feed rate is directly proportional to the laser power and, therefore, throughput increases in almost similar proportions. When cutting thick-gage stainless steel with high-pressure nitrogen, the feed rate increases only modestly with each kW of power increase, while corresponding operating costs increase by close to 40%.

REFERENCES

Bell, David. 2000, November. "True Cost with Cutting with a CO_2 Laser." Fabtech International, Session 208, Cleveland, OH. Dearborn, MI: Society of Manufacturing Engineers.

Julian, Al. 2002, June. "Comparative Economics of Thermal Cutting Technologies." Technical Forum. Advanced Thermal Processing of Metal Sheets and Plates: Cutting, Welding, and Inspection. The Ohio State University, Columbus, OH. Dearborn, MI: Association for Forming and Fabricating Technologies of the Society of Manufacturing Engineers.

Safety and Environment

"The dying of an Elder is like a library that burns."

—Amadou H. Diop

INTRODUCTION

The safety information in this chapter offers general guidance and is not a substitute for a safety program specific to each individual laser-cutting operation and environment. Although laser cutting of metals has one of the best safety records of all metal fabrication processes, its biggest danger remains complacency. A safe operation takes a sustained effort by all employees in a workplace to maintain proper safety procedures at all times. The bibliography at the back of this chapter lists several safety standards, certifications, and regulation documents that are additional sources of information.

SAFETY PRECAUTIONS

In the early 1980s, it was estimated that 180,000–600,000 workers were routinely involved with laser devices (OSHA 1991). This estimate was predicted to jump to 500,000–1,000,000 by the mid-1990s. Although no known recent study confirming this forecast has come to the attention of the author of this book, it can be conservatively claimed that these numbers have probably been surpassed, especially due to the economic boom of the past decade, including medical applications. This growing number of laser-exposed workers increases the risk of injury unless proper safety guidelines are enforced and workers are educated in laser safety. It is important to protect our environment as well. Safety concepts can be extended to protect the communities outside the plant operation.

Clothing

Even though this book is focused on laser metal processing, the process also operates within traditional metalworking environments. As such, standard safety precautions, such as protective clothing, should be used:

- leather gloves for hand protection when handling sheet metal; and
- safety boots with steel toes.

Wool and cotton clothing offers better protection against burning spatters than synthetics such as nylon, rayon, and polyester (Jeffus 1993). Synthetic materials burn easily and produce hot ash that sticks to the skin and can produce severe burns—from first degree burns that mildly affect the epidermis to third degree burns that also destroy the dermis and subcutaneous layers of tissue (see *Figure 12-1*). A first-degree burn mildly affects the skin surface (epidermis) and can be initially treated with cold-water compresses. A second-degree burn severely damages the epidermis with blisters or breaks and the dermis may be exposed. The temperature of the skin must be reduced as soon as possible with, for example, cold-water compresses (no ice) to avoid more blisters and breaks. A sterile bandage helps prevent infection. A third-degree burn damages the skin as deep as through the subcutaneous layers, destroying hair and blood vessels. Pain may not be felt for some time period after destruction of some nerve endings. In all cases, immediate medical attention may be necessary.

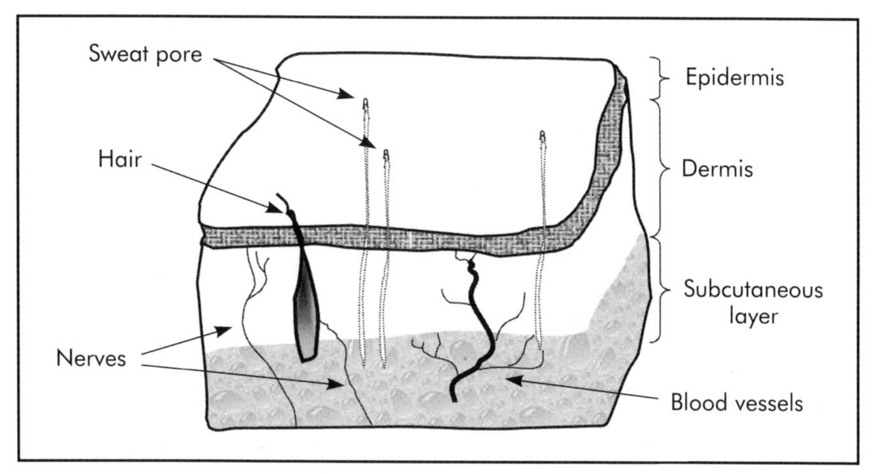

Figure 12-1. Human skin and its layers.

Noise

Varying with local OSHA regulations, noise protection warrants wearing ear plugs whenever the time-averaged decibel level in the plant exceeds about 85 decibels in a shift, or if occasional 140-decibel or higher noise spikes are generated in one shift. Laser-cutting systems generally produce much less than 85 decibels, contrary to punch-press systems. The noisiest components are water chillers and air filters.

Machinery

Common machinery safety engineering and procedural regulations apply, such as European Community (CE) or Underwriters' Laboratories (UL) marking, safety mats, safety curtains, safety interlocks and, very important for laser safety, labeling.

Fire Protection

The right type of fire extinguishers (types A through D) should be easily accessible at clearly visible locations and inspected periodically. Some water sprinklers installed overhead risk destroying electrical devices such as lasers, while extinguishing a fire elsewhere.

Flammable compounds, such as oil and alcohol, are to be stored in a special certified yellow safety cabinet. Gas cylinders must be chained to prevent them from being accidentally knocked over. Oxygen and fuel-gas cylinders or flammable compounds must be stored separately from one other by at least 20 ft (6 m) or by a 5-ft (1.5-m) high minimum separation wall.

Eye and Skin Protection

The Laser Institute of America (LIA) is the publisher of the ANSI Z136.1 standard, "The Safe Use of Lasers" (Laser Institute of America 2000). It recommends that any U.S.-based operation involving lasers for metal cutting hire or train a laser safety officer who is present on site. "The laser safety officer shall have responsibility and authority to monitor and enforce the control of laser hazards." In the standard, lasers and laser systems fall into one of four main classes based on maximum accessible emission limits and maximum permissible exposure limits. Maximum permissible exposure (MPE), measured in J/cm^2, represents a level of laser radiation to which a person may be exposed without hazardous effects or adverse biological changes to the eyes or skin. It varies with wavelength and time of exposure. Refer to ANSI Z136.1 for MPE tables. LIA also provides further in-depth laser safety information, training, and guidelines.

Industrial lasers for metal-cutting systems with open beams fall in the class-four category of lasers, which requires specific engineering, administrative, and procedural control measures based on accessible emission limits. One of the responsibilities of the laser safety officer is to be aware of or determine the nominal hazard zones illustrated in *Figure 12-2*. A nominal hazard zone describes the space within which the level of direct, reflected, or scattered radiation exceeds the applicable maximum permissible exposure limit. A thorough experimental risk analysis (Heberer 2000) reveals the presence of laser stray-energy hot spots. Laser paper indicates places with potentially hazardous diffuse reflections and stray energy, which could not have been known otherwise.

It should be common sense and common knowledge that a laser beam should never be looked at with direct exposure to the eyes. Because of its coherence and monochromaticity, a laser beam can be focused by the human eye lens to a tiny spot on the retina. This can induce possible permanent damage even at incident power densities well below 0.1 W/cm^2. Permanent eye damage can range from loss of blue vision by nonthermal photochemical retinal injury to retinal burning beyond recovery and total vision loss. This

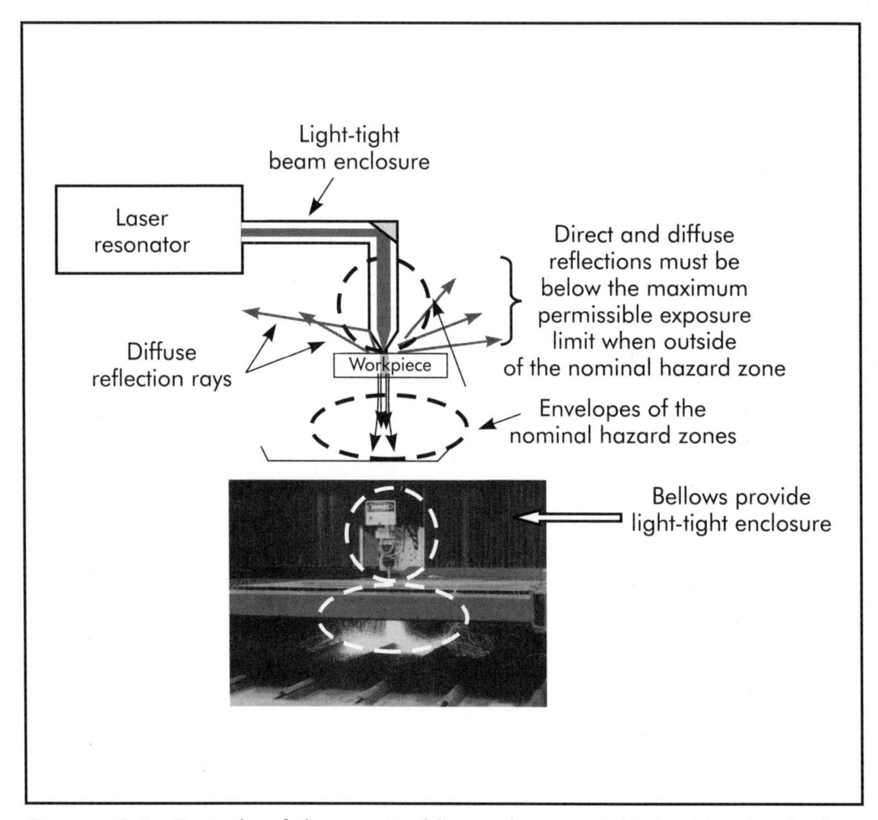

Figure 12-2. Outside of the nominal hazard zones delimited by the dashed lines, scattered radiation has an energy density below the applicable maximum permissible exposure limit. (Courtesy Rofin-Sinar, Inc.)

makes even stray reflections of multi-kilowatt lasers dangerous to the eyes, let alone direct exposure. Eye protection must be worn in a laser shop at all times.

CO_2 laser radiation at 10.6 μm wavelength is effectively absorbed by most polycarbonate plastics. Worn at all times, ANSI-approved, clear-plastic safety goggles with side shields provide eye protection for CO_2 laser operations. More expensive goggles with KG-3 filter glass give even better protection. In facilities with CO_2 laser-cutting system installations, workers and visitors must wear safety goggles at all times. Several degrees of enclosures are nevertheless offered, from a totally open laser-cutting machine to an open ceiling or total enclosure as illustrated in *Figure 12-3*.

None of the previously mentioned goggles for CO_2 laser beams are sufficient to absorb Nd:YAG laser radiation. YAG laser eye protection requires special multilayer dark safety goggles to stop the shorter 1.06-μm radiation. Such goggles are significantly more expensive than standard clear-plastic goggles. They also reduce the clarity of vision of the workers who wear them. Nd:YAG laser-cutting machines generally have a complete light-tight enclosure around them, enabling workers not to need to wear the special dark safety goggles outside of the enclosure.

Most industrial laser systems for metal cutting contain a small He-Ne laser or a diode laser emitting a visible red (about 0.63 μm wavelength) laser beam aligned with the main industrial laser beam. These small lasers have only a few milliwatts of power distributed over a cross-section of diameter reaching about 0.25 in. (6.5 mm). Such visible laser beams are not stopped by clear-plastic goggles. They too can be focused in a tiny spot beyond the cornea, which can result in burning the retina and vision loss (see *Figure 12-4*).

Fumes and Dust

Fume and dust accumulation over several days, weeks, months, or years could become hazardous to worker health. Iron, aluminum, and other metals and their alloying components contained

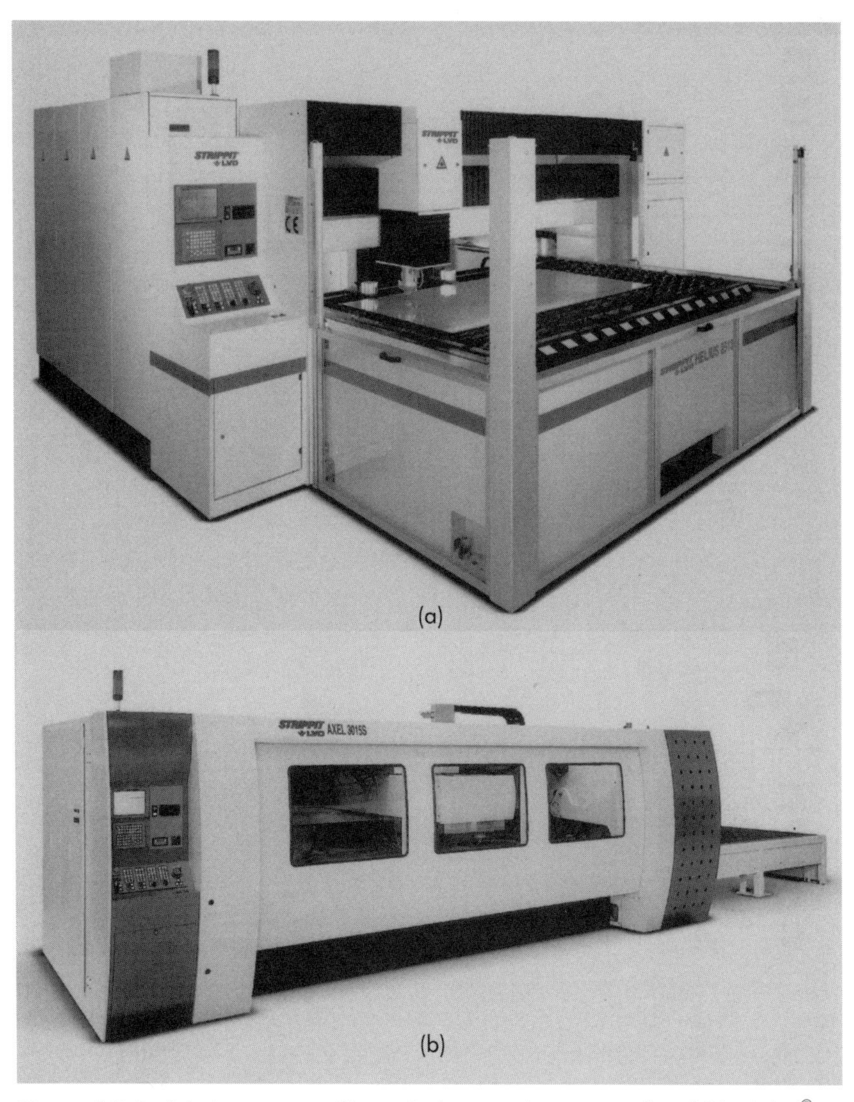

Figure 12-3. (a) An open-ceiling window enclosure made of Plexiglas® or lexane provides additional safety from beam reflections around the perimeter of the work envelope. The nominal hazard zone lays within this perimeter. (b) Total enclosure provides maximum protection from CO_2 laser beams. Both enclosures are retractable to enable access for load/unload, setup, and maintenance. (Courtesy Strippit/LVD)

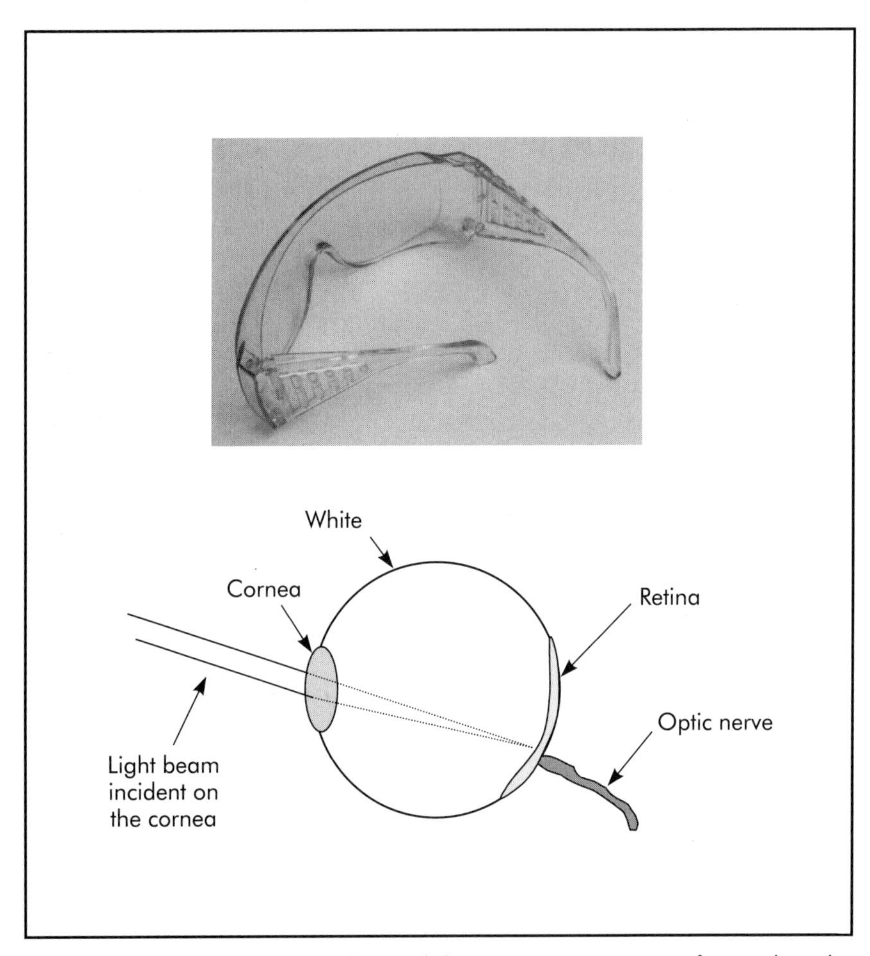

Figure 12-4. The human eye: beyond the cornea, images are focused on the retina; however, coherent monochromatic light from visible and YAG lasers can focus very efficiently into a hazardous high-power-density spot on the retina. CO_2 laser wavelengths are absorbed by the cornea and can eventually lead to vision loss.

in fumes and dust must be adequately extracted and collected in proper containers by an air-filter suction system integrated with the cutting head. These containers must be properly disposed of in accordance with local safety, health, and environmental regulations. Nonmetal fumes and dusts are generally at least as toxic as metal ones. They include oil for lubrication and organic coatings for protecting some material surfaces against corrosion and scratches. Material safety data sheets (MSDS) for organic coatings must be reviewed to verify that, when burning from a laser cut, they will not release toxic by-products such as hydrogen chloride and cyanide.

Acrylic mode burns release an obnoxious-smelling toxic fume. It is recommended to perform acrylic mode burns in a well-ventilated area and/or use a local air-suction-filter element to collect fumes and prevent them from propagating inside a facility.

OTHER HAZARDS

Most lethal accidents that occur in laser-equipped installations are related to electrocution. The presence of high voltage calls for handling only by qualified electrical maintenance engineers who are also trained on laser material processing.

Although CO_2 laser focusing lenses look like candies, they are made of a poisonous substance, zinc selenide (ZnSe), which should not be put in the mouth.

Any chemical compound used for optics cleaning must be dealt with according to recommendations from its MSDS sheet.

REFERENCES

Bell, David. 2000, November. "True Cost with Cutting with a CO_2 Laser." Fabtech International, Session 208, Cleveland, OH. Dearborn, MI: Society of Manufacturing Engineers.

Heberer, Erwin Martin. 1993. "Risk Analysis for Laser Guards in the Automotive Industry." International Congress on Applications of Lasers and Electro-Optics (ICALEO), pp. F52-to F61. Orlando, FL: Laser Institute of America.

Jeffus, Larry. 1993. *Welding Principles and Applications*, Fourth Edition. New York: Delmar Publishers.

Laser Institute of America. 2000. ANSI Z136.1. "Safe Use of Lasers." Orlando, FL: Laser Institute of America (www.laserinstitute.org)/ American National Standards Institute (ANSI).

Occupational Safety and Health Administration (OSHA). 1991. "Guidelines for Laser Safety and Hazard Assessment." Washington, DC: Occupational Safety and Health Administration.

BIBLIOGRAPHY

American National Standards Institute (ANSI). ANSI B11.21. 1997. "Machine Tools Using Lasers for Processing Materials—Safety Requirements for Design, Construction, Care, and Use." Washington, DC: American National Standards Institute/Association for Manufacturing Technology (AMT).

Center for Devices and Radiological Health (CDRH) of the U.S. Food and Drug Administration (FDA). 2003. 21 CFR 1040. Code of Federal Regulations. "Standard for Laser Radiation Emission Machine." Washington, DC: CDRH/FDA.

International Electrotechnical Commission (IEC)/International Organization for Standardization (ISO). 1993. IEC TC 172/SC 9, ISO 11252. "Lasers and Laser-related Equipment—Laser Devices—Minimum Requirements for Documentation." Geneva, Switzerland: International Electrotechnical Commission (IEC).

——. 1993. IEC TC 172/SC 9, ISO 11553 (EN 12626). "Safety of Machine—Laser Processing Machines—Safety Requirements." Geneva, Switzerland: International Electrotechnical Commission (IEC).

——. 2001. IEC TC 76, IEC 60825. "Safety of Laser Products." Geneva, Switzerland: International Electrotechnical Commission (IEC).

——. 2003. ISO TC 44, ISO 15616. "Acceptance Tests for CO_2 Laser-beam Machines for Welding & Cutting." Geneva, Switzerland: International Electrotechnical Commission (IEC).

Laser Institute of America (LIA). "Guide for the Selection of Laser Eye Protection." Orlando, FL: Laser Institute of America.

——. Laser Safety Officer Certification. Orlando, FL: Laser Institute of America.

Occupational Safety and Health Administration (OSHA). 1991. "Guidelines for Laser Safety and Hazard Assessment." PUB 8-1.7. Washington, DC: Occupational Safety and Health Administration.

thirteen

The Six-sigma Approach

"Laws and institutions are constantly tending to gravitate. Like clocks, they must be occasionally cleansed, wound up, and set to true time."

—Henry Ward Beecher

INTRODUCTION

In an ideal world, a quality operation serves quality customers with quality employees and quality processes. Realistically, the generic term "quality" does not have the same perceived meaning in the three aforementioned uses of the word. The manufacturing world has evolved from the monochromatic days of the black Ford Model T with go/no-go quality gages along the chain, to sophisticated multivariate process controls and analysis in an evolving technological and competitive environment. There must be a holistic strategy for decision making encompassing more than just product specifications. Decisions must also satisfy operation productivity, conform to environmental regulations and safety and occupational constraints, and lead to profit.

Dr. Genichi Taguchi attempted to develop an advanced concept of quality that extends beyond engineering to economics by defining quality in terms of quantifiable loss to society, particularly loss due to variations in product performance (Ross 1988; Wadsworth 1990). This concept of quality can be extended to include performance of administrative tasks, sales, purchasing, and logistics—all activities whether commercial, administrative, or technical, which take away from or contribute to value in an organization.

Six Sigma^{SM} is a service mark registered by Motorola, Inc. It encompasses a quality methodology aimed at continuously improving outputs based on criteria set by customers. Customers can be external recipients of products as well as intermediate users internal to an organization. Products can come in any combination of hardware, software, and services. Outputs are generally chosen as specific key critical specifications within the five outputs listed in the fishbone diagram of *Figure P-1*—environment, safety, quality, productivity, and profitability.

Out-of-control processes sooner or later yield out-of-specification output, which is a general definition for defective product. A six-sigma methodology primarily aims to reduce the variation of key process parameters, thereby reducing the number of defects per product unit. What makes the six-sigma methodology appealing to the corporate world is that the end result translates macroscopically but directly into tangible financial savings by improving capacity and productivity while reducing the cost of poor quality. What slows down its propagation is the perceived ambiguity of the methodology and the uncertainty of its scientific validation. In the following sections, an effort is made to shed more light on this powerful tool and clarify the methodology.

THE ROOT OF SIX SIGMA

In the absence of special causes, random events tend to be solely influenced by nature in a way that can be modeled after a well-known statistical function called Gaussian or "normal" distribution:

$$f(x) = \frac{1}{\sigma\sqrt{2\pi}}\, e^{-\frac{1}{2}\left(\frac{x-\mu}{\sigma}\right)^2} \quad (13\text{-}1)$$

where:

x = value of a critical output variable
σ = a positive number called standard deviation for x; that is, a characteristic deviation on either side from the mean μ, within which 68.3% majority of outputs x fall
μ = the average value taken by output x

This is also called the "bell-shaped-curve" function for obvious reasons explicit in *Figure 13-1*. The function is normalized because, regardless of the values of σ and μ, its integration for x, varying from $+\infty$ to $-\infty$, is equal to 1, or in statistical terms, 100%. In other words, function $f(x)$ represents the statistical occurrence distribution for this critical output to have the exact value x. The

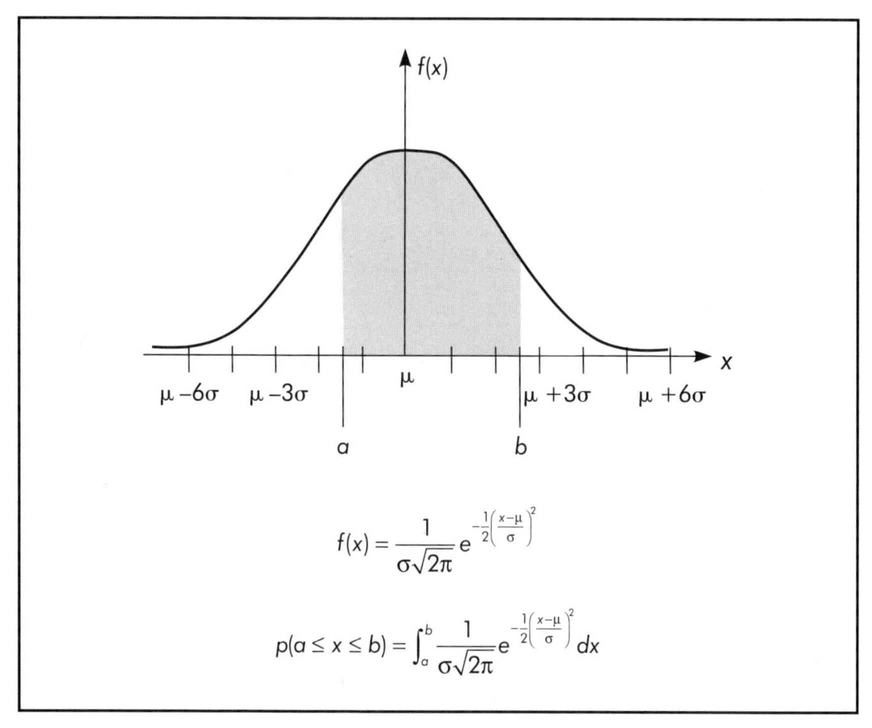

Figure 13-1. In most processes, the statistical occurrence of event x can be approximately represented by the well-known function f(x). The shaded area under the curve represents the probability, P(a ≤ x ≤ b), to have output x take value between a and b.

probability for this critical output to have a value x, such that $a \leq x \leq b$, is given by:

$$P(a \leq x \leq b) = \int_a^b \frac{1}{\sigma\sqrt{2\pi}} \; e^{-\frac{1}{2}\left(\frac{x-\mu}{\sigma}\right)^2} dx \qquad (13\text{-}2)$$

$P(a \leq x \leq b)$ is represented in *Figures 13-1* and *13-2* by the shaded area under the bell curve. Note that the term "probability" makes sense only for a range of values for x, that is, for $a \neq b$. A single isolated value for x would by definition of *Equation 13-2* be an

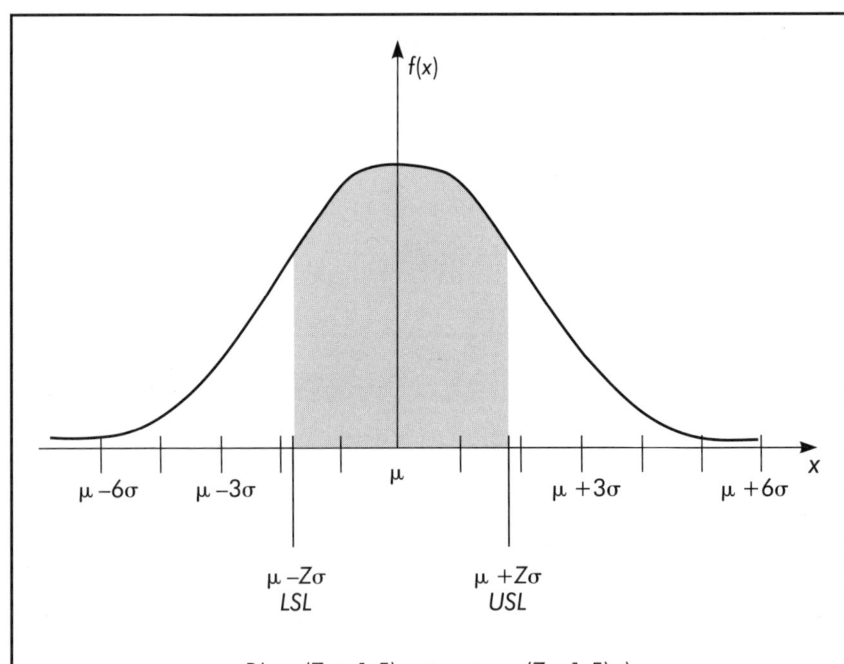

Figure 13-2. Zσ process-capability definition: an arbitrary shift of 1.5σ is applied to compute the associated defect-free production rate.

improbable event, that is, probability $P(a \leq x \leq a) = 0\%$. For practical reference using *Table 13-1*, the probability function in *Equation 13-2* can be formulated as:

$$P(a \leq x \leq b) = P(-\infty \leq x \leq b) - P(-\infty \leq x \leq a) \tag{13-3}$$

A $Z\sigma$ value can be defined such that output x can be written as the number of σ-unit distance from mean μ. For $a = \mu - Z_L\sigma$ and $b = \mu - Z_U\sigma$: Z_L, and respectively Z_U, are either positive or negative numbers that can represent a lower specification limit, $LSL = a$, or respectively an upper specification limit, $USL = b$.

$$Z_L = \frac{\mu - LSL}{\sigma} \text{ and } Z_U = \frac{\mu - USL}{\sigma} \tag{13-4}$$

Equations 13-3 and *13-4* yield:

$$P(\mu - Z_L\sigma \leq x \leq \mu - Z_U\sigma) = \text{defect-free production rate} \tag{13-5}$$

or

$$P(-\infty \leq x \leq \mu - Z_U\sigma) - P(-\infty \leq x \leq \mu - Z_L\sigma) = \text{defect-free production rate} \tag{13-6}$$

A process for which $P(\mu - Z_L\sigma \leq x \leq \mu - Z_U\sigma) = 99\%$ is capable of generating 99% defect-free and 1% defective output. The probability $P(-\infty \leq x \leq \mu - Z\sigma)$ can be obtained from *Table 13-1* or by using a spreadsheet function such as NORMSDIST (Z) in Microsoft Excel®.

Process Capability

If the process-output tolerances for x are defined by LSL and USL such that μ is not necessarily centered between LSL and USL as exemplified in *Figure 13-3*, then a standard definition for process capability, C_{pk}, is defined by statisticians as the minimum between two expressions:

$$C_{pk} = \min\left(\frac{|\mu - LSL|}{3\sigma}; \frac{|\mu - USL|}{3\sigma}\right) \tag{13-7}$$

Table 13-1. Quick reference spreadsheet for probability $P(-\infty \le x \le \mu - Z\sigma)$ as a function of Z

	A	B	C	D	E	F	G	H	I	J	K
1	Z	0.00	0.01	0.02	0.03	0.04	0.05	0.06	0.07	0.08	0.09
2	**6.0**	0.0000001	0.0000001	0.0000001	0.0000001	0.0000001	0.0000001	0.0000001	0.0000001	0.0000001	0.0000001
3	**5.9**	0.0000002	0.0000002	0.0000002	0.0000002	0.0000001	0.0000001	0.0000001	0.0000001	0.0000001	0.0000001
4	**5.8**	0.0000003	0.0000003	0.0000003	0.0000003	0.0000003	0.0000002	0.0000002	0.0000002	0.0000002	0.0000002
5	**5.7**	0.0000006	0.0000006	0.0000005	0.0000005	0.0000005	0.0000004	0.0000004	0.0000004	0.0000004	0.0000004
6	**5.6**	0.0000011	0.0000010	0.0000010	0.0000009	0.0000009	0.0000008	0.0000008	0.0000007	0.0000007	0.0000006
7	**5.5**	0.0000019	0.0000018	0.0000017	0.0000016	0.0000015	0.0000014	0.0000014	0.0000013	0.0000012	0.0000011
8	**5.4**	0.0000033	0.0000032	0.0000030	0.0000028	0.0000027	0.0000025	0.0000024	0.0000023	0.0000021	0.0000020
9	**5.3**	0.0000058	0.0000055	0.0000052	0.0000049	0.0000047	0.0000044	0.0000042	0.0000039	0.0000037	0.0000035
10	**5.2**	0.0000100	0.0000095	0.0000090	0.0000085	0.0000080	0.0000076	0.0000072	0.0000068	0.0000065	0.0000061
11	**5.1**	0.0000170	0.0000161	0.0000153	0.0000145	0.0000138	0.0000130	0.0000124	0.0000117	0.0000111	0.0000105
12	**5.0**	0.0000287	0.0000273	0.0000259	0.0000246	0.0000233	0.0000221	0.0000210	0.0000199	0.0000189	0.0000179
13	**4.9**	0.0000480	0.0000456	0.0000433	0.0000412	0.0000391	0.0000372	0.0000353	0.0000335	0.0000318	0.0000302
14	**4.8**	0.0000794	0.0000756	0.0000719	0.0000684	0.0000650	0.0000618	0.0000588	0.0000559	0.0000531	0.0000505
15	**4.7**	0.0001302	0.0001240	0.0001181	0.0001124	0.0001070	0.0001018	0.0000969	0.0000922	0.0000878	0.0000835
16	**4.6**	0.0002115	0.0002015	0.0001921	0.0001830	0.0001744	0.0001661	0.0001583	0.0001508	0.0001436	0.0001368
17	**4.5**	0.0003401	0.0003244	0.0003095	0.0002952	0.0002815	0.0002685	0.0002560	0.0002441	0.0002327	0.0002218
18	**4.4**	0.0005417	0.0005173	0.0004939	0.0004716	0.0004502	0.0004297	0.0004102	0.0003914	0.0003736	0.0003564
19	**4.3**	0.0008546	0.0008169	0.0007807	0.0007461	0.0007130	0.0006812	0.0006508	0.0006217	0.0005939	0.0005672
20	**4.2**	0.0013354	0.0012777	0.0012223	0.0011692	0.0011183	0.0010696	0.0010228	0.0009780	0.0009351	0.0008940
21	**4.1**	0.0020669	0.0019794	0.0018954	0.0018148	0.0017375	0.0016633	0.0015922	0.0015239	0.0014584	0.0013956
22	**4.0**	0.0031686	0.0030374	0.0029113	0.0027902	0.0026739	0.0025622	0.0024549	0.0023519	0.0022530	0.0021580
23	**3.9**	0.0048116	0.0046167	0.0044293	0.0042491	0.0040758	0.0039092	0.0037491	0.0035952	0.0034473	0.0033052
24	**3.8**	0.0072372	0.0069507	0.0066749	0.0064094	0.0061539	0.0059081	0.0056715	0.0054438	0.0052248	0.0050142

Table 13-1. *Continued*

	A	B	C	D	E	F	G	H	I	J	K
	Z	**0.00**	**0.01**	**0.02**	**0.03**	**0.04**	**0.05**	**0.06**	**0.07**	**0.08**	**0.09**
25	**3.7**	0.0107830	0.0103659	0.0099641	0.0095768	0.0092038	0.0088445	0.0084983	0.0081650	0.0078440	0.0075349
26	**3.6**	0.0159146	0.0153135	0.0147337	0.0141746	0.0136353	0.0131154	0.0126141	0.0121308	0.0116649	0.0112158
27	**3.5**	0.0232673	0.0224097	0.0215816	0.0207822	0.0200105	0.0192656	0.0185467	0.0178530	0.0171836	0.0165377
28	**3.4**	0.0336981	0.0324865	0.0313156	0.0301840	0.0290906	0.0280341	0.0270135	0.0260276	0.0250753	0.0241555
29	**3.3**	0.0483483	0.0466538	0.0450144	0.0434286	0.0418948	0.0404113	0.0389767	0.0375895	0.0362482	0.0349515
30	**3.2**	0.0687202	0.0663738	0.0641016	0.0619014	0.0597711	0.0577086	0.0557122	0.0537798	0.0519095	0.0500996
31	**3.1**	0.0967671	0.0935504	0.0904323	0.0874099	0.0844806	0.0816419	0.0788912	0.0762260	0.0736440	0.0711429
32	**3.0**	0.1349967	0.1306308	0.1263943	0.1222838	0.1182960	0.1144276	0.1106754	0.1070363	0.1035071	0.1000851
33	**2.9**	0.1865880	0.1807211	0.1750225	0.1694878	0.1641129	0.1588938	0.1538264	0.1489068	0.1441311	0.1394956
34	**2.8**	0.2555191	0.2477136	0.2401244	0.2327463	0.2255740	0.2186026	0.2118270	0.2052424	0.1988442	0.1926276
35	**2.7**	0.3467023	0.3364211	0.3264148	0.3166769	0.3072013	0.2979819	0.2890125	0.2802872	0.2718003	0.2635461
36	**2.6**	0.4661222	0.4527147	0.4396526	0.4269282	0.4145342	0.4024631	0.3907076	0.3792607	0.3681155	0.3572649
37	**2.5**	0.6209680	0.6036575	0.5867760	0.5703147	0.5542646	0.5386170	0.5233635	0.5084954	0.4940046	0.4798829
38	**2.4**	0.8197529	0.7976255	0.7760251	0.7549411	0.7343633	0.7142815	0.6946857	0.6755661	0.6569129	0.6387167
39	**2.3**	1.0724081	1.0444050	1.0170414	0.9903053	0.9641850	0.9386687	0.9137452	0.8894029	0.8656308	0.8424177
40	**2.2**	1.3903399	1.3552534	1.3209339	1.2873678	1.2545420	1.2224433	1.1910588	1.1603756	1.1303811	1.1010627
41	**2.1**	1.7864357	1.7429116	1.7002962	1.6585747	1.6177325	1.5777551	1.5386280	1.5003369	1.4628679	1.4262068
42	**2.0**	2.2750062	2.2215525	2.1691624	2.1178201	2.0675095	2.0182148	1.9699203	1.9226106	1.8762701	1.8308836
43	**1.9**	2.8716493	2.8066539	2.7428881	2.6803350	2.6189776	2.5587990	2.4997825	2.4419115	2.3851694	2.3295398
44	**1.8**	3.5930266	3.5147838	3.4379445	3.3624911	3.2884058	3.2156713	3.1442700	3.0741845	3.0053974	2.9378914
45	**1.7**	4.4565432	4.3632903	4.2716185	4.1815099	4.0929468	4.0059114	3.9203858	3.8363523	3.7537931	3.6726904
46	**1.6**	5.4799289	5.3698923	5.2616130	5.1550737	5.0502569	4.9471451	4.8457206	4.7459659	4.6478632	4.5513949
47	**1.5**	6.6807229	6.5521737	6.4255510	6.3008383	6.1780193	6.0570771	5.9379950	5.8207562	5.7053437	5.5917403
48	**1.4**	8.0756711	7.9269891	7.7803888	7.6358555	7.4933743	7.3529300	7.2145075	7.0780913	6.9436656	6.8112148

Table 13-1. *Continued*

	A	B	C	D	E	F	G	H	I	J	K
	Z	0.00	0.01	0.02	0.03	0.04	0.05	0.06	0.07	0.08	0.09
49	**1.3**	9.6800549	9.5097982	9.3417573	9.1759198	9.0122734	8.8508052	8.6915021	8.5343508	8.3793378	8.2264493
50	**1.2**	11.5069732	11.3139509	11.1232501	10.9348617	10.7487762	10.5649839	10.3834747	10.2042381	10.0272634	9.8525394
51	**1.1**	13.5666102	13.3499557	13.1356927	12.9238161	12.7143201	12.5071989	12.3024458	12.1000541	11.9000166	11.7023256
52	**1.0**	15.8655260	15.6247655	15.3864244	15.1505020	14.9169971	14.6859081	14.4572328	14.2309686	14.0071125	13.7856610
53	**0.9**	18.4060092	18.1411225	17.8786354	17.6185520	17.3608762	17.1056112	16.8527597	16.6023240	16.3543057	16.1087061
54	**0.8**	21.1855334	20.8970026	20.6107994	20.3269335	20.0454139	19.7662492	19.4894473	19.2150158	18.9429614	18.6732906
55	**0.7**	24.1963578	23.8851994	23.5762424	23.2695018	22.9649924	22.6627280	22.3627221	22.0649876	21.7695369	21.4763817
56	**0.6**	27.4253065	27.0930848	26.7628834	26.4347230	26.1086235	25.7846044	25.4626846	25.1428824	24.8252158	24.5097021
57	**0.5**	30.8537533	30.5025719	30.1531771	29.8055944	29.4598489	29.1159655	28.7739682	28.4338808	28.0957264	27.7595276
58	**0.4**	34.4578303	34.0903014	33.7242763	33.3597852	32.9968580	32.6355241	32.2758126	31.9177519	31.5613701	31.2066949
59	**0.3**	38.2088643	37.8280543	37.4484230	37.0700045	36.6928327	36.3169410	35.9423626	35.5691301	35.1972760	34.8268323
60	**0.2**	42.0740313	41.6833866	41.2935613	40.9045927	40.5165176	40.1293726	39.7431943	39.3580186	38.9738814	38.5908182
61	**0.1**	46.0172104	45.6204636	45.2241530	44.8283177	44.4329967	44.0382288	43.6440527	43.2505067	42.8576291	42.4654580
62	**0.0**	**50.0000000**	49.6010621	49.2021646	48.8033473	48.4046501	48.0061127	47.6077747	47.2096760	46.8118560	46.4143544

Example: cell J50 (lower tail area) yields a probability of 10.0272634% corresponding to $Z = 1.2 + 0.08 = 1.28$; and cell B62 confirms that for $Z = 0.00$, the probability is 50.0000000%.

Note: to retrieve probability for $-Z$, the following relationship can be used: $P(-\infty \leq x \leq \mu + Z\sigma) = 100\% - P(-\infty \leq x \leq \mu - Z\sigma)$.

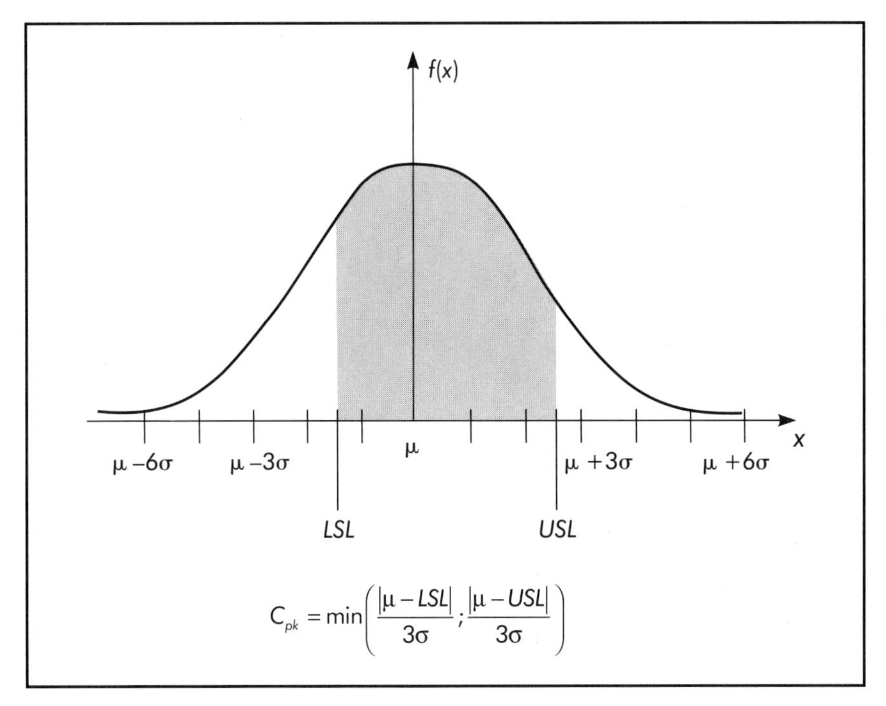

Figure 13-3. C_{pk} process capability: the shaded area under the curve represents P(LSL ≤ x ≤ USL). For the distributions that are not centered between LSL and USL, a C_{pk} definition makes sense.

The six-sigma definition of process capability differs from C_{pk} in that it considers arbitrarily skewing by 1.5σ from a normal distribution, for which mean value μ is centered between *LSL* and *USL*. In the case illustrated in *Figure 13-2*, μ is centered between specification limits, $Z_L = -Z_U = Z$, with Z being a positive number. Here a $Z\sigma$ process capability generates a defect-free production rate given by:

$$P(\mu - (Z + 1.5)\sigma \leq x \leq \mu + (Z - 1.5)\sigma) \tag{13-8}$$

Table 13-2 provides a quick conversion between $Z\sigma$ process capability and a defect-free production rate.

Based on many more practical representations of sigma capability similar to the real scenarios in *Table 13-3* and on the standard C_{pk} definition of *Equation 13-7*, six sigma is chosen by many

Table 13-2. Defects per million opportunities, defect-free production rate, and $Z\sigma$ capability conversion

Defects per Million Opportunities	Defect-free Production Rate, %	$Z\sigma$ Capability
933,000	6.70000	0.0
919,000	8.10000	0.1
903,000	9.70000	0.2
885,000	11.50000	0.3
864,000	13.60000	0.4
841,000	15.90000	0.5
816,000	18.40000	0.6
788,000	21.20000	0.7
758,000	24.20000	0.8
726,000	27.40000	0.9
691,000	30.90000	1.0
655,000	34.50000	1.1
618,000	38.20000	1.2
579,000	42.10000	1.3
540,000	46.00000	1.4
500,000	50.00000	1.5
460,000	54.00000	1.6
421,000	57.90000	1.7
382,000	61.80000	1.8
345,000	65.50000	1.9
309,000	69.10000	2.0
274,000	72.60000	2.1
242,000	75.80000	2.2
212,000	78.80000	2.3
184,000	81.60000	2.4
159,000	84.10000	2.5
136,000	86.40000	2.6
115,000	88.50000	2.7
96,800	90.32000	2.8
80,800	91.92000	2.9
66,800	93.32000	3.0
54,800	94.52000	3.1

Table 13-2. *Continued*

Defects per Million Opportunities	Defect-free Production Rate, %	$Z\sigma$ Capability
44,600	95.54000	3.2
35,900	96.41000	3.3
28,700	97.13000	3.4
22,800	97.72000	3.5
17,900	98.21000	3.6
13,900	98.61000	3.7
10,700	98.93000	3.8
8,200	99.18000	3.9
6,210	99.37900	4.0
4,660	99.53400	4.1
3,470	99.65300	4.2
2,560	99.74400	4.3
1,870	99.81300	4.4
1,350	99.86500	4.5
968	99.90320	4.6
687	99.93130	4.7
483	99.95170	4.8
337	99.96630	4.9
233	99.97670	5.0
159	99.98410	5.1
108	99.98920	5.2
72	99.99280	5.3
48	99.99520	5.4
32	99.99680	5.5
21	99.99790	5.6
13	99.99870	5.7
9	99.99910	5.8
5	99.99950	5.9
3.4	99.99966	6.0

Table 13-3. Practical examples of approximated output expectations in USA

99% Defect-free Output Means 3.8σ Capable	99.99966% Defect-free Output Means 6σ Capable
22,000 surgical mistakes/month	9 surgical mistakes per month
7 hr/month of electricity blackout	1 hr of electricity blackout every 34 years
170,000 automobile recalls/year	5,780 automobile recalls/year
500,000 lost articles of mail/day	168 lost articles of mail/day

as a realistic target for output expectation. Rare are the manufacturing processes that are truly six sigma or more capable.

CONTINUOUS IMPROVEMENT ACTIONS

The path to six-sigma capability may take several iterations of continuous improvement actions. These actions are to be decided and implemented in a five-phase process: define, measure, analyze, improve, and control (DMAIC) highlighted in *Figure 13-4* (Chowdhury 2001; Bertels 2003; Wireman 1991).

Define Phase

To justify a six-sigma project, a problem must be identified. The case must be defined by a simple, clear, and focused statement. There must be a champion within the organization who can evaluate its magnitude and assign appropriate resources to solve the problem or make improvements. The champion supports the formation of a six-sigma project team composed of active participants who are directly or indirectly involved with the problem. A customer is precisely identified, whether internal or external to the organization. A strong knowledge or direct survey of customers helps define product features that are critical to a specific customer, that is, the critical-to-quality (CTQ) specifications.

The six-sigma team's first action after its formation consists of discussing and agreeing on a definition of a defect associated with

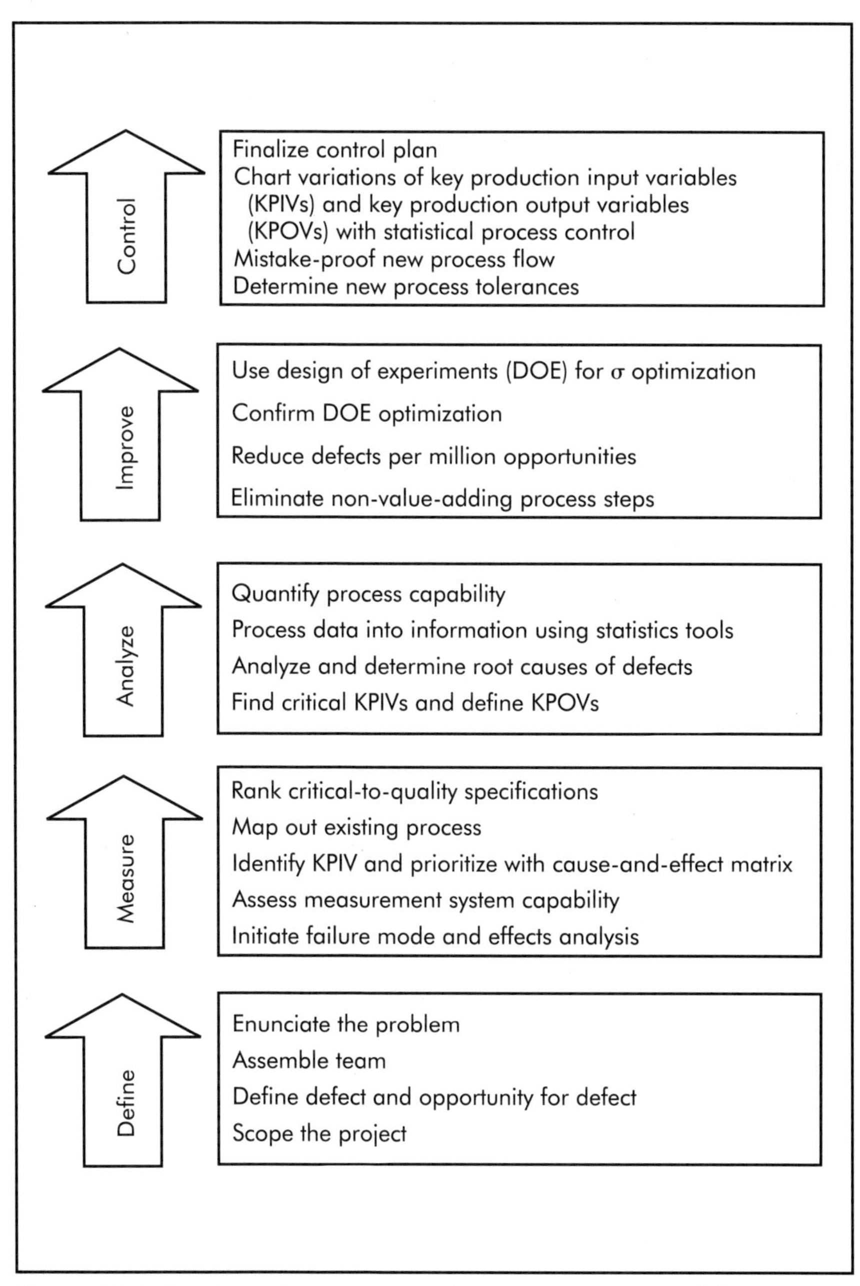

Figure 13-4. Six-sigma improvement of an existing process follows a five-phase process: define, measure, analyze, improve, and control.

the stated problem and the identified CTQ specifications. The team must establish a project goal with an estimate of the financial impact to the organization and customer. A project tracking system with target dates for project milestones is put in place. The defect definition task ensures the essential quantification of a problem that may have been only qualitatively stated. With the defect definition goes a definition of "opportunity for defect," in other words, any instances in a process step when a defect can be generated. A measurement of success can be represented by a defect-free production rate, which translates into defects per million opportunities (DPMO) using the following relationship:

$$\text{defect-free production rate} = 100\% - DPMO \times 10^{-6} \quad (13\text{-}9)$$

DPMO can be converted mathematically into a sigma capability by using *Table 13-2* or a programmed spreadsheet function such as the NORMSINV function in Microsoft Excel. This function determines the sigma capability from the defect-free production rate by inverting the formulas in *Equations 13-2* and *13-4*:

$$Z\sigma \text{ capability} = \text{NORMSINV}(\text{defect-free production rate}) + 1.5 \quad (13\text{-}10)$$

Case Study

Consider a two-shift-per-day laser-cutting operation that is expected to produce a target average of 30 good parts per hour for each 10-hour shift. With a 100% visual inspection system, parts produced with bad cuts are identified and discarded before shipment to the customer. The 100% visual inspection performed in real time reduces the scrap rate to a negligible level as the operator stops production at the first instance of a bad cut and uses the same scraped plate repeatedly for parameter tweaking and optimizing.

The production manager states the problem, "with two shifts of 10 hours per day, shipments of good parts do not meet target volume, forcing costly overtime on weekends and jeopardizing just-in-time (JIT) production capability in the eyes of the customer." He decides to champion a six-sigma project aimed at improving the production rate of good parts. A team is formed, which includes a first-shift operator, a maintenance engineer handling both shifts, and a purchasing agent. Roles for each team member are clearly defined and accepted by each.

In this case, the user of the product is an external customer who would benefit from a productivity improvement with better JIT capability and possibly a lower price. A first CTQ characteristic for the external customer is JIT complete delivery on a shift, that is, 30 good parts per hour.

In the course of defining defects, the operator stated, "we are capable of running the laser at up to 55 in./min (1.4 m/min), but the machine is unstable and unreliable and requires constant tweaking adjustments." The maintenance engineer agreed that a feed rate of 55 in./min (1.4 m/min) would solve the problem but remarked that a lot of the instabilities may be due to the material's surface condition inconsistency with scales and rust. The purchasing agent warned that the material was specified by the customer and that scale-free and rust-free pickled and oiled material would be way too costly at this time.

To help in defect definition, the team decides to look at the past 120 weekdays of production. Supervisory control of the machine recorded the number of good parts per hour averaged over each shift, as summarized in *Table 13-4*. The first-shift team shipped 34,900 good parts, while the second-shift team shipped 35,500 good parts, both short of the target 36,000 parts. A team analysis of the report in *Table 13-4* established that most of the low-production-rate shifts are due to elevated tweaking downtime when attempting to cut fast. By maintaining cutting feed rate at 40 in./min (1 m/min), the target 36,000 good parts per shift should be achieved by both shifts.

The team defines a defect as an average production rate of either less than 30 good parts per hour or more than 40 good parts per hour. Each shift represents one opportunity for a defect. Based on these criteria, the first shift had 88 defects for 120 opportunities, an initial 733,333 DPMO (0.88σ), whereas the second shift had an initial 416,667 DPMO (1.71σ). Pareto histograms illustrating the number of shifts and occurrence rate versus the defect-free production rate are plotted in *Figure 13-5* separately for the first and second shifts. The Pareto distributions

Table 13-4. Supervisory control report for 120 weekdays of production

Feed Rate, in./min (m/min)	Number of Good Parts/hr	Number of Occurrences First Shift	Number of Occurrences Second Shift
55 (1.4)	0–10	15	2
50 (1.3)	10–20	20	6
35 (0.9)	20–30	26	32
40 (1.0)	30–40	32	70
45 (1.1)	40–50	17	8
50 (1.3)	50–60	7	2
55 (1.4)	60–70	3	0
		120	120

When operating at 40 in./min (1 m/min) feed rate, average production yields 30–40 good parts/hours. Out of 120 first and second shifts, only 32 first shifts were operated at a feed rate of 40 in./min (1 m/min), whereas 70 second shifts were operated at 40 in./min (1 m/min). The first-shift team attempted to cut faster than 40 in./min (1 m/min) in a total of 62 shifts, 27 of which were successful attempts; the remaining 35 attempts degenerated into significant tweaking downtime, averaging less than the targeted 30 good parts/hr.

are approximated by normal distributions characterized by two different sets of μ and σ.

In the define phase, the team must complete a critical scope exercise to break down goals, roles and responsibilities, and processes and procedures to within specific guiding boundaries. The purpose of determining the scope is to ensure team focus and planning of executable actions. In the case example, the team could scope the project to include or exclude specific input parameters influencing defect-free production-rate improvement. For example, the scope could force the team to evaluate material specifications, such as surface condition, which impact the defect-free production rate. Alternatively, it could lead to a design of experiments (DOE) troubleshooting exercise to optimize key cutting-method parameters other than restricting the cutting speed to 40 in./min (1 m/min). The scope could include determining the training level of operators in each shift and many other process inputs, as well as definition of the output characteristics to be studied. A defect-free production rate could be ranked as the first CTQ output and scrap rate the second. CTQ characteristics must be identified and ranked in order of importance to the customer.

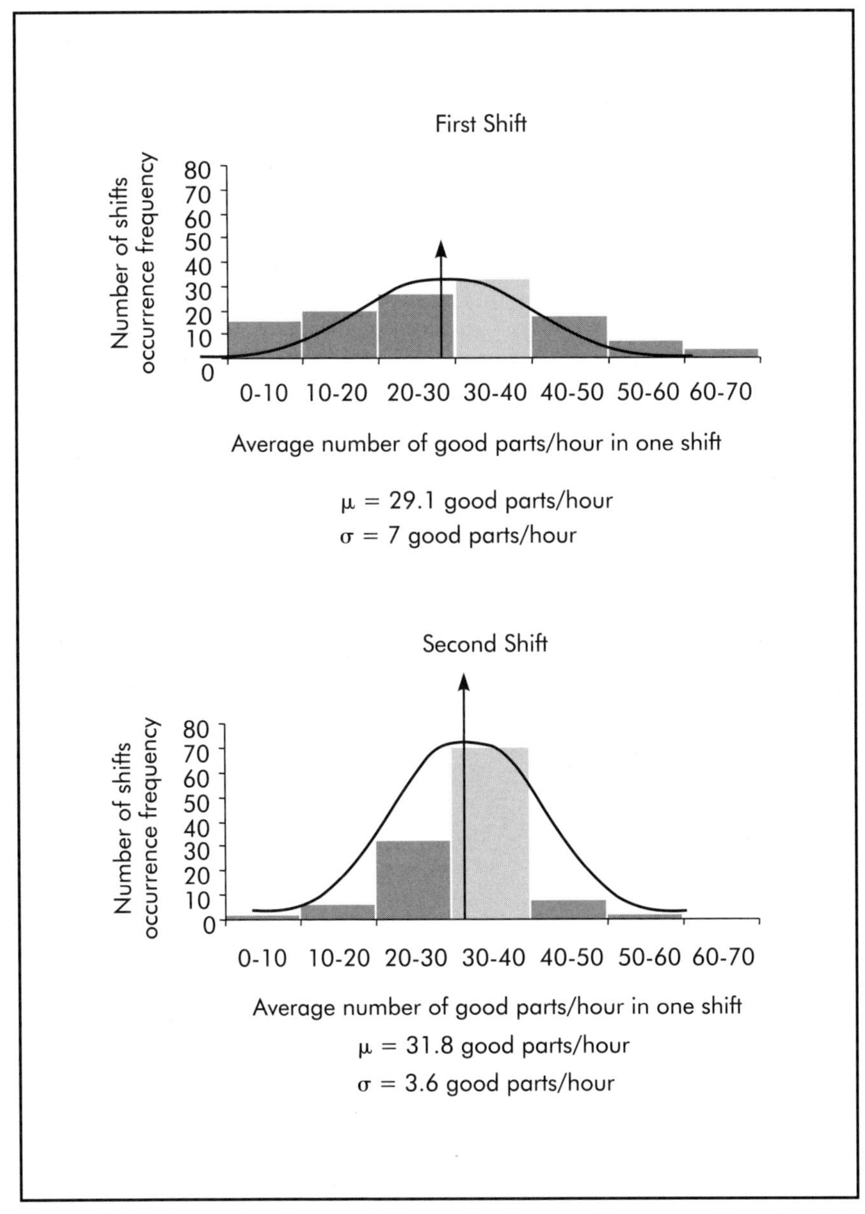

Figure 13-5. Example of a two-shift-per-day laser-cutting operation: the first-shift diagram is approximated by a normal curve characterized by $\mu = 29.1$ and $\sigma = 7$. For the second shift, $\mu = 31.8$ and $\sigma = 3.6$. LSL = 30 good parts/hour and USL = 40 good parts/hour. For the first shift $C_{pk} = 0.04$ and for the second shift $C_{pk} = 0.17$.

Measure Phase

With goals, key process input variables (KPIVs), and CTQ characteristics identified and ranked, mapping of a process is in order. Using a graphical tool, mapping synthesizes a comprehensive view of the process steps, linking inputs to outputs (see *Figure 13-6*). Process mapping helps identify value-adding versus non-value-adding steps, controllable and uncontrollable (noise) key process inputs, and their links to process outputs critical to the customer. Ultimately, a process map provides a snapshot vision for "lean" transformation by revealing where non-value-adding process steps can be eliminated. *Figure 13-7* lists flow-chart symbols used in process-control plans and process mapping.

A process map can indicate KPIV data-collection points and which types of data-processing control are in effect. The next step is to prioritize the indicated KPIVs, which should be monitored by order of importance for reduction of DPMO. This prioritization process can be executed with a cause-and-effect matrix. A cause-and-effect matrix, such as the example in *Figure 13-8*, sorts out the KPIVs that influence the CTQ specifications most. Generally, the 20/80 rule applies. Variations in the top 20% of KPIVs cause 80% of CTQ defects. In *Figure 13-8*, feed rate appears singled out of four KPIVs that account for the most impact on CTQ variations. Generally, the feed rate is accurately commanded and monitored by a machine's numerical control based on setup data, and therefore does not suffer from random variations. Commanded feed-rate data can be carefully monitored or designed such that access to override it is only allowed with management approval.

Failure Mode and Effects Analysis

A more in-depth tool than a cause-and-effect diagram, failure mode and effects analysis (FMEA) analyzes the root causes for failure to meet CTQ specifications, quantifies their risk priority levels, and recommends corrective actions. FMEA can be executed for processes and applications involving hardware, software, and services. It must be reviewed and adjusted periodically. FMEA is a prevention-oriented discipline that eases detection of failure

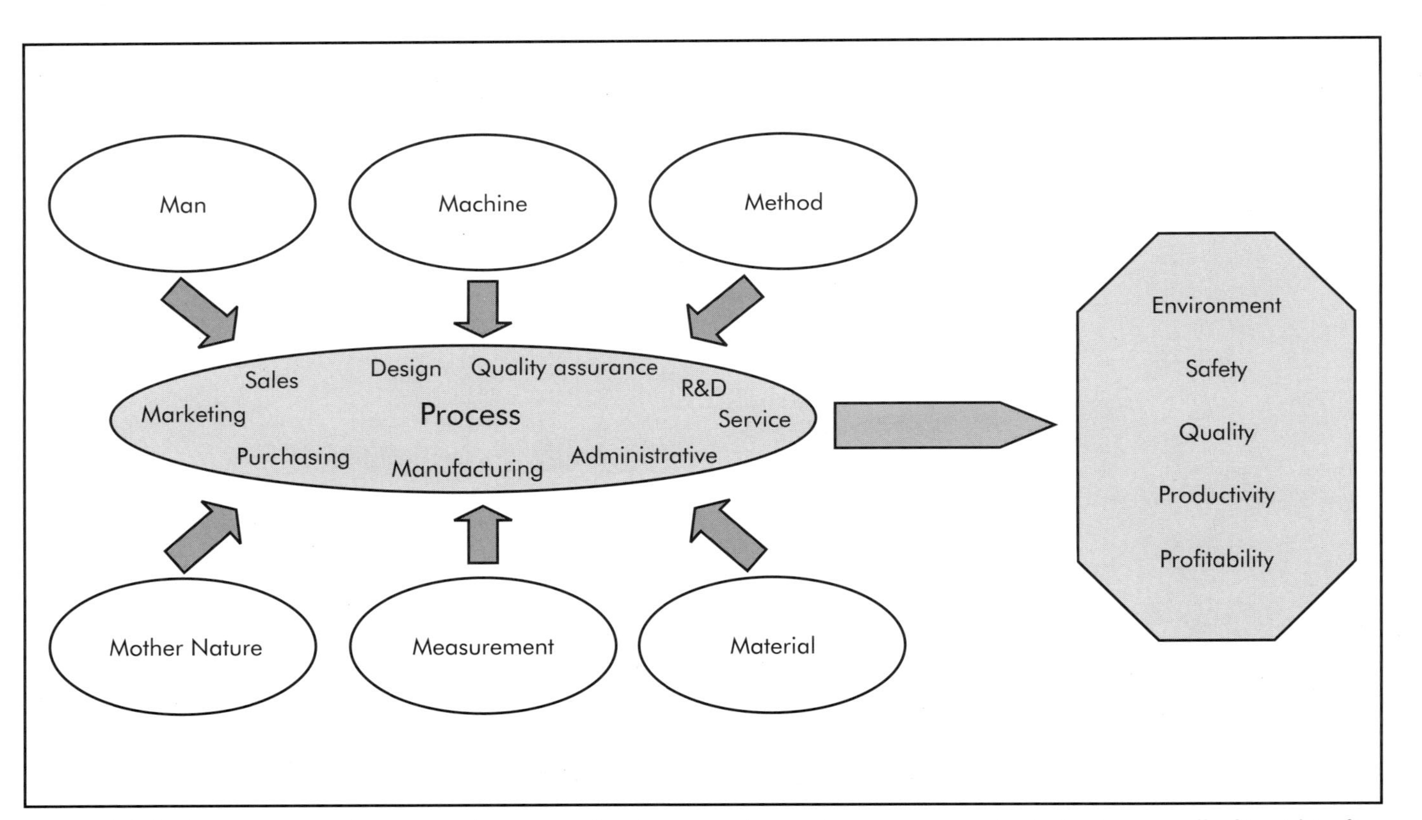

Figure 13-6. A process receives input from the six M categories and generates outputs that generally fit within five categories: environment, safety, quality, productivity, and profitability.

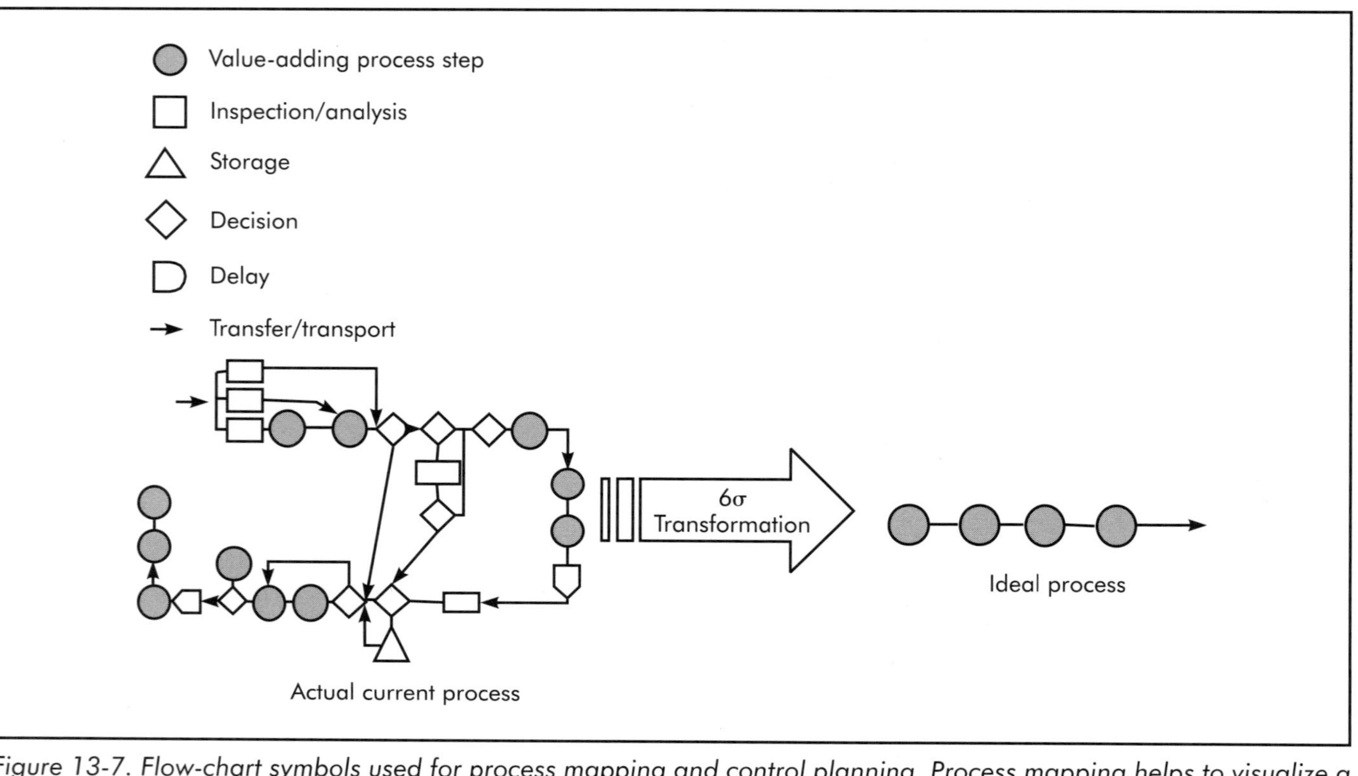

Figure 13-7. Flow-chart symbols used for process mapping and control planning. Process mapping helps to visualize a leaner and more productive process in which ideally only value-adding process steps take place. In practice, the improved process map fits between the current one and the ideal lean one.

	Cause-and-effect Matrix						
Importance of CTQ specification	10	5	8	2			
	CTQ #1	CTQ #2	CTQ #3	CTQ #4	5	6	
	Defect-free production rate	Scrap rate	Contour accuracy	Burr	CTQ	CTQ	Total
KPIV: Feed rate	10	5	1	3			102
KPIV: Day or night shift	8	3	1	2			78
KPIV: Operator training and experience	5	9	5	6			84
KPIV: Material's surface quality	7	4	1	8			85

$= 10 \times 10 + 5 \times 5 + 8 \times 1 + 2 \times 3$

Figure 13-8. A cause-and-effect matrix provides a first glimpse at which KPIVs have the most overall influence on CTQ specifications. For each KPIV, the total impact is computed as the sum over each CTQ specification of the product of a KPIV influence strength number by the relative importance ranking number of the CTQ specification.

causes, reduces DPMO failure occurrences, and limits the severity of their effects on the customer's CTQ specifications.

Figure 13-9 illustrates the content of an FMEA spreadsheet. For each potential failure mode, an analysis of root causes yields three numbers between 1 and 10—the occurrence frequency, severity of the effect, and detection indices. A high occurrence scores a 10 while a low one scores a 1. The severity of the effect scores 10 if it yields high DPMO and 1 if it does not have a significant impact on DPMO. If the failure mode is easy to detect, the index is 1, whereas for extremely difficult-to-detect failure modes, the index would be 10. The product of the three indices yields a risk priority number (RPN) by which failure modes are ranked. Failure modes with the highest RPN are given priority for corrective actions. Implementation of recommended actions leads to iterative revisions of RPN computations.

Measurement systems suggested by process mapping and prioritized by a cause-and-effect matrix and FMEA should be put in place for in-depth analysis. Before collection of data, trust and confidence in the measurement method and in the measurement's accuracy and precision must be secured. *Figure 13-10* illustrates the difference between precision and accuracy. Accuracy quantifies how close the hits' average is to the target, whereas precision measures the spread among several hits on the same target.

Precision is ultimately limited by a gage's repeatability and reproducibility (R&R) of measurements. A *gage* is an instrument used to take a measurement. It may have built-in variation representative of its capability to measure a certain quantity within given environmental conditions. For non-automated measurements, a human appraiser will also introduce added variation in a final reading and recording of a measurement. Appraiser and instrument variations are the contributors to gage R&R. If R&R varies within a wide tolerance, the lack of precision of a measurement may lead to a wrong analysis and thus to inappropriate corrective actions.

Repeatability quantifies the variation in repeated measurements of the same characteristic on the same part with the same gage, by the same appraiser, in steady environmental conditions. The result of a repeatability test is characterized by a standard deviation $\sigma_{Repeatability}$. *Reproducibility* quantifies the variation in several

Failure Mode and Effects Analysis

Process Step/Part Number	Potential Failure Mode	Potential Failure Effects	Severity	Potential Causes	Occurrence	Current Controls	Detection	RPN	Actions Recom-mended	Responsibility	Actions Taken
What are the process steps?	In what ways can the process step lead to failure?	What is the impact of the failure mode on the customer?	How severe is the effect on the customer (1 = least, 10 = most)?	What are the causes of the failure mode?	How frequent is the cause of failure mode (1 = least, 10 = most)?	What are the existing controls and procedures that prevent the cause of the failure mode?	How difficult is it to detect the cause of the failure mode?	Calculated risk priority number	What are the actions for reducing occurrence, decreasing severity, or easing detection?	Who is responsible for the recommend-ed action?	What are the completed actions?

RPN = severity × occurrence × undetectability

Figure 13-9. FMEA identifies potential failure modes and renders an analysis of root causes, their effect, and occurrence frequency, along with methods to detect and prevent failures. An FMEA ranks failure mode by risk priority number.

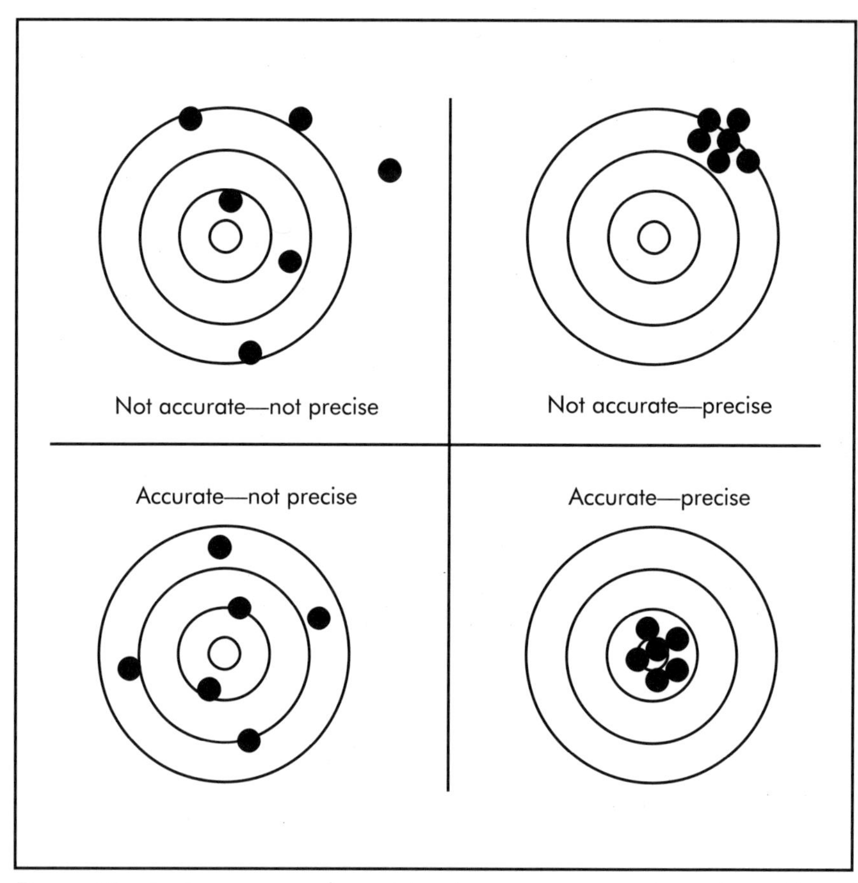

Figure 13-10. Accuracy and precision in a measurement can be achieved only within a measurement gage's repeatability and reproducibility limits.

measurements of an identical characteristic on the same part, made by different appraisers with the same gage, under different environmental conditions. The result of a reproducibility test is characterized by a standard deviation $\sigma_{Reproducibility}$. Together they yield an R&R standard deviation:

$$\sigma^2_{R\&R} = \sigma^2_{Repeatability} + \sigma^2_{Reproducibility} \tag{13-11}$$

If σ_{output} represents the process output's standard deviation, then the acceptability of a measurement system is quantified with a gage R&R contribution percentage:

$$\text{Gage R\&R contribution} = \frac{\sigma^2_{R\&R}}{\sigma^2_{R\&R} + \sigma^2_{output}} \qquad (13\text{-}12)$$

A gage R&R contribution of more than 5% should generally start raising concerns about the capability of a measurement system.

Analyze Phase

Data collection and analysis are key to six-sigma methodology because they establish factual cases that justify an organization's decision to invest in process, product, service, and application changes. Statistical methods and tools such as analysis of variance (ANOVA) multivariate studies, relations tests such as Chi Square tests, histograms and regressions, Pareto diagrams, and statistical process control (SPC) charts help process data to yield information (Aft 1992).

SPC charting provides a powerful defect-prevention-oriented analysis of the trends of averages, $\overline{X}$, and their ranges, R, for selected key input and output variables. An example of an SPC chart showing control limits is given in *Figure 13-11*. $\overline{X}$ represents variable X averaged over a subgroup of collected data. The subgroup's size is preferably at least seven measurements (Ford Motor Company 1990). R represents the range of variable X over each subgroup of measurements. Upper and lower control limits (UCL and LCL), upper and lower specification limits (USL and LSL), and C_{pk} (process capability) can be dynamically computed from $\overline{X}$ and R data using known parameter tables (Wadsworth 1990). UCL and LCL control limits are process-inherent values for $\overline{X}$ and R data, corresponding to a distance of 3σ from centerline average $\overline{\overline{X}}$ and $\overline{R}$. Control limits UCL and LCL have no relationship to USL and LSL. A process can be under control and still generate out-of-specification outputs. Inversely, a process can be out of control and generate outputs within specification for a period of time. In $\overline{X}$ and R charts, criteria that determine whether or not a process is under control are based on the following plot patterns:

- data beyond UCL or LCL ($\pm 3\sigma$);
- repeated patterns/cycles;

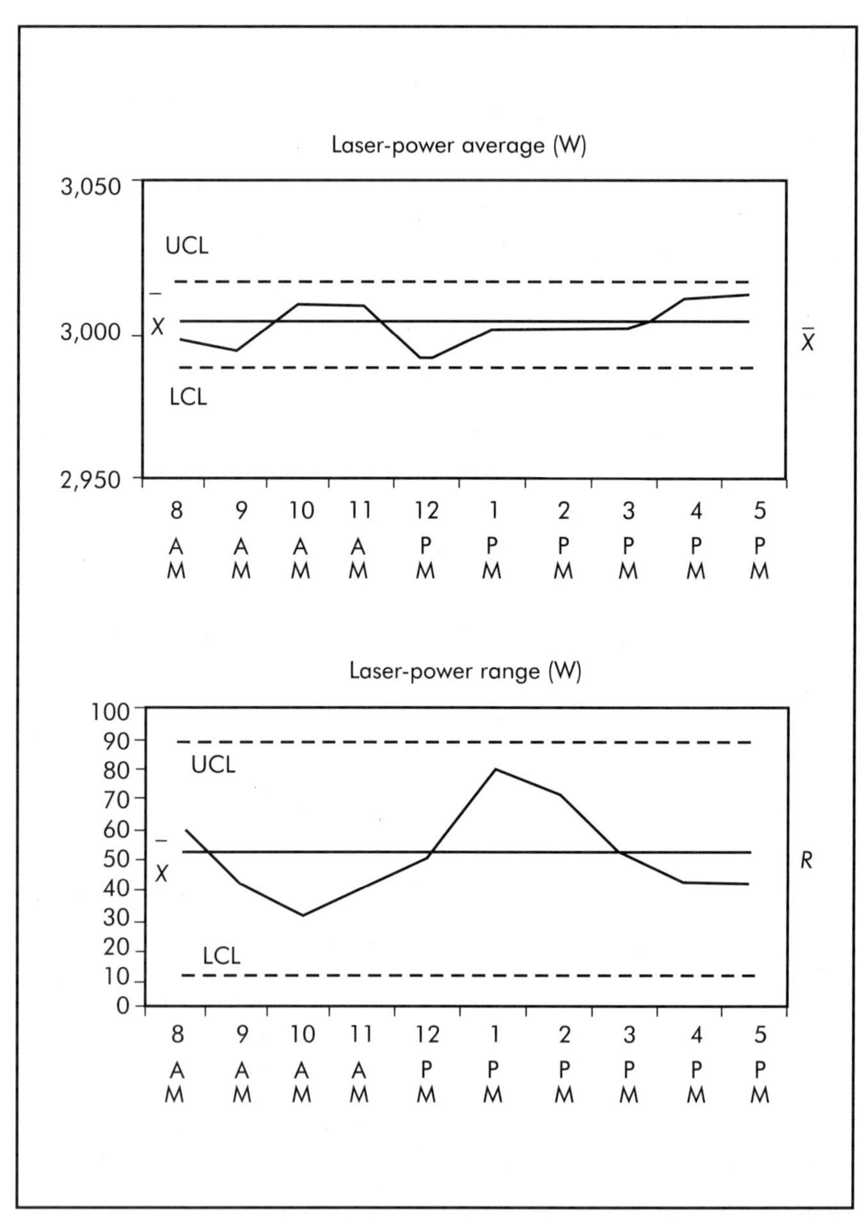

Figure 13-11. SPC charts monitor trends in averages and ranges and indicate special or common causes for out-of-control outputs. LCL and UCL are recomputed after each corrective action to re-establish process control. C_{pk} can be deduced from SPC charts (Mombo Caristan, Koch, and Prange 1991).

- six consecutive points steadily increasing or decreasing; and
- seven consecutive points on the same side of the centerline.

Additional criteria can be customarily drafted.

Improve and Control Phases

Data collected and properly analyzed turn into information that helps identify areas for improvement. Since most processes are under the influence of several key variables, it can become tedious, expensive, and sometimes erroneous to account for all key variables as if they had independent influences on an output. For example, for processes having a large number of KPIVs, an analysis of each KPIV taken in isolation would result in an even larger number of experiments in which one KPIV would vary while all other KPIVs are unchanged. The extended number of experiments increases costs. It also causes error because the interdependency of a KPIV on a key process output variable (KPOV) is ignored, resulting in choices of individual KPIV settings that do not yield process optimization when combined as a whole.

A DOE uses an orthogonal matrix to set a preferred minimum number of experiments sequenced in a specific combination. It scientifically separates the influence of controllable factors on KPOVs (Peace 1993). The example of *Figure 13-12* illustrates three KPIVs named *Z*, *V*, and *R* (labeled A, B, and C). Each has an interdependent influence on two KPOVs measured by R1 and R2. The larger the better is the optimization criteria for R1 and R2. The KPIVs can each take one of three levels labeled 1, 2, and 3. The aim of this DOE is to find out what combination of levels for *Z*, *V*, and *R* would optimize R1 and R2. In a regular experiment, for each level of Z, $3 \times 3 = 9$ combinations of levels of *V* and *R* would be tested. This would result in a total of $3^3 = 27$ experiments needed. In general, for n controllable factors with each m levels, the number of experiments needed is m^n. Using the three-level L9 orthogonal matrix depicted in *Figure 13-12*, only nine experiments would be needed for controllable factor $n = 4$ or less. Compared to traditional techniques, not only is the number of experiments far less, but the use of an orthogonal matrix insures a separation of the

Column	Unit	Controllable Factors	Levels 1	2	3
A	mm	Z	–0.2	0	0.2
B	m/min	V	15	25	30
C	in.	R	–0.02	0	0.02

R1 is part drop = 1, does not drop = 0
R2 = surface roughness appearance

	Orthogonal Matrix			Result			
Exp. #	A	B	C	R1	R2	R3	R4
1	1	1	1	1.00	6.00		
2	1	2	2	1.00	5.00		
3	1	3	3	0.00	0.00		
4	2	1	2	1.00	3.00		
5	2	2	3	1.00	2.00		
6	2	3	1	0.00	0.00		
7	3	1	3	1.00	10.00		
8	3	2	1	1.00	8.00		
9	3	3	2	1.00	1.00		

Average	A	B	C	R
Level 1	0.67	1.00	0.67	1
	3.67	6.33	4.67	2
	0.00	0.00	0.00	3
	0.00	0.00	0.00	4
Level 2	0.67	1.00	1.00	1
	1.67	5.00	3.00	2
	0.00	0.00	0.00	3
	0.00	0.00	0.00	4
Level 3	1.00	0.33	0.67	1
	6.33	0.33	4.00	2
	0.00	0.00	0.00	3
	0.00	0.00	0.00	4

Figure 13-12. A design of experiment with use of a three-level L9 orthogonal matrix for optimum production cutting setup. Three controllable factors were used: cutting speed, V, nozzle standoff, Z, and focus position, R. Results were based on two criteria: whether or not the cut part drops under its own weight in the collection bin, and the cut-edge quality as measured by the angle of striations. Setup at Z = 0.2, V = 15, and R = –0.02 was optimum, however, for productivity, Z = 0.2, V = 25, and R = –0.02 was preferred (Mombo Caristan et al. 1999).

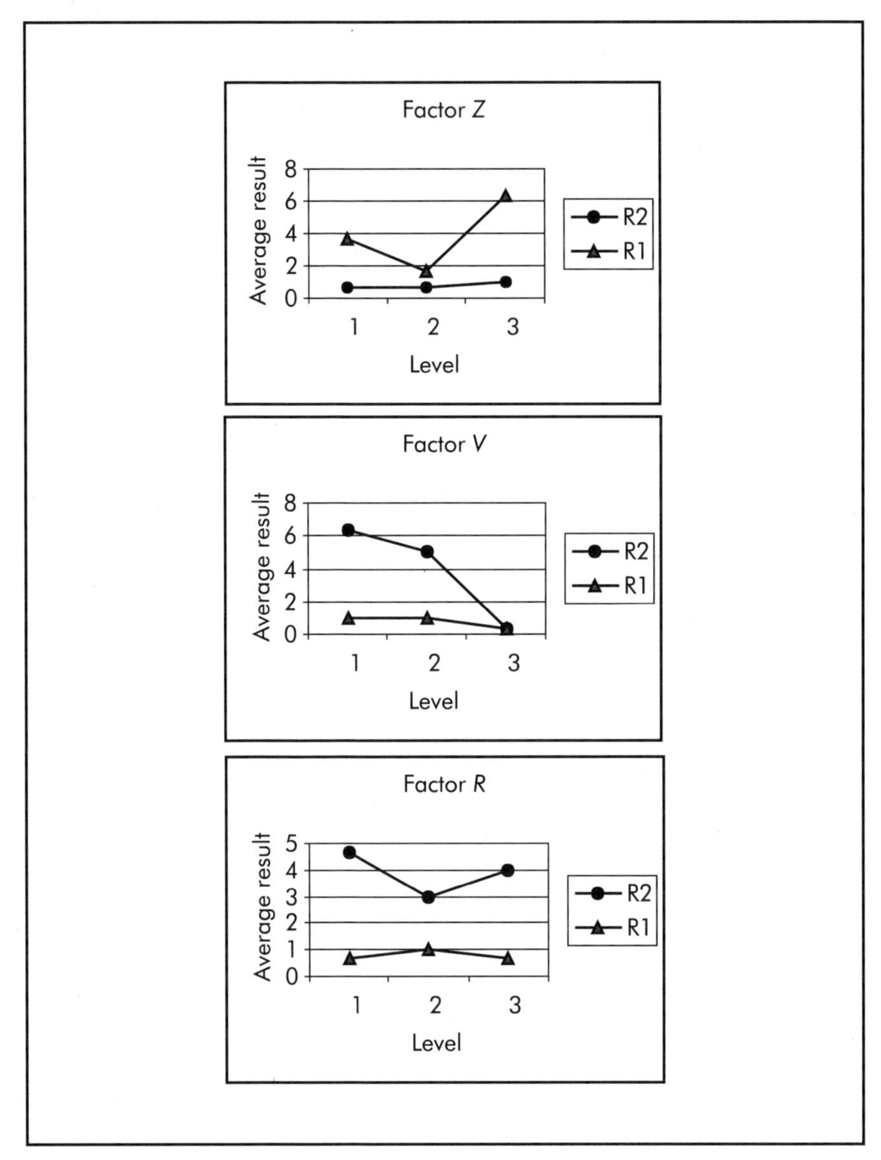

Figure 13-12. continued.

influences of each KPIV, and even an analysis of how their interaction impacts the process outputs. To maximize the outputs R1 and R2, an optimized set of KPIVs is determined rather than a set of individually optimized KPIVs.

DESIGN FOR SIX SIGMA

Although SPC charting is a powerful tool for monitoring and predicting defects before they are generated, ultimately an ideal process is one that always generates outputs within specification limits. The addition of measurement systems for KPIV variations and defect detection, as well as the use of SPC charting for defect prevention, are non-value adding sequences that cost time and money. A perfect process is an ideal process that does not need any measurement system. It should be designed to produce with zero defects at all times, regardless of which definition for a defect applies. A perfect system has an impossible infinite sigma capability. Though such a design is illusive, a design for six sigma is certainly executable.

Design-for-six-sigma projects apply to non-existing processes or processes that still fail to improve sigma capability despite DMAIC improvement attempts. Similar to DMAIC, design-for-six-sigma projects follow a five-phase methodology charted in *Figure 13-13*—define, measure, analyze, design, and verify. It aims at optimizing a design for a new product, process, or service for minimum defects, with the criteria for defects predefined by the customer.

Define Phase

The define phase must clearly identify the hardware, software, service, process, applications, and design specifications. The business case must be completed and approved by a champion who has authority to assign resources and facilitate cross-functional cooperation with other departments. The team must scope the project and establish a project-tracking system with target dates for project milestones all the way to completion and achievement of the stated goal.

Measure Phase

The measure phase deals with methods for building the foundations of the new design. A survey of the projected customer base

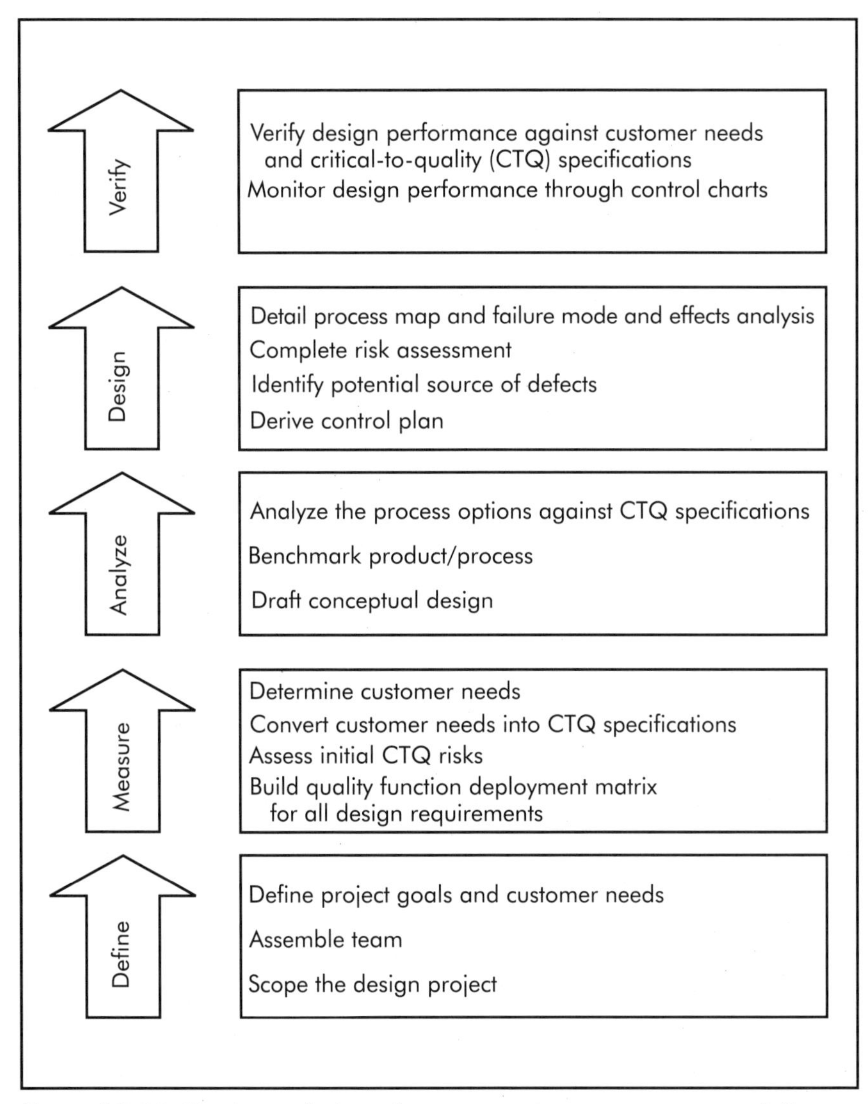

Figure 13-13. Six-sigma design of a new product or new process follows a five-phase methodology: define, measure, analyze, design, and verify.

for the new product or process feature yields important information on customer needs, which can be converted to CTQ specifications. Benchmarking the new product or process with existing ones provides another value-added input to the prioritization of customer needs and ranking of CTQ specifications by order of importance. Once KPIVs and KPOVs are also identified, a measurement system must be planned. Two key tools play a powerful role at this juncture: a CTQ risk assessment and a quality-function-deployment (QFD) multiple-level matrix.

A CTQ risk assessment provides a broader evaluation of a design beyond CTQ specifications and determines the potential risk in a design process. It takes into account internal and external fringe influences deemed pertinent by the project team, for example, company policy, state occupational safety and health regulations, federal regulations, and local weather.

QFD is a trickle-down process of translating the customer's requirements into product/process design specifications, while determining features, functionality, and resource requirements at every level of development, production, sale, and service. *Figure 13-14* illustrates an example of a two-level QFD matrix, which establishes links between a customer's top requirements and research and development (R&D) task needs. A level III QFD can be deployed to link R&D task needs to R&D resource requirements in personnel and time. Parallel QFD matrices can link customer requirements to feature functionality which, in turn, could be linked to product specifications. Many levels of QFD matrices can be iterated until all requirements are identified and ranked within the project scope.

Analyze Phase

In the analyze phase, a benchmarking report will be generated along with the QFD results to deploy CTQ specifications into a high-level conceptual design.

Design Phase

In the design phase, a detailed process map can be used to conduct an FMEA, identify potential sources of defects, and draft a detailed system design. A detailed risk assessment can be finalized along with a control plan and pilot plan.

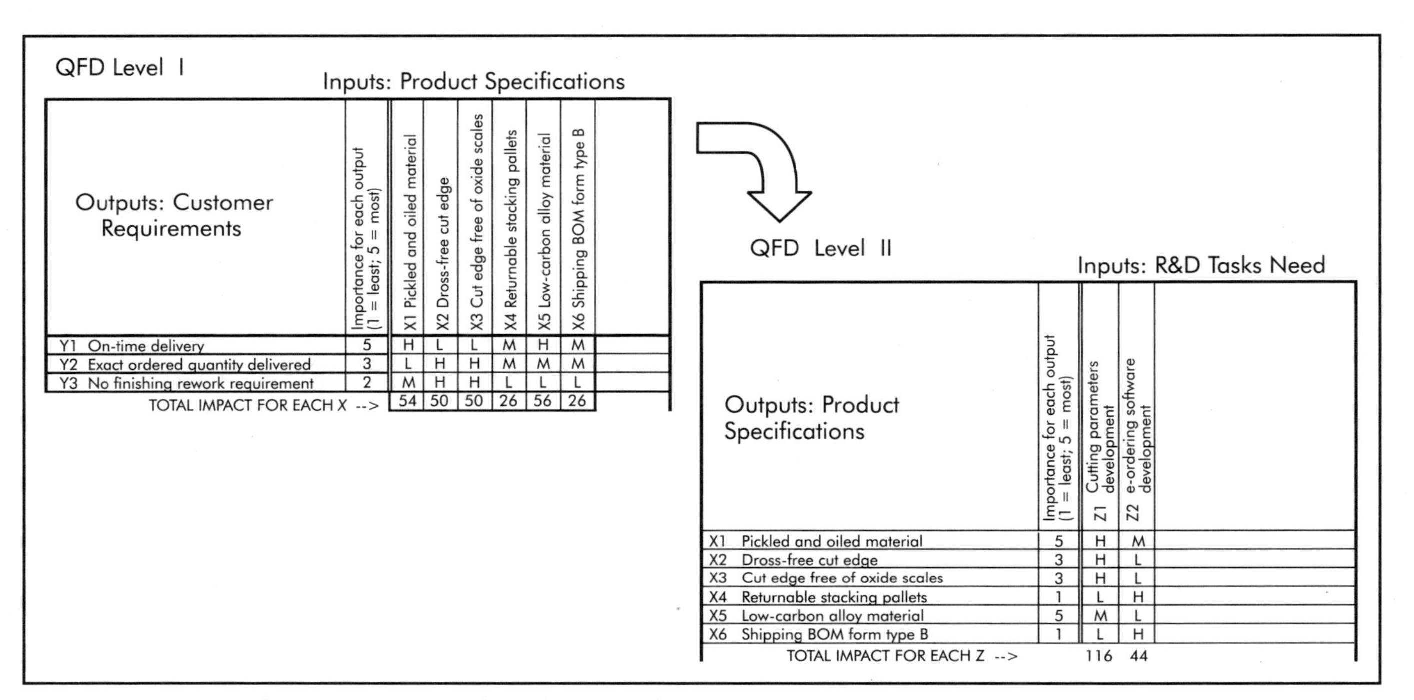

Outputs: Customer Requirements	Importance for each output (1 = least; 5 = most)	X1 Pickled and oiled material	X2 Dross-free cut edge	X3 Cut edge free of oxide scales	X4 Returnable stacking pallets	X5 Low-carbon alloy material	X6 Shipping BOM form type B
Y1 On-time delivery	5	H	L	L	M	H	M
Y2 Exact ordered quantity delivered	3	L	H	H	M	M	M
Y3 No finishing rework requirement	2	M	H	H	L	L	L
TOTAL IMPACT FOR EACH X -->		54	50	50	26	56	26

Outputs: Product Specifications	Importance for each output (1 = least; 5 = most)	Z1 Cutting parameters development	Z2 e-ordering software development
X1 Pickled and oiled material	5	H	M
X2 Dross-free cut edge	3	H	L
X3 Cut edge free of oxide scales	3	H	L
X4 Returnable stacking pallets	1	L	H
X5 Low-carbon alloy material	5	M	L
X6 Shipping BOM form type B	1	L	H
TOTAL IMPACT FOR EACH Z -->		116	44

Figure 13-14. QFD always starts at Level I with outputs being customer requirements. Critical inputs that impact outputs must be identified. The importance of each output is entered (1 = least and 5 = most), and the impact level of each input on each output is evaluated (H = high, M = medium, and L = low). In this example, three critical customer requirements, Y1, Y2, and Y3 are listed and six key inputs, X1 through X6, are identified at Level I. X1 through X6 could, for example, be six product specifications. A total impact is computed for each input. In Level II, X1 through X6 have become outputs for which key inputs must be identified. In the example, two inputs, Z1 and Z2, have been listed.

Verify Phase

In the verify phase, the product/process is built and evaluated against the CTQ specifications.

REFERENCES

Aft, Lawrence. 1992. *Fundamentals of Industrial Quality Control*. Boca Raton, FL: Ste Lucie Press.

Bertels, Thomas, ed. 2003. *Rath & Strong's Six-sigma Leadership Handbook*. Hoboken, NJ: John Wiley.

Chowdhury, Subir. 2001. *The Power of Six Sigma*. Chicago, IL: Dearborn Trade Publishing.

Ford Motor Company. 1990. Statistical Methods Office. "Continuing Process Control and Process Capability Improvement." Dearborn, MI: Ford Motor Company.

Mombo Caristan, J. C., Koch, M., and Prange, W. 1991. "Seam Geometry Monitoring for Tailored Welded Blanks." Proceedings of the International Congress on Applications of Lasers and Electro-optics (ICALEO), San Jose, CA, Vol. 74, pp. 123-132. Orlando, FL: Laser Institute of America.

Mombo Caristan, J. C., Penn, W., Mudiam, S., Karube, N. 1999. "High-speed, High-power Laser-blank Cutting and Welding." Proceedings of the International Congress on Applications of Lasers and Electro-optics (ICALEO), San Diego, CA, Vol. 87a, pp. A23-31. Orlando, FL: Laser Institute of America.

Peace, Glen Stuart. 1993. *Taguchi Methods: A Hands-on Approach*. Reading, MA: Addison-Wesley.

Ross, Philipp J. 1988. *Taguchi Techniques for Quality Engineers*. New York: McGraw Hill.

Wadsworth, Harrison M., ed. 1990. *Handbook of Statistical Methods for Engineers and Scientists*. Kacker, Raghu N. "Taguchi Methods." Woodhall, William and Adams, Benjamin M. "Statistical Process Control." New York: McGraw Hill.

Wireman, Terry. 1991. *Total Productive Maintenance, An American Approach*. New York: Industrial Press.

Appendix A

Basics of Lasers

"I have always felt that independence of mind and thought are very important, not just in science but for civilization in general."

—Charles Townes

HISTORICAL BACKGROUND

Nobel Prize laureate Charles Townes, shown in *Figure A-1*, reveals in his book, *How the Laser Happened*, the 1953 invention and theory of the "maser" (Townes 1999). The maser was developed to amplify microwave signals detected from distant stars for astrophysics research. Townes later extended the same principle to amplify light waves. Also significant, another Nobel laureate, Nicolas Bloembergen (also shown in *Figure A-1*), theorized a three-level, solid-state maser at Harvard University in 1956.

The solid-state ruby laser was the first evidenced laser oscillation, thanks to the ingenuity of Theodore Maiman in 1960 at the Hughes laboratories in California. Arthur Shawlow was the first to demonstrate a true visible red laser-beam output from a ruby laser at the Bell Laboratories in New Jersey later that same year. The ruby laser is a three-level, solid-state laser. In 1961, Ali Javan, William Bennet, and Donald Herriot invented the He-Ne gas laser at Bell Laboratories. In 1962, at the General Electric laboratories in New York, Robert Hall invented a solid-state semi-conductor

Figure A-1. Nobel Prize laureates Charles Townes (center) and Nicolas Bloembergen (right) pose with Charles Caristan (left), the author of this book, at the ICALEO Laser Congress in Detroit, MI in 2000.

laser—the type found in every laser printer, laser pointer, and CD player—which now plays a huge role in telecommunications (Karube 2001).

In 1964, four years after the demonstration of the first laser beam, a Nobel Prize was co-awarded to Charles Townes at Columbia University and A. M. Prokhorov and N.G. Basov of the Lebedev Institute in Moscow. It was awarded for "fundamental work in the field of quantum electronics, which has led to the construction of oscillators and amplifiers based on the maser-laser principle." During the same year at Bell Laboratories, Kumar Patel invented the CO_2 laser and a team composed of J.E. Geusic, H.M. Markos, and L.G. Van Uiteit invented the Nd:YAG laser.

In his book, Townes humorously describes how his students and colleagues at the time at Columbia University proposed names for the new invention such as "iraser," "gaser," "raser," and even "dasar" suggested by his brother-in-law and fellow Nobel laureate Arthur Shawlow. Townes explains how Gordon Gould coined the term "laser" for the first time around late 1958 to indicate an optical cavity based on the maser principle, which amplifies waves of short enough length to qualify as light. After a long and bitter legal battle, the U.S. Patent and Trademark Office credited Gould with the patent rights for the invention of the laser-optical oscillator. Maser and laser share one important quantum principle that was theorized as early as 1916 by Albert Einstein, that is, the stimulated emission of radiation—the portion "ser" of both words.

ACTIVE MEDIUM

Laser mediums are made of atoms and/or molecules. An *atom* is composed of one or more electrons gravitating around a nucleus within a well-established base of distribution patterns, each defining discrete (discontinuous) quantum electronic-energy levels. Helium (He) and Argon (Ar) are two examples of atoms existing in nature, argon being 10 times heavier than helium.

An assembly of two or more atoms bound together by intramolecular forces is called a *molecule*. A molecule also exhibits quantum electronic-energy levels resulting from the combination and interaction of each of its atoms. Within each electronic level, smaller quantum vibrational energy levels, characteristic of modes of vibrational motion of the interatomic bonds in a molecule, can be observed. Within each vibrational energy level, smaller quantum rotational energy levels, characteristic of the modes of rotation of a molecule, can be equally distinguished. All of these types of energy levels are illustrated in *Figure A-2*. The lowest energy level of a molecule or atom is called *ground level*.

CO_2 and N_2 are examples of molecules existing naturally in the atmosphere in gas form. A mixture of He, CO_2, and N_2 constitutes the lasing gas for CO_2 lasers. The CO_2 molecule is called the active medium as it is the source for the laser emission as shown in *Figure A-3*.

In some cases, atoms combine in crystals, giving them a stable molecular structure in solid-state. Ruby (Al_2O_3), and respectively yttrium-aluminum-garnet (YAG) ($Y_3Al_5O_{12}$), are examples of solid-state crystals. When contaminated/doped with active medium Cr^{3+} chromium ions, respectively active medium Nd^{3+} neodimium rare earth ions, they constitute the lasing mediums for ruby and Nd:YAG lasers. *Figure A-4* details the energy levels of Nd^{3+} involved in a Nd:YAG lasing mechanism.

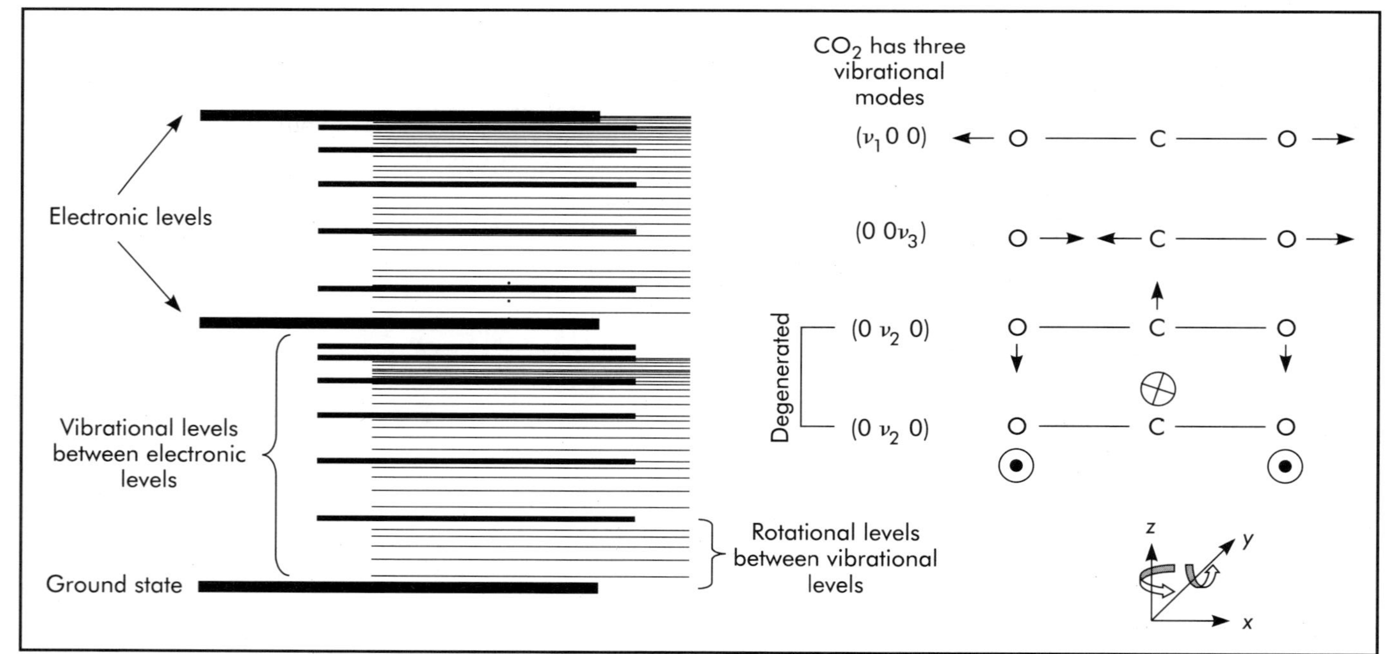

Figure A-2. CO_2 is a linear triatomic molecule. It has four vibrational degrees of freedom yielding three modes of vibration (the bending mode is actually degenerated into bending in the plane of and in the plane perpendicular to the figure), and two modes of rotation about the Z and Y axes (rotation about the X axis of a linear molecule is not considered a mode of rotation). Each mode of vibration generates many harmonic quantum vibrational energy levels between electronic energy levels corresponding to integer values for v_1, v_2, and v_3. Each mode of rotation generates many quantum rotational energy levels between vibrational energy levels.

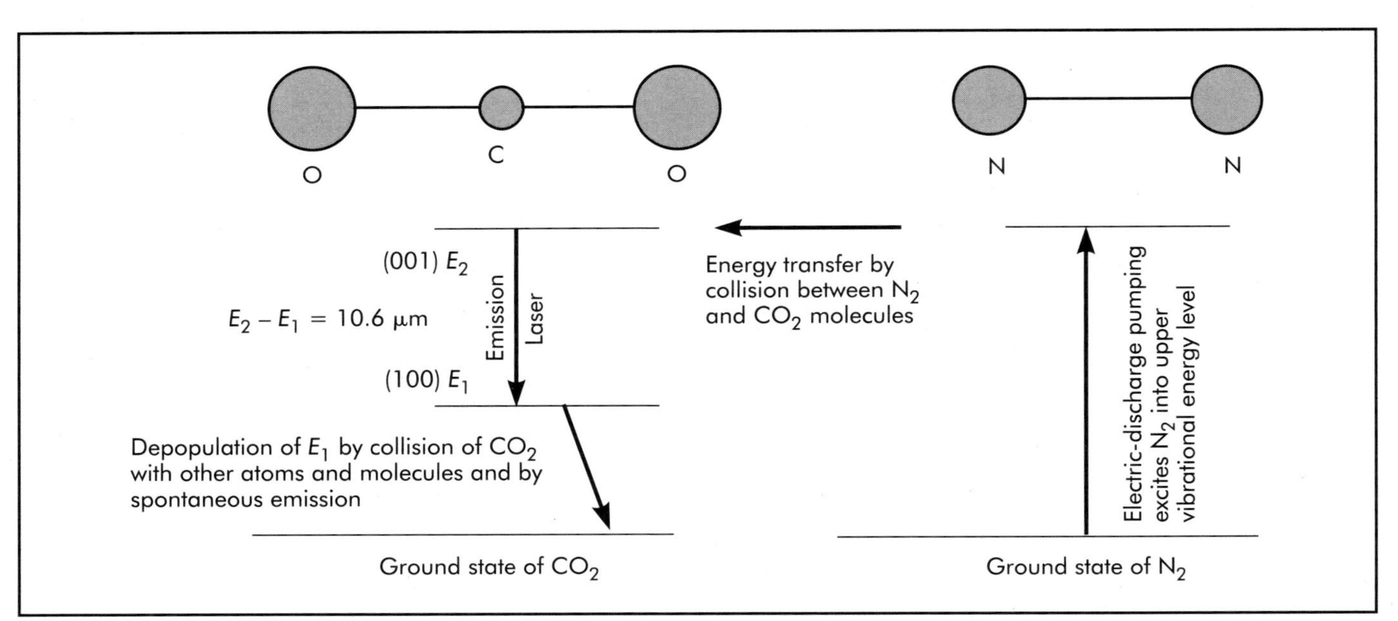

Figure A-3. The lasing medium for industrial CO_2 lasers is composed of $CO_2 + N_2 + He$ mixture. E_2 and E_1 represent two vibrational energy levels of CO_2. The pumping mechanism by electrical discharge excites N2. Molecular collisions between CO_2 and N_2 actually populate upper level E_2 of CO_2 while de-exciting N_2 back to its ground state. Other collisions depopulate the lower energy level E_1 of CO_2, which translates into heating of the gas mixture. Population inversion between E_2 and E_1 makes laser emission possible. The quantum efficiencies of the pumping mechanism of N_2, the energy transfer to E_2 of CO_2, the depopulation of E_1 of CO_2, and the stimulated emission between E_2 and E_1 are the main components for the computation of the overall efficiency of a laser. Other key parameters are gas, velocity, composition, purity, cavity-mirror reflectivity, curvatures, cleanliness, etc.

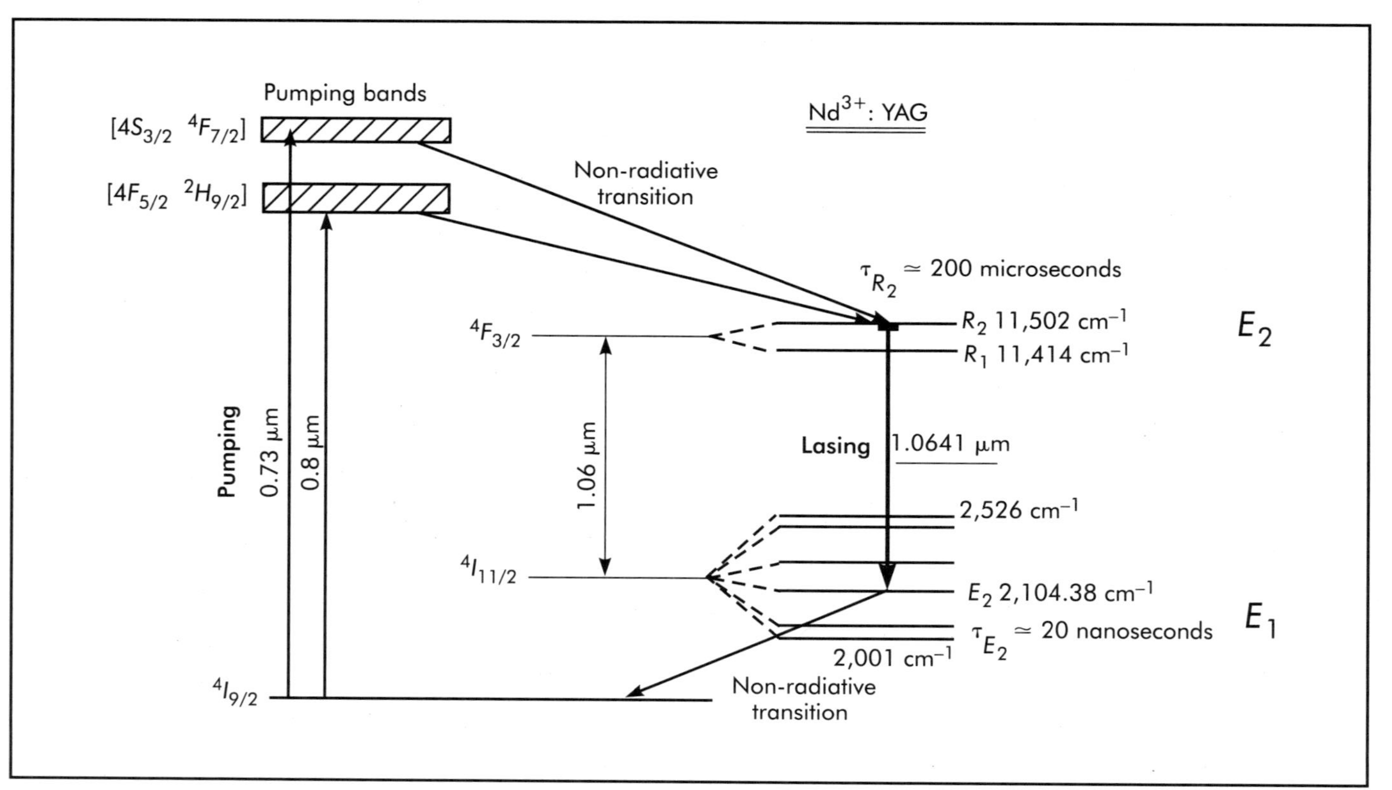

Figure A-4. Shown is the lasing mechanism for industrial Nd:YAG lasers. Non-radiative transitions translating into heat depopulate the lower-energy level E_1, while populating the upper-energy level E_2 from even higher pumped energy levels.

Wavelength

Considering two energy levels of a molecule, E_2 and E_1 (the same reasoning is applicable to atoms), the difference of energy between them is often expressed in terms of an equivalent wavelength λ.

$$E_2 - E_1 = \frac{hc}{\lambda} \quad \text{(A-1)}$$

where:

h = known Planck constant
c = known speed of light in a vacuum
λ = equivalent wavelength corresponding to energy difference, $E_2 - E_1$

For example, two particular energy levels of CO_2, labeled (001) and (100) after vibrational modes of this linear triatomic molecule, differ by 10.6 μm. Two particular energy levels of ion Nd^{3+} differ by 1.0641 μm or of Cr^{3+} differ by 0.6943 μm.

A *wavelength* is a quantitative measurement used to identify color in the visible light spectrum, which goes from indigo at 0.4 μm to red at 0.7 μm, with all colors of the rainbow in between. A wavelength larger than 0.7 μm is invisible to humans and corresponds to infrared (IR) light. A wavelength shorter than 0.4 μm is also invisible to humans and corresponds to ultraviolet (UV) light. At a shorter wavelength than UV light are x-ray radiations followed by even shorter wavelengths called gamma-ray radiations. On the other end of the spectrum, at wavelengths larger than IR light are microwave radiations, followed by radio waves at even longer wavelengths.

Wavelength measurement characterizes light as an electromagnetic field wave. The only wavelengths used for commercial lasers so far go from near UV for telecommunications applications to IR for material processing, detection, and sensor technology. A ruby laser emits a visible red light at 0.6943 μm wavelength. CO_2 lasers at 10.6 μm and Nd:YAG lasers at 1.06 μm emit invisible IR light. During metal processing, intense visible plume light can be seen where the focused beam impinges on the workpiece. This visible plume light is just hot-plasma radiative heat and should not be confused with laser light. However, it is definitely indicative of the presence of the IR laser beam, including invisible reflections of it from which people should be guarded with at least appropriate goggles.

Pumping Mechanism

In a natural equilibrium state, molecules are more likely to rest on a lower energy level, E_1, than on a higher energy level, E_2, following the statistics of Boltzmann law:

$$\left.\frac{N_2}{N_1}\right|_{Boltzmann\ Equilibrium} = \exp\left(\frac{E_1 - E_2}{kT}\right) \tag{A-2}$$

where:

N_2, respectively N_1 = population, that is, the number of molecules with energy level E_2, and respectively E_1

k = known Boltzmann constant

T = temperature of the molecules, ° F (° C)

An external source of energy (intense electrical discharge, intense flash lamp, diode emission, etc.) can excite atoms or molecules enough to inverse the Boltzmann law by making population N_2, of the higher energy level, E_2, become larger than population N_1 of the lower energy level E_1. The method by which the upper-energy level E_2 is populated is called the *pumping mechanism*. Population inversion between E_2 and E_1 will enable lasing. It is conceivable that lasing could occur as soon as the Boltzmann equilibrium is perturbed in favor of the upper energy level E_2, even if total population inversion with E_1 is not achieved. For example:

$$\frac{N_2}{N_1} \geq \left.\frac{N_2}{N_1}\right|_{Boltzmann\ Equilibrium} \quad \text{but} \quad N_1 \geq N_2 \tag{A-3}$$

In industrial CO_2 lasers, the gas medium is a mixture of mainly CO_2, N_2, and He. An electrical discharge excites N_2 molecules from the ground state to upper energy levels. By way of collisions between excited N_2 and CO_2 molecules in the ground state, excited N_2 returns to the ground state by transferring energy to CO_2 molecules. This creates CO_2 molecules with largely populated upper energy levels E_2 (see *Figure A-3*). Collisions between much lighter He atoms and CO_2 are particularly efficient at depopulating the lower energy level E_1. This results in a population inversion between E_1 and E_2, which is ideal for lasing.

In the case of Nd:YAG lasers, a flash-lamp system or diode-laser-system pumping mechanism excites the Nd^{3+} ions from the ground state to a high-level energy state. Non-radiative spontaneous de-excitation occurs from these high energy levels to another upper energy level, E_2 (see *Figure A-4*). Concurrently, due to non-radiative spontaneous de-excitation, energy level E_1, which is lower than E_2, is being depopulated. This creates a population inversion between E_2 and E_1, which is ideal for lasing. This describes a four-level, laser-active medium. The non-radiative transitions translate into heat in the Nd:YAG crystal that must be evacuated with appropriate cooling.

Pumping and transitions between quantum energy levels occur with certain probabilities that will determine the overall efficiency of the laser. Each of these probabilities varies with parameters such as temperature, velocity, intensity, and the type of pumping mechanism.

Photons

When a molecule or atom relaxes (transitions from an upper energy level to a lower energy level), it generally does so by emitting a particle of energy called a photon. *Photons* have no mass. They are characterized by the equivalent wavelength corresponding to the difference between the upper and lower energy levels of the particular transition that generated them (see *Equation A-1*). Most industrial CO_2 lasers emit photons of 10.6-μm wavelength, whereas most Nd:YAG lasers emit 1.06-μm photons.

Light Wave

In 1860, physicist James C. Maxwell theorized the interpretation of *light* as an electromagnetic field wave characterized by its amplitude and wavelength. This electromagnetic interpretation enables the explanation of the phenomena of interference. At the turn of the 20th century, physicist Max Planck proposed a corpuscular interpretation: light is an emission of particles of energy called photons, that is, a radiation. The word *radiation* applies here to light wavelengths and should not be associated with nuclear radioactivity, which occurs at much shorter wavelengths. Light waves are emitted from neon and bulb lights, laser lights, sunlight, and combustion firelight. These lights are radiation and are not considered radioactive on Earth. Both the corpuscular and the electromagnetic interpretations of light are accepted to this day.

Spontaneous Emission

Adhering to the Boltzmann law of *Equation A-2*, excited molecules, if left alone, tend to naturally relax (they transition spontaneously back to a lower energy level). In this naturally spontaneous process, they emit photons of light isotropically, that is, in random directions. This is the case with sunlight, firelight, and neon and bulb lights. In a neon light, an electrical discharge excites neon-based gas until it starts radiating photons of light spontaneously.

Stimulated Emission

Consider a medium composed of molecules already excited on an upper-energy level, E_2, by a pumping mechanism. Further consider an incoming light wave composed of photons, for which wavelength, λ, corresponds exactly to the difference between the upper-energy level, E_2, and the lower-energy level, E_1, of the medium. When this incoming wave encounters the excited molecules, a de-excitation of the molecules into the lower-energy level, E_1, may be stimulated along with a corresponding emission of photons forming a stimulated wave. This stimulated wave possesses three important characteristics:

- monochromaticity, or a single color, which has the same defined wavelength, λ, as the incoming wave;
- directionality—contrary to spontaneous emission, the stimulated wave is not emitted isotropically, it is emitted in the same direction as the incoming wave; and
- coherence—the stimulated wave is in phase with the incoming wave.

Coherence insures that the waves produced are in phase and thus, their amplitudes add to one another in constructive interference instead of canceling each other's amplitude by destructive interference as illustrated in *Figure A-5*. The intensity of a wave is proportional to the square of its amplitude. In that regard, all living things on Earth should be thankful that sunlight is not a coherent light, as life as we know it would not be possible.

Monochromaticity enables all rays of light in a laser beam to be focused at a much smaller point instead of suffering from spectral dispersion as illustrated in *Figure A-6*. This also can be shown in a prism demonstration common in high school classrooms (see wavelength dependence of focus position shown by *Equation B-22*).

Directionality minimizes the divergence of the laser light beam and enables its delivery and collection through optical means with minimum loss by dispersion.

Monochromaticity, directionality, and coherence enable smaller focus points through a focusing lens or mirror. A smaller focus point yields the high power density required to cut metals. Monochromaticity, directionality, and coherence are the main characteristics that distinguish laser light from any other light. Diode-laser lights are coherent and monochromatic but are an exception as they do not necessarily exhibit emission directionality. Their beams are also notably less focusable than other laser beams having a directionality property.

Amplification

Considering stimulated emission as a "black box," its net result is that for one incoming photon, two identical photons come out. This multiplication of photons is not systematic and occurs

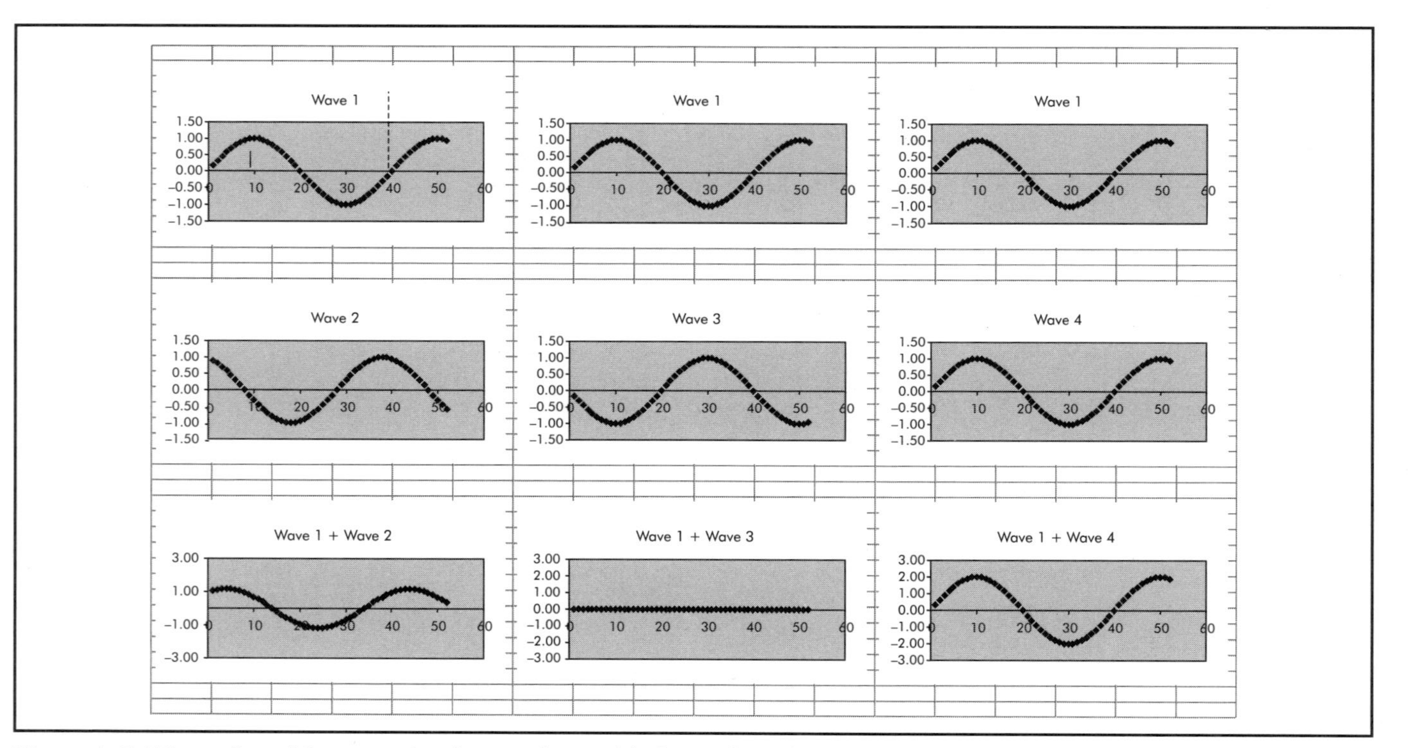

Figure A-5. Waves 1 and 2 are not in phase: when added together, they result in a small-amplitude wave (low intensity). Waves 1 and 3 are in opposition of phase: when added together, they result in a wave of 0 intensity. Waves 1 and 4 are in phase and indicate coherence: when added together, they result in a wave, for which the amplitude is the sum of each wave's amplitude (high intensity).

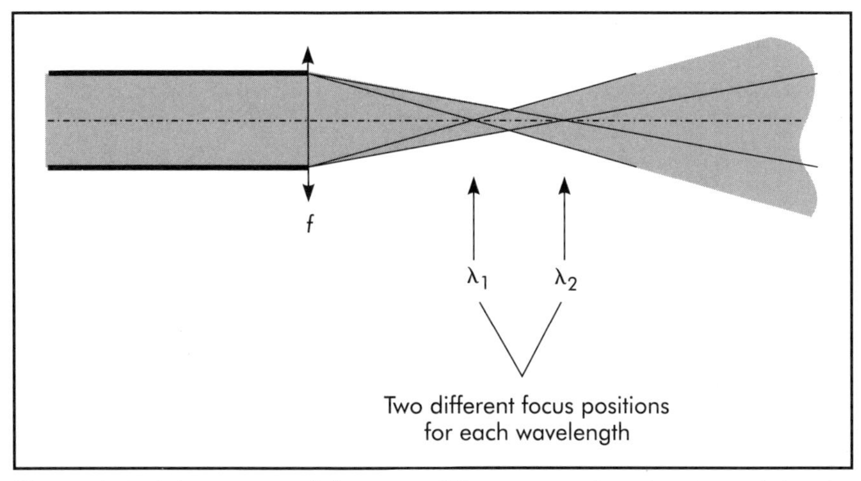

Figure A-6. A beam containing two different wavelengths, λ_1 and λ_2: the focus position through the same lens, f, varies with the wavelength.

with a certain probability each time that a photon encounters an excited molecule.

Figure A-7 shows a medium placed between two reflecting mirrors. Together they form an optical cavity with an optical axis. Some photons traveling parallel to the optical axis keep being reflected back and forth between these mirrors. During each trip through the medium, photon multiplication yields an increasing number of stimulated photons until saturation power is achieved. This phenomenon, by which saturation gain is obtained by feeding back a portion of the increased signal to a system that produces this gain in the first place, is well known from basic electronic amplification systems such as shown in *Figure A-8*.

RESONATOR CAVITY

A cavity is composed of one end mirror called the rear mirror (RM), another end mirror called the output-coupler (OC) mirror, and a lasing medium placed along the optical path between the OC and rear mirrors. The cavity's amplification results in the oscillation of a light wave between the two end mirrors. This wave oscillation can be broken down into a coherent wave traveling

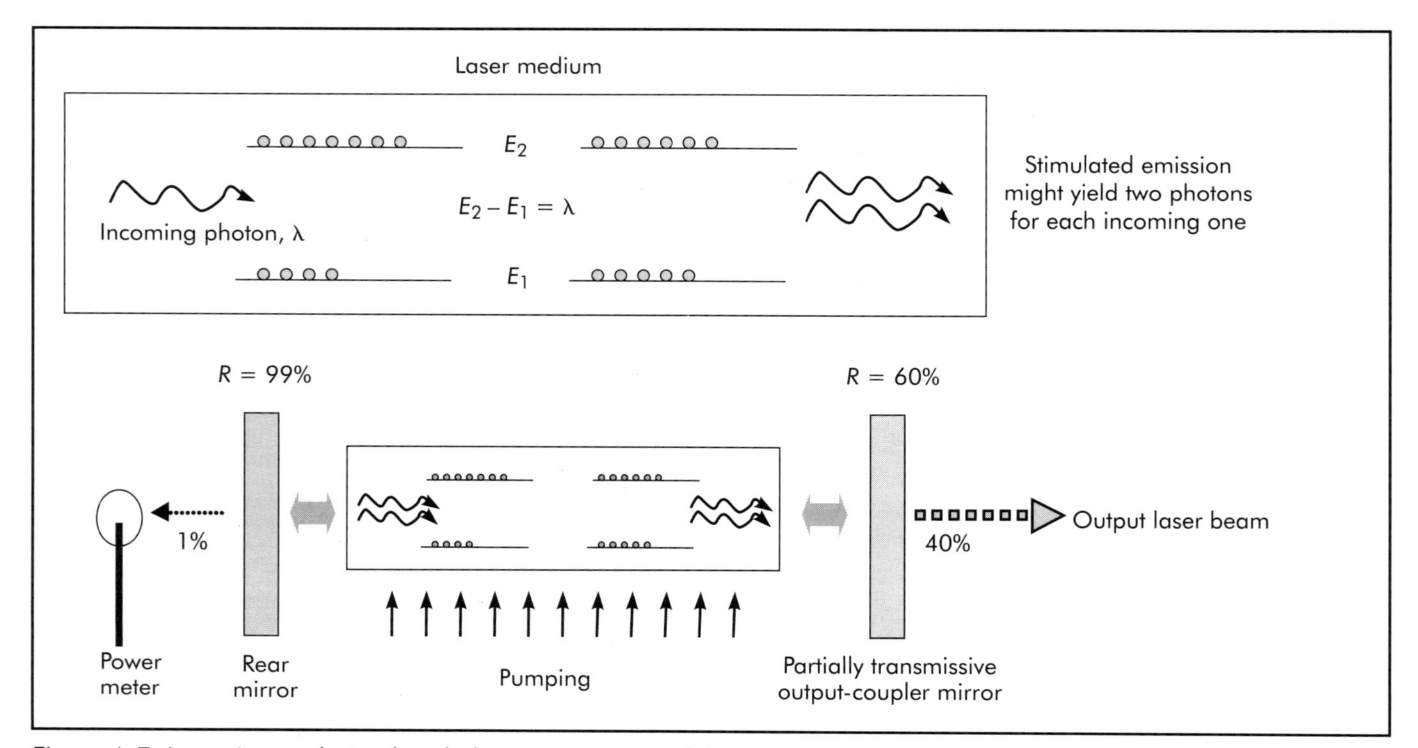

Figure A-7. Incoming and stimulated photon waves are of the same wavelength, λ, same propagation direction, and in phase. When repeated until saturation inside an optical cavity, photon multiplication becomes amplification. The output-coupler mirror can allow an output laser beam to exit through it by transmission (stable resonator) or by dispersion (unstable resonator) beside it.

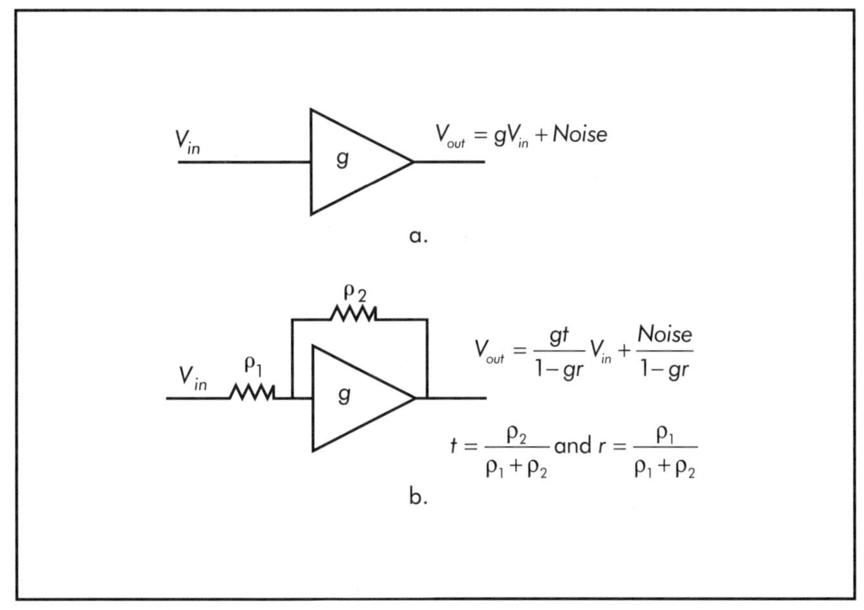

Figure A-8. (a) A basic electronic amplifier multiplies input signal, V_{in}, by gain, g, and also yields amplified noise. (b) When a portion of the amplified output signal is fed back to the input of the amplifier, the resultant output, V_{out}, can have a larger signal-to-noise ratio if the right impedances, ρ_1 and ρ_2, are chosen. An optical resonator is similar to such electronic amplification as a portion of an amplified light wave is reflected back into the cavity by end mirrors.

from the OC mirror to the rear mirror and another coherent wave traveling back from the rear mirror to the OC mirror. If both waves are in opposition of phase, their amplitudes will cancel each other and no laser-beam intensity will be detected. On the other hand, if the optical distance between the OC and rear mirrors is precisely adjusted to within less than a quarter wavelength precision (2.52 μm in a CO_2 laser), then both waves may be in phase and their amplitudes will be combined in a resultant intense laser beam. In this case, the amplified waves are said to be resonating in the cavity. A percentage of the stimulated light can be transmitted out of the cavity through the OC mirror. It outputs a coherent, monochromatic, and monodirectional light wave—a light beam that is the result of light amplification by stimulated emission of radiation (LASER).

Cavity Modes

Light waves will be amplified only if their spatial oscillation modes allow them to resonate in phase in a particular cavity. A mode is recognizable by its spatial energy distribution across a beam cross-section, that is, a transverse electromagnetic mode, TEM_{mn}, characterized by two integers, m and n. Based mainly on the curvatures of the end mirrors, the cavity aperture, and the optical distance between them, several modes are generally possible in a cavity. Mode sorting can be achieved using optical and electronic means. *Figure A-9* illustrates some observable individual pure circular and rectangular modes. A laser beam's quality is often measured in terms of an M^2 number, which for pure TEM_{mn} modes, relates to integers m and n as follows (Luxon and Parker 1992; Petring 1995):

$$M^2 = 2m + n + 1 \quad \text{(A-4)}$$

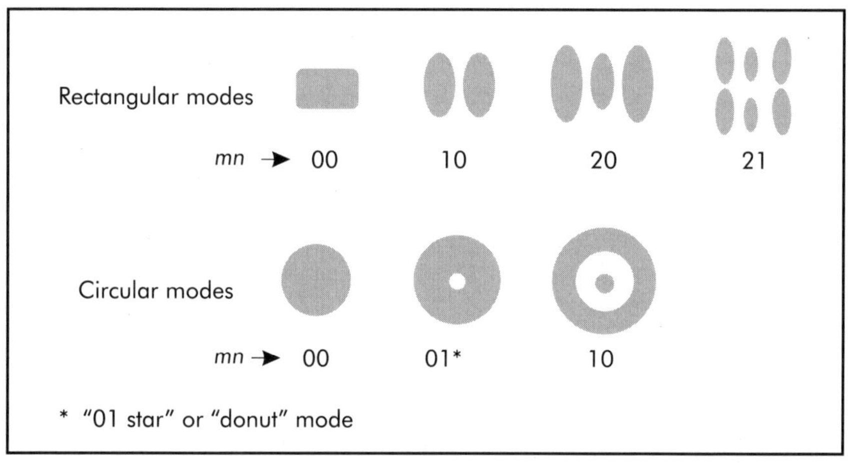

Figure A-9. Possible individual modes of a cavity are represented in their cross-section. The shapes of optics and of all physical elements along the optical path of the beam in the cavity can limit which transverse electromagnetic modes (TEM_{mn}) will resonate. Gaussian modes correspond to m = 0 and n = 0 circular mode and are generally smallest in size. High-order numbers m and n yield large-size TEM_{mn} modes and large divergence. Only circular modes can possess axis-symmetry when the laser's oscillator cavity is tuned properly.

It is important to note that the higher the mode order (large m and n values and, therefore, large M^2 value per *Equation A-4*), the larger the transverse dimensions of the beam and its divergence. Despite a directionality property, laser beams have a natural divergence dictated by diffraction limitations—output beam dimensions will sooner or later naturally increase with distance from the OC mirror (see *Figure A-10*). High-order modes have a larger divergence than low-order modes (see *Equation B-29*).

Industrial laser beams are generally *multimode*, meaning a combination of individual modes. Their resultant M^2 number is a weighted combination of the M^2 numbers of each individual pure mode. The resultant output beam power is distributed among each individual pure mode allowed to resonate. Resonance can be achieved if the cavity is aligned adequately. Laser-beam intensity can then be detected. *Figure A-11* shows that although intensity at or above the rated power can be detected and measured, acrylic

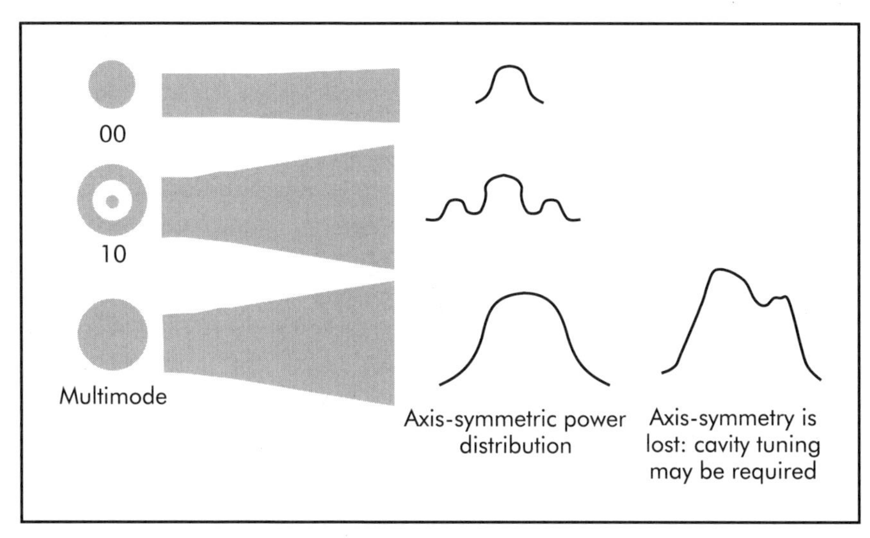

Figure A-10. Examples of spatial transverse power distribution vary from mode to mode: Gaussian mode is TEM_{00}, *the next higher-order mode is* TEM_{10}. *Shown is an example of the asymmetry of a multimode beam observable on a mode burn when a cavity is not optimally tuned. Some output beams diverge right from the OC mirror with a waist at the OC mirror or intra-cavity. Other output beams converge first toward an extra-cavity waist position before diverging downstream from it.*

mode burns of the output beam could show insufficient axis-symmetry if the cavity is not precisely tuned. Cavity tuning generally involves OC, rear, and folding-mirror alignment to achieve the proper axis-symmetry necessary for contour cutting.

If a spatial-filter object is placed intra-cavity (between the rear and OC mirrors) along the optical-path length and with an aperture large enough to let low-order modes through but too small to prevent high-order modes from resonating, then the higher modes will vanish from the output laser beam. The resultant output beam mode will have a smaller M^2 number and a smaller power. If the same spatial-filter aperture is placed extra-cavity, then it will not eliminate higher modes altogether. It will spatially mask a portion of the higher mode too large to pass through the aperture, and the resultant output beam mode will not have a changed M^2 number.

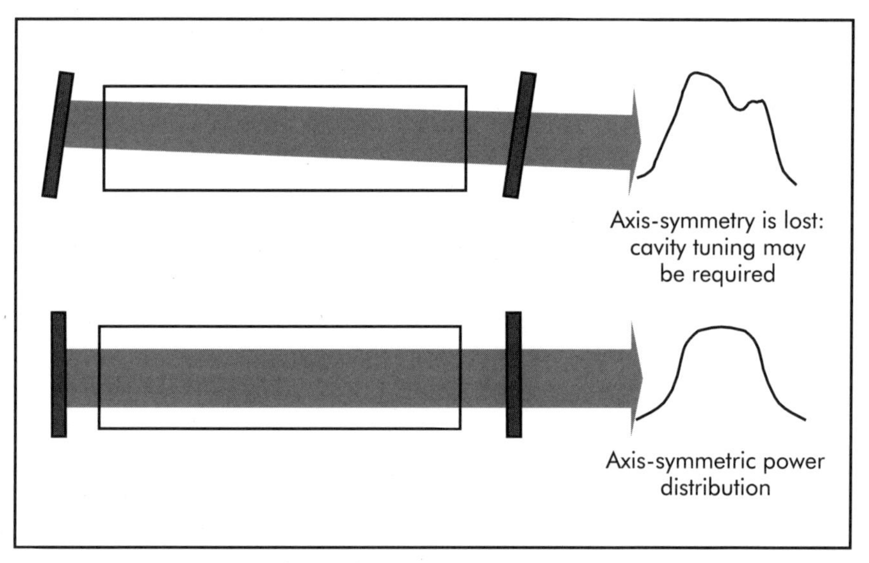

Figure A-11. Tuning realigns the mirrors of the cavity to achieve an axis-symmetric beam mode. Once this is achieved, fine-tuning adjustment will yield a maximum power reading, which should be at least equal to the rated power of the laser. As a word of caution, the maximum power reading can be higher with an asymmetric mode than with an axis-symmetric mode; nevertheless, axis-symmetry at rated power must take precedence over maximum power capability when tuning a cavity.

REFERENCES

Karube, Norio. 2001. *The Light of the 21st Century*. Japan: ISBN 4-8355-2264-8.

Luxon, James T. and Parker, David E. 1992. *Industrial Lasers and Their Applications*. Englewood Cliffs, NJ: Prentice Hall.

Petring, Dirk. 1995. "Anwendungsorientierte Modellierung des Laserstrahlschneidens zur rechnergestutzten Prozeßoptimierung." Ph.D. thesis. Aachen, Germany: University of Aachen.

Townes, Charles. 1999. *How The Laser Happened: Adventures of a Scientist*. Cary, NC: Oxford University Press.

Appendix B

Laser-beam Propagation

"Let us not mistake imagination for lie. They are actually opposite."

—Daniel Pennac

Classical optics theory becomes grossly inaccurate and imprecise when describing laser-beam propagation. For example, diffraction limitation cannot be demonstrated using classical lens equations and Snell's law. A different approach is necessary. This appendix details how laser-beam-mode propagation can be derived by an extension of Gaussian beam-propagation calculations to give a more accurate and precise prediction of shape, size, and focusing characteristics.

RESONATOR-CAVITY DESIGN

Consider the example cavity in *Figure B-1*, which has a periodical structure of lenses that dictate beam propagation inside and outside of the cavity. A mirror of curvature R is equivalent to a lens of focal length $f = R/2$. If $R < 0$, then the lens is a diverging lens. If $R > 0$ it is a converging lens. If the periodic optical structure tends to have light rays propagating back and forth, moving progressively further away from the optical axis shared by the mirrors, then the cavity is that of an unstable resonator. If the rays

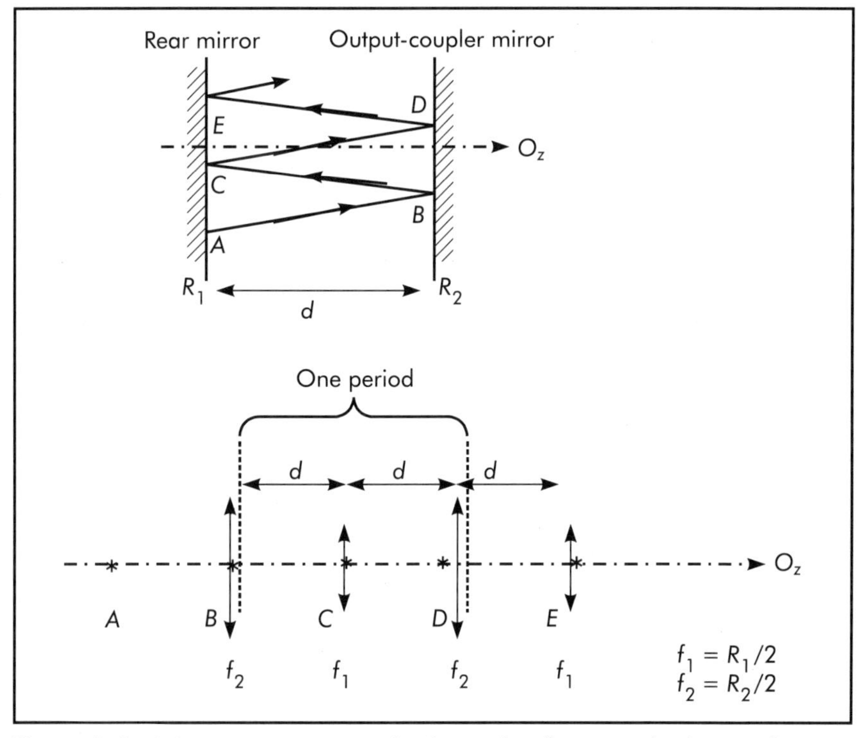

Figure B-1. A laser-resonator cavity is made of two end mirrors, the rear mirror (RM) and output-coupler (OC) mirror, with curvatures R_1 *and* R_2*, respectively. They share the same optical axis,* O_z*. A ray of light travels back and forth between the mirrors along the ABCDE . . . path. The equivalent structural optics system for this cavity is a periodical sequence of lenses.*

propagate back and forth and are periodically forced back toward the optical axis of the cavity as seen in *Figure B-2*, then the cavity is that of a stable resonator. The output laser beam of the stable cavity resonator can be extracted through the partially transmissive output-coupler (OC) mirror. In an unstable cavity, the rays bouncing back and forth between the output-coupler and rear mirror are progressively dispersed away from the optical axis of the cavity until they are reflected beyond the physical aperture boundary of the cavity. For most unstable resonators, the OC mirror is totally reflective and does not allow any laser-ray transmission. The rays escaping from the cavity by dispersion constitute the output laser beam of the unstable resonator cavity.

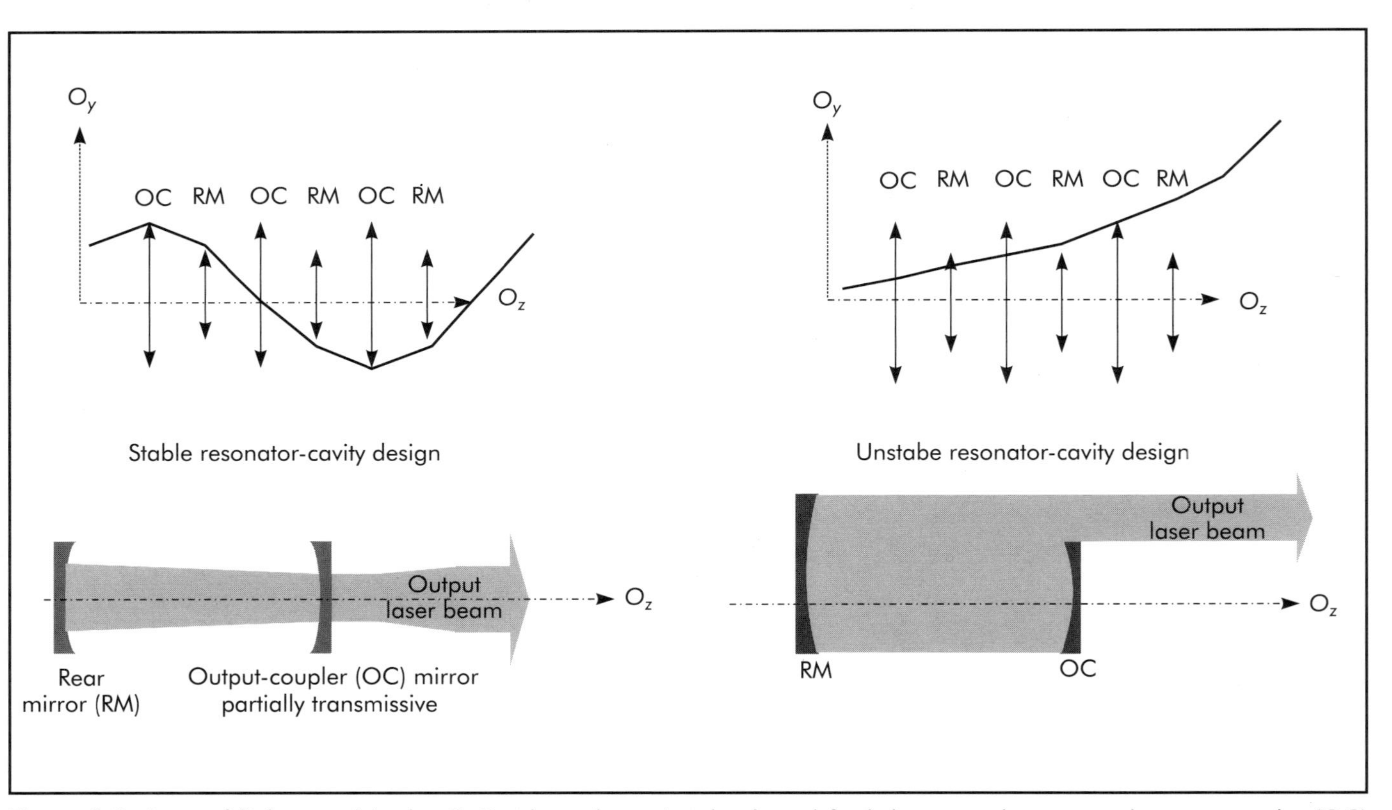

Figure B-2. Rays of light travel in the O_yO_z plane, bouncing back and forth between the rear and output-coupler (OC) mirrors in the laser-resonator cavity.

Cavity stability is strongly dependent on the curvatures of the end mirrors and the optical distance between them along the optical axis. Here, *stability* characterizes a design of a cavity and has no relation to the stability of the output beam. There are many industrial lasers with unstable resonator-cavity designs yet with perfectly stable output-beam characteristics and performance.

OPTICAL SETUPS

The following derivations and developments apply to practical and realistic optical setups. They lead to final beam-propagation characteristics that are applicable to many industrial beam-delivery systems. The complex derivations of beam transformations can be skipped to find the final solutions in *Equations B-31* through *B-40* (or their approximated versions in *Equations B-26* and *B-27*) for focus position, focus-spot radius, and Rayleigh range corresponding to beam transformation of a known input beam through the optical system depicted in *Figure B-3*.

Beam Transformation Matrix

A ray of light along optical axis, O_z, can be represented by its elevation, y_{in}, and its slope, y'_{in}, with respect to O_z at a particular start position 1 as shown in *Figure B-4*. The elevation, y_{out}, and slope, y'_{out}, of this ray after traveling a distance, d_{in}, in free space can be simply stated as:

$$y_{out} = y_{in} + d_{in} y'_{in} \text{ and } y'_{out} = y'_{in} \quad \text{(B-1)}$$

or, in matrix annotation:

$$\begin{pmatrix} y_{out} \\ y'_{out} \end{pmatrix} = \begin{pmatrix} 1 & d_{in} \\ 0 & 1 \end{pmatrix} \begin{pmatrix} y_{in} \\ y'_{in} \end{pmatrix} \quad \text{(B-2)}$$

wherein:

$$T_a = \begin{pmatrix} 1 & d_{in} \\ 0 & 1 \end{pmatrix}$$

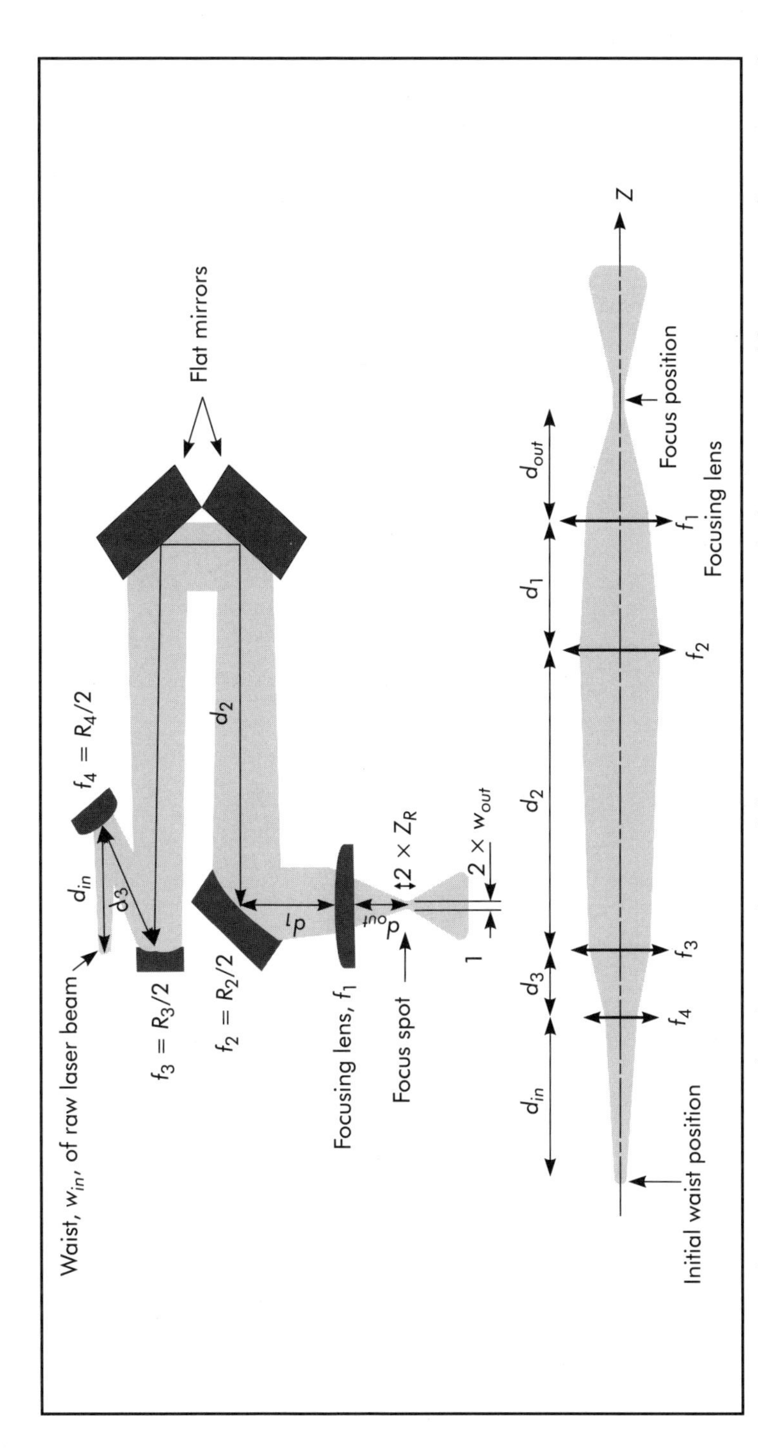

Figure B-3. Shown is a practical and generic beam-delivery system composed of a sequence of free-space distances and lenses: d_1, f_1, d_2, f_2, d_3, f_3, d_{in}, and f_4. A mirror of curvature R is equivalent to a lens of focal length R/2. A flat folding mirror has an infinite radius of curvature, R; that is, infinite focal length and equivalent to no mirror at all. The M^2 value and the initial waist position distance from the output-coupler mirror can be obtained from the laser-resonator manufacturer.

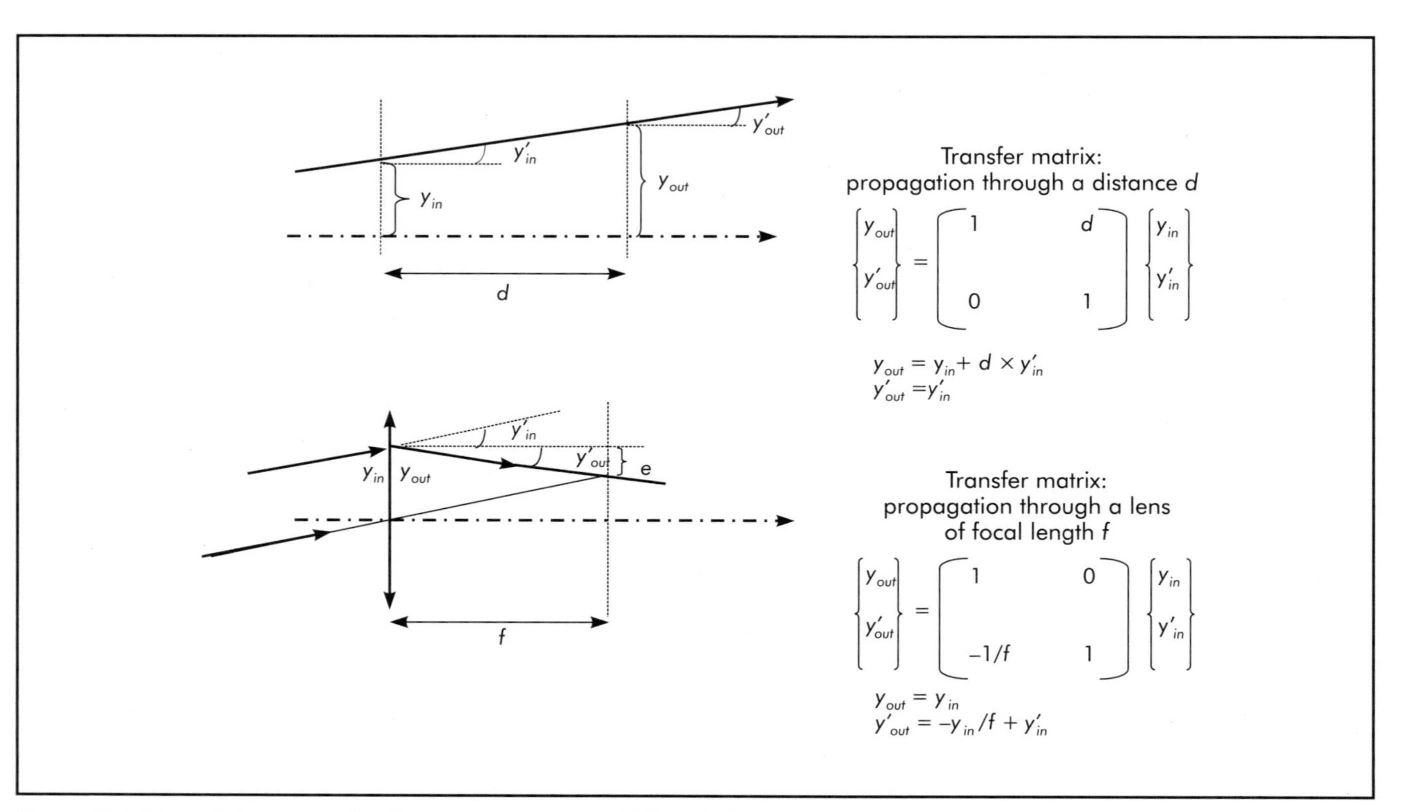

Figure B-4. Paraxial rays are by definition quasi-parallel and close to the optical axis of the lens. Their propagation can be expressed by transfer matrices.

is a transfer matrix for propagation through a linear homogene medium such as free space of length d_{in}.

Similarly, beam position y_{out} and its slope y'_{out} immediately after a thin lens of focal length f is compared to the same characteristics immediately before the lens (*Figure B-4*), and can be derived as follows:

$$y_{out} = y_{in} \text{ and } y'_{out} = -\frac{e}{f} = -\frac{1}{f}(y_{in} - f y'_{in}) \tag{B-3}$$

or, in matrix annotation:

$$\begin{pmatrix} y_{out} \\ y'_{out} \end{pmatrix} = \begin{pmatrix} 1 & 0 \\ -\frac{1}{f} & 1 \end{pmatrix} \begin{pmatrix} y_{in} \\ y'_{in} \end{pmatrix} \tag{B-4}$$

wherein:

$$T_b = \begin{pmatrix} 1 & 0 \\ -\frac{1}{f} & 1 \end{pmatrix}$$

is a transfer matrix for propagation through a lens of focal length f. Note that the determinant of the transfer matrices T_a and T_b is equal to 1. The transfer matrix for an optical system containing free-space distance d_{in}, a lens of focal length f, and free-space distance d_{out} as shown in *Figure B-5,* is a product of three matrices and results in:

$$T = \begin{pmatrix} 1 & d_{out} \\ 0 & 1 \end{pmatrix} \begin{pmatrix} 1 & 0 \\ -\frac{1}{f} & 1 \end{pmatrix} \begin{pmatrix} 1 & d_{in} \\ 0 & 1 \end{pmatrix}$$

$$= \begin{pmatrix} 1 - \frac{d_{out}}{f} & d_{in} - \frac{d_{in} d_{out}}{f} + d_{out} \\ -\frac{1}{f} & -\frac{d_{in}}{f} + 1 \end{pmatrix} \tag{B-5}$$

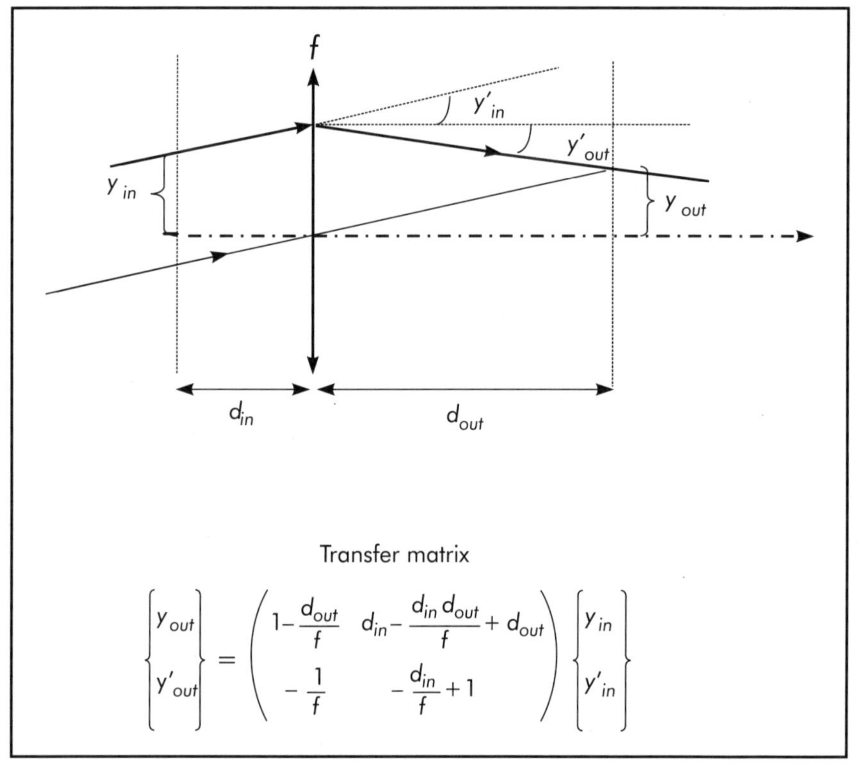

Figure B-5. Shown is an example of a transfer matrix for a paraxial ray traveling through a distance, d_{in}, of free space, then a lens of focal length f, and then again a distance d_{out} of free space.

Note that the determinant of the matrix product T equals the product of the determinants and is equal to 1.

Complex Radius of Curvature

In a developed analysis of laser beams, it has been established that laser beams propagate like spherical waves with radius of curvature $R(z)$ and beam cross-section with radius $W(z)$ (Kogelnick and Li 1966). $R(z)$ and $W(z)$ are functions of distance z on the optical axis. As contradictory as it sounds, to simplify equation derivations, a complex radius of curvature $q(z)$ (with an imaginary number component) is defined such that:

$$q(z) = z + i\frac{\pi w_0^2}{\lambda} \quad \text{(B-6)}$$

or alternatively,

$$\frac{1}{q(z)} = \frac{1}{R(z)} - i\frac{\lambda}{\pi W^2(z)}$$

where:

$q(z)$ = complex radius of curvature
z = real component of complex number $q(z)$
i = imaginary number such that $i^2 = -1$
$\frac{\pi w_0^2}{\lambda}$ = imaginary component of complex number $q(z)$
λ = wavelength,

$$R(z) = z\left[1 + \left(\frac{\pi w_0^2}{\lambda z}\right)^2\right] \quad \text{(B-7)}$$

and $$W(z) = w_0\left[1 + \left(\frac{\lambda z}{\pi w_0^2}\right)^2\right]^{\frac{1}{2}} \quad \text{(B-8)}$$

where:

w_0 = waist or radius of the beam at its smallest cross-section, which corresponds to the origin position $z = 0$ of the spherical wave where the radius of curvature $R(z)$ is infinite

A ray can be represented by its complex radius of curvature $q(z)$ at every position, z, rather than being represented by elevation y and slope y'. It can be demonstrated that if

$$T = \begin{pmatrix} A & B \\ C & D \end{pmatrix}$$

is a beam-propagation transfer matrix between positions 1 and 2 along an optical axis, then y_{out}, y'_{out}, and q_{out} complex curvature at position 2 can be derived from y_{in}, y'_{in}, and q_{in} complex curvature at position 1 as follows (Yariv 1991):

$$y_{out} = Ay_{in} + By'_{in} \tag{B-9}$$

$$y'_{out} = Cy_{in} + Dy'_{in} \tag{B-10}$$

and

$$q_{out} = \frac{Aq_{in} + B}{Cq_{in} + D} \tag{B-11}$$

Beam Transformation Through a Single Focusing Lens

From *Figure B-6*, if $q_{in}(z)$ represents the complex curvature before the lens with waist w_{in} at distance d_{in} upstream from the lens, then $q_{in}(z)$ at the left of the lens can be expressed according to *Equation B-6* as:

$$q_{in}(z) = (z + d_{in}) + i\frac{\pi w_{in}^2}{\lambda} \tag{B-12}$$

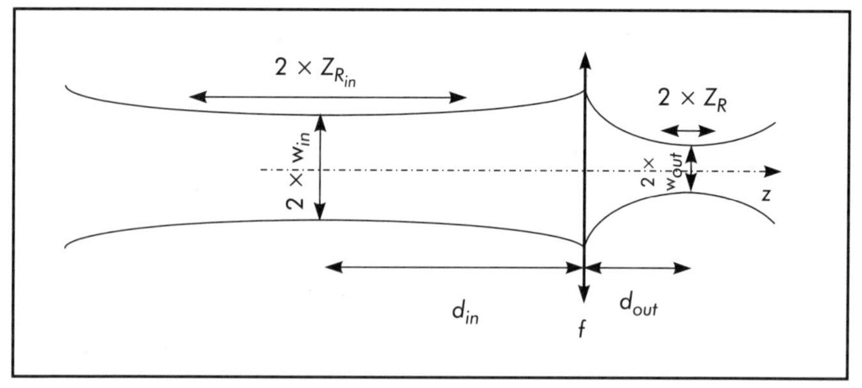

Figure B-6. After focusing lens f, a new waist, w_{out}, defines the position of the origin for the spherical wave of complex curvature $q_{out}(z)$ to the right-hand side of the lens. The focusing lens is at a variable distance, d_{in}, from the incident beam's waist, w_{in}.

where:

z varies from $-d_{in}$ to 0 and $z = 0$ indicates the position of the lens

However, because $q_{in}(z)$ is a "real" beam, a correction factor, M^2 (defined in Appendix A), must be introduced at this point in the calculation (Carter 1980; Phillips and Andrews 1983; Belanger 1991). *Equation B-12* should be rewritten as:

$$q_{in}(z) = (z + d_{in}) + i\frac{\pi w_{in}^2}{M^2\lambda} \tag{B-13}$$

Similarly, if $q_{out}(z)$ is the complex curvature at distance z after the lens, with waist w_{out} at distance d_{out} to the right of the lens (see *Figure B-6*), then $q_{out}(z)$ to the right of the lens can be expressed as:

$$q_{out}(z) = (z - d_{out}) + i\frac{\pi w_{out}^2}{M^2\lambda} \tag{B-14}$$

where:

z varies from 0 to d_{out} and $z = 0$ indicates the position of the lens

Derivation of $q_{out}(z)$, d_{out}, and w_{out} as a function of parameters d_{in}, w_{in}, f, M^2, and variable z, and knowing transfer matrix A, B, C, D from *Equation B-5* can be shown as:

$$\begin{pmatrix} A & B \\ C & D \end{pmatrix} = \begin{pmatrix} 1 - \frac{z}{f} & d_{in} - \frac{d_{in} z}{f} + z \\ -\frac{1}{f} & -\frac{d_{in}}{f} + 1 \end{pmatrix} \tag{B-15}$$

$$q_{out}(z) = \frac{Aq_{in} + B}{Cq_{in} + D} \tag{B-16}$$

where:

$q_{in} = i\frac{\pi w_{in}^2}{M^2\lambda}$, which leads to

$$q_{out}(z) = \frac{\left(B + Ai\frac{\pi w_{in}^2}{M^2\lambda}\right)\left(D - Ci\frac{\pi w_{in}^2}{M^2\lambda}\right)}{D^2 + \pi^2 C^2 \frac{w_{in}^4}{M^4\lambda^2}} \tag{B-17}$$

or,

$$q_{out}(z) = \frac{BD + AC\frac{\pi^2 w_{in}^4}{M^4\lambda^2} + i(AD - BC)\frac{\pi w_{in}^2}{M^2\lambda}}{D^2 + C^2\frac{\pi^2 w_{in}^4}{M^4\lambda^2}} \tag{B-18}$$

$AD - BC$ is the determinant of the resultant transfer matrix and is equal to 1. The position $z = d_{out}$ of the focus point is a new waist position and can be established by equating the real component of complex number $q_{out}(z)$ to 0. In other words $q_{out}(d_{out})$ becomes a purely imaginary number:

$$BD + AC\frac{\pi^2 w_{in}^4}{M^4\lambda^2} = 0 \tag{B-19}$$

implying

$$\left(d_{in} - \frac{d_{in}d_{out}}{f} + d_{out}\right)\left(-\frac{d_{in}}{f} + 1\right) + \left(1 - \frac{d_{out}}{f}\right)\left(-\frac{1}{f}\right)\frac{\pi^2 w_{in}^4}{M^4\lambda^2} = 0 \tag{B-20}$$

and

$$d_{out}\left(1 - 2\frac{d_{in}}{f} + \frac{d_{in}^2}{f^2} + \frac{\pi^2 w_{in}^4}{M^4 f^2\lambda^2}\right) = \left(\frac{d_{in}^2}{f} - d_{in} + \frac{\pi^2 w_{in}^4}{M^4 f\lambda^2}\right) \tag{B-21}$$

lastly,

$$d_{out} = \frac{\frac{d_{in}^2}{f} - d_{in} + \frac{\pi^2 w_{in}^4}{M^4 f\lambda^2}}{\left(1 - \frac{d_{in}}{f}\right)^2 + \frac{\pi^2 w_{in}^4}{M^4 f^2\lambda^2}} \tag{B-22}$$

It should be acknowledged that d_{out} is also a function of wavelength λ, incident beam waist w_{in}, and M^2. Similarly, the radius w_{out} of the waist at the focus point can be derived by equating the imaginary components of complex number $q_{out}(z)$ in *Equations B-14* and *B-18*.

$$Z_R = \frac{\pi w_{out}^2}{M^2\lambda} = \frac{(AD - BC)\dfrac{\pi w_{in}^2}{M^2\lambda}}{D^2 + C^2\dfrac{\pi^2 w_{in}^4}{M^4\lambda^2}} \tag{B-23}$$

that is:

$$Z_R = \frac{\dfrac{\pi w_{in}^2}{M^2\lambda}}{\left(1 - \dfrac{d_{in}}{f}\right)^2 + \dfrac{\pi^2 w_{in}^4}{M^4 f^2 \lambda^2}} \tag{B-24}$$

and

$$w_{out}^2 = \frac{w_{in}^2}{\left(1 - \dfrac{d_{in}}{f}\right)^2 + \dfrac{\pi^2 w_{in}^4}{M^4 f^2 \lambda^2}} \tag{B-25}$$

Incidentally, Z_R is called the *Rayleigh range*, defined as the distance around the waist under which the beam can be considered almost cylindrical, that is, within about ±41.4% variation in radius w_{out}. Laser operators prefer to define a depth of focus, which is equivalent to a Rayleigh range of much less than ±40% variation in radius w_{out}, such that within the depth-of-focus range, cutting performance remains fairly unchanged. Nonetheless, Rayleigh ranges indicate theoretical estimates and trends of tolerances in depth of focus. In many practical metal laser-cutting situations, *Equations B-22*, *B-24*, and *B-25* are approximated with:

$$d_{out} = f \text{ and } w_{out} = \frac{M^2\lambda f}{\pi w_{in}} \tag{B-26}$$

$$Z_R = \frac{M^2 \lambda f^2}{\pi w_{in}^2} \qquad \text{(B-27)}$$

These approximations are to be handled with caution. The user should verify the conditions as they apply to a specific design. They generally assume that the beam incident on the focusing lens is perfectly collimated, that is, the constant cross-section radius is equal to the waist radius. Knowing Z_R, d_{out}, and w_{out}, beam radius $W_{out}(z)$ can be computed as a function of distance z from the lens with the following:

$$W_{out}(z) = w_{out} \left[1 + \left(\frac{z - d_{out}}{Z_R} \right)^2 \right]^{\frac{1}{2}} \qquad \text{(B-28)}$$

For laser beams, the full divergence angle of beam propagation is small enough to be approximated to the tangent of the divergence angle in radians.

$$\theta = 2 \lim_{z \to \infty} \frac{W_{out}(z)}{z} \text{ and } \theta = \frac{2\lambda M^2}{\pi w_{out}} \qquad \text{(B-29)}$$

Beam Transformation Through One Focusing Lens and Three Non-flat Mirrors

Figure B-3 illustrated a more complex sequence of beam-delivery optics composed of one focusing lens f_1, and at most three non-flat mirrors f_2, f_3, and f_4. A collimator could be formed from f_3 and f_4, and f_2 could be an adaptive optic with adjustable focal length. Bending mirrors with flat surfaces are ignored since their focal length is infinite, and thus equivalent to no mirror at all for this calculation. Incidentally, the system described in *Figure B-3* would become equivalent to the sequence of *Figure B-6* if $f_2 = f_3 = f_4 = \infty$ and $d_1 = d_2 = d_3 = 0$.

Knowing parameters d_1, d_2, d_3, d_{in}, f_1, f_2, f_3, and f_4, then focus position d_{out}, beam radius at focus position w_{out}, Rayleigh range Z_R, and beam radius $W_{out}(z)$ can be expressed as a function of variable distance z to the right of focusing lens f_1 by starting with *Equations B-19* and *B-23*, and using the following expression for transfer matrix $ABCD$:

$$\begin{pmatrix} A & B \\ C & D \end{pmatrix} \tag{B-30}$$

where:

$A = \alpha + \beta z$
$B = \beta + \delta z$
$C = \gamma$
$D = \delta$

with

$$\alpha = (1-\frac{d_1}{f_2})(1-\frac{d_3}{f_4}) - (d_2 + d_1 - \frac{d_1 d_2}{f_2})(\frac{1}{f_3} + \frac{1}{f_4} - \frac{d_3}{f_3 f_4}) \tag{B-31}$$

$$\beta = (1-\frac{d_1}{f_2})\left[d_{in} - \frac{d_3 d_{in}}{f_4} + d_3\right] + (d_2 + d_1 - \frac{d_1 d_2}{f_2})\left[1 - \frac{d_{in}}{f_3} - \frac{d_{in}}{f_4} - \frac{d_3}{f_3} + \frac{d_3 d_{in}}{f_3 f_4}\right] \tag{B-32}$$

$$\gamma = (1-\frac{d_3}{f_4})(-\frac{1}{f_1} - \frac{1}{f_2} + \frac{d_1}{f_1 f_2}) + (-\frac{1}{f_3} - \frac{1}{f_4} + \frac{d_3}{f_3 f_4})\left[1 - \frac{d_2}{f_1} - \frac{d_2}{f_2} - \frac{d_1}{f_1} + \frac{d_1 d_2}{f_1 f_2}\right] \tag{B-33}$$

$$\delta = (\frac{d_1}{f_1 f_2} - \frac{1}{f_1} - \frac{1}{f_2})\left[d_{in} - \frac{d_3 d_{in}}{f_4} + d_3\right] + \left[1 - \frac{d_2}{f_1} - \frac{d_2}{f_2} - \frac{d_1}{f_1} + \frac{d_1 d_2}{f_1 f_2}\right]\left[1 - \frac{d_{in}}{f_3} - \frac{d_{in}}{f_4} - \frac{d_3}{f_3} + \frac{d_3 d_{in}}{f_3 f_4}\right] \tag{B-34}$$

Note that α, δ, A, and D are dimensionless, whereas β and B are proportional to a distance and γ and C are inversely proportional to a distance. The determinant is $AD - BC = 1$. The equivalent of *Equations B-22, B-24*, and *B-25* can be derived to find the following:

$$d_{out} = \frac{-\beta\delta - \alpha\gamma \frac{\pi^2 w_{in}^4}{M^4\lambda^2}}{\delta^2 + \gamma^2 \frac{\pi^2 w_{in}^4}{M^4\lambda^2}} \tag{B-35}$$

$$Z_R = \frac{\frac{\pi w_{in}^2}{M^2\lambda}}{\delta^2 + \gamma^2 \frac{\pi^2 w_{in}^4}{M^4\lambda^2}} \tag{B-36}$$

$$w_{out}^2 = \frac{w_{in}^2}{\delta^2 + \gamma^2 \frac{\pi^2 w_{in}^4}{M^4\lambda^2}} \tag{B-37}$$

$$W_{out}(z) = w_{out}\left[1 + \left(\frac{z - d_{out}}{Z_R}\right)^2\right]^{\frac{1}{2}} \tag{B-38}$$

Similarly to *Equation B-6*, *Equation B-14* can be rewritten as:

$$\frac{1}{q_{out}(z)} = \frac{1}{R(z)} - i\frac{\lambda M^2}{\pi W_{out}^2(z)} \tag{B-39}$$

and consequently *Equation B-38* can be rewritten in the following form:

$$W_{out}^2(z) = \frac{w_{in}^2 + \left[\frac{M^2\lambda}{\pi w_{in}}(\beta\delta + \delta^2 z) + \frac{\pi w_{in}^3}{M^2\lambda}(\alpha\gamma + \gamma^2 z)\right]^2}{\delta^2 + \gamma^2 \frac{\pi^2 w_{in}^4}{M^4\lambda^2}} \tag{B-40}$$

Impact of Incident Beam Waist Size and M^2 Number

An example of a CO_2 laser beam is given. It has a 7.9-in. (200-mm) focusing lens which, in the near field (NF), is positioned 236.2 in. (6,000 mm) downstream from the incident beam's waist position, and in the far field (FF), is positioned 472.4 in. (12,000 mm) downstream from the incident beam's waist position. *Figure B-7* illustrates the variations of the focus-point diameter, Rayleigh range, and focus position as a function of M^2 and the incident beam's waist size. Generally speaking, when M^2 increases, the differences between NF and FF increase. When the incident beam's waist increases, the differences between NF and FF decrease. Based on the sole criterion of stability, it would make sense to seek a laser system with a small M^2 number and a large incident-beam waist. This combination provides for a smaller focus-spot diameter and, therefore, higher power density at the workpiece.

When cutting thick material, it is critical to maintain beam characteristics between the NF and FF positions on a work envelope as identical as possible. For example, compare the case of a 0.8-in. (20-mm) diameter beam waist with an M^2 value of 3 between NF and FF in the absence of a system guaranteeing absolute constant optical-path length. The positions of the focus spot are changed at 7.944 in. (201.77 mm) from the focusing lens in the NF, versus 7.952 in. (201.99 mm) in the FF. This is a tolerable 0.009 in. (0.22 mm) difference because it is well within the large depth-of-focus windows hinted by large Rayleigh range (Z_R) values of 0.119 in. (3.01 mm) in the NF and 0.066 in. (1.67 mm) in the FF. However, the focus-spot diameters are 0.014 in. (0.35 mm) in the NF and 0.010 in. (0.26 mm) in the FF. This represents a worrisome 45% difference in power density at the workpiece. This explains why a constant beam-path option or adaptive optics helps to make NF and FF data identical. An alternative is to compromise by using a collimator (possibly mirrors f_3 and f_4 of *Figure B-3*). This has an effect almost equivalent to an inflation of the incident beam's waist size by a magnification factor, f_3/f_4, and reduction of M^2 value by a factor, f_4/f_3 (strict use of *Equations B-30* through *B-38* would give the more accurate effect of a collimator).

Considering the same beam waist of 0.8-in. (20-mm) diameter with an M^2 value of 3 going through a collimator of magnification

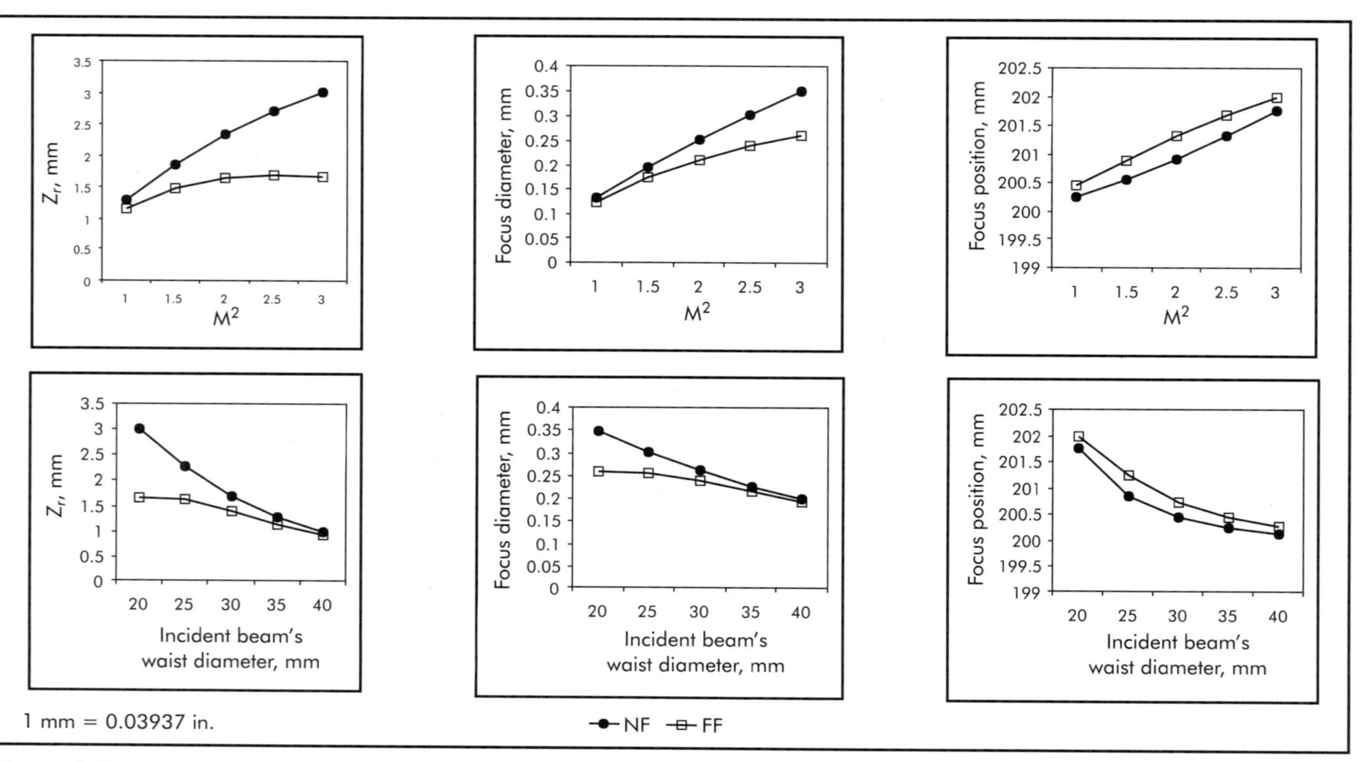

Figure B-7. For a CO_2 laser at 10.6 μm wavelength and f = 7.9 in. (200 mm), variations of focus-point diameter, Rayleigh range, and focus position are shown as a function of M^2 (top row at constant incident-beam waist diameter = 20 mm), and as a function of the incident beam's waist diameter (bottom row at constant M^2 = 3).

1.5, the result of collimation would correspond in *Figure B-7* to an equivalent beam diameter of 1.2 in. (30 mm) with an M^2 value of 2. Such a collimator would make NF and FF beam characteristics almost identical. However, with a beam diameter of 1.2 in. (30 mm) at the collimator lens f_3, despite a reduced divergence, the diameter of this beam incident on the focusing lens may probably be too large for the beam-delivery conduit or the focusing lens. A magnification reduction to an appropriate maximum value is needed. *Table B-1* compares three magnifications.

The beam diameter at the focusing lens f_1 can be estimated by following these steps:

1. Calculate α, β, γ, and δ in *Equations B-31* through *B-34* by setting $f_1 = +\infty$ (that is, no focusing lens).
2. Determine corresponding values for d_{out}, w_{out}, and Z_R from *Equations B-35* through *B-37*.
3. Calculate the beam radius at the lens by using *Equation B-38* with $z = 0$.

An experimental acrylic mode burn at the focusing-lens position can be used to confirm the calculations.

Table B-1. Collimator magnification comparison

	Magnification 1.5		Magnification 1.2		Magnification 1†	
Parameter	NF	FF	NF	FF	NF	FF
Z_r	1.16	1.07	2.10	1.59	3.01	1.67
Focus diameter	0.18	0.17	0.27	0.23	0.35	0.26
Focus position	200.20	200.38	200.71	201.10	201.77	201.99

† No collimation

CONCLUSION

The considerations given in this appendix hint at the complexity of decision criteria for machine and beam-delivery design. A complex set of input variables such as focal length, beam waist, collimation requirement, metal type, metal thickness, etc., must be taken into account. The output variables to be considered range among the specifics of quality, productivity, profitability, environment, and safety. A systematic approach using six-sigma tools such as design of experiments (Taguchi techniques) with an orthogonal matrix can save development time and cost when many input variables must be compared.

REFERENCES

Belanger, P. A. 1991, February. "Beam Propagation and the *ABCD* Ray Matrices." *Optics Letters*, Vol. 16, pp. 196-198.

Carter, William. 1980, March. "Spot Size and Divergence for Hermite-Gaussian Beams of Any Order." *Applied Optics*, pp. 1,027-1,029.

Kogelnick, H. and Li, T. 1966, October. "Laser Beams and Resonators." *Applied Optics*, vol. 5, pp. 1,550-1,567.

Phillips, R. L. and Andrews, L.C. 1983, March. "Spot Size and Divergence for Laguerre-Gaussian Beams of Any Order." *Applied Optics*, pp. 643-644.

Yariv, Amnon. 1991. *Optical Electronics*. New York: Saunders College Publishing.

Appendix C

Nozzle Gas Dynamics

"Gravitation is not responsible for people falling in love."

—Albert Einstein

Nozzle gas dynamics are a crucial yet often neglected aspect of thermal metal cutting. "Stick on a nozzle tip and it should work" is the response to most inquiries. Few understand the important optimization and troubleshooting parameters. This appendix will shed more light on the fluid mechanics essentials useful to understand compressible gas flow through a nozzle. Derivations can be skipped to the end results for subsonic and supersonic volume flow rate (*Equations C-40, C-41, C-46*, and *C-47*). *Table C-1* gives volume flow-rate numerical data in increments of pressure and nozzle diameter for common assist-gases.

NOZZLE TYPES

Figure C-1 shows three common types of nozzle orifice geometries. For laser cutting, types (b) and (c) are the most commonly used. Type (a) is the rarest, probably due to its prohibitive cost, but also because it reduces the range of nozzle standoff by the length of the diverging segment. The exact geometry and dimensions of (a) are suited for only a very narrow range of stagnation

Table C-1. Flow rates for assist-gas

Gage Reading psi (bar)		Pressure P, psi (bar)		Nozzle Diameter, in. (mm)								
				0.040 (1.00)	0.050 (1.25)	0.060 (1.50)	0.070 (1.75)	0.080 (2.00)	0.090 (2.25)	0.100 (2.50)	0.110 (2.75)	0.120 (3.00)
Nitrogen												
14.7	(1)	29.4	(2)	37	57	82	112	147	186	229	277	330
29.4	(2)	44.1	(3)	55	86	124	168	220	278	344	416	495
44.1	(3)	58.8	(4)	73	115	165	224	293	371	458	554	660
58.8	(4)	73.5	(5)	92	143	206	281	367	464	573	693	825
73.5	(5)	88.2	(6)	110	172	247	337	440	557	687	832	990
88.2	(6)	102.9	(7)	128	200	289	393	513	649	802	970	1,155
102.9	(7)	117.6	(8)	147	229	330	449	586	742	916	1,109	1,319
117.6	(8)	132.3	(9)	165	258	371	505	660	835	1,031	1,247	1,484
132.3	(9)	147.0	(10)	183	286	412	561	733	928	1,145	1,386	1,649
147.0	(10)	161.7	(11)	202	315	454	617	806	1,021	1,260	1,525	1,814
161.7	(11)	176.4	(12)	220	344	495	673	880	1,113	1,374	1,663	1,979
176.4	(12)	191.1	(13)	238	372	536	730	953	1,206	1,489	1,802	2,144
191.1	(13)	205.8	(14)	257	401	577	786	1,026	1,299	1,604	1,940	2,309
205.8	(14)	220.5	(15)	275	430	619	842	1,100	1,392	1,718	2,079	2,474
220.5	(15)	235.2	(16)	293	458	660	898	1,173	1,484	1,833	2,217	2,639
235.2	(16)	249.9	(17)	312	487	701	954	1,246	1,577	1,947	2,356	2,804
249.9	(17)	264.6	(18)	330	515	742	1,010	1,319	1,670	2,062	2,495	2,969
264.6	(18)	279.3	(19)	348	544	783	1,066	1,393	1,763	2,176	2,633	3,134
279.3	(19)	294.0	(20)	367	573	825	1,122	1,466	1,856	2,291	2,772	3,299
294.0	(20)	308.7	(21)	385	601	866	1,179	1,539	1,948	2,405	2,910	3,464

Table C-1. *Continued*

Gage Reading psi (bar)	Pressure *P*, psi (bar)	Nozzle Diameter, in. (mm) 0.040 (1.00)	0.050 (1.25)	0.060 (1.50)	0.070 (1.75)	0.080 (2.00)	0.090 (2.25)	0.100 (2.50)	0.110 (2.75)	0.120 (3.00)
Air										
14.7 (1)	29.4 (2)	36	56	81	110	144	182	225	272	324
29.4 (2)	44.1 (3)	54	84	122	165	216	273	338	409	486
44.1 (3)	58.8 (4)	72	113	162	221	288	365	450	545	648
58.8 (4)	73.5 (5)	90	141	203	276	360	456	563	681	810
73.5 (5)	88.2 (6)	108	169	243	331	432	547	675	817	972
88.2 (6)	102.9 (7)	126	197	284	386	504	638	788	953	1,134
102.9 (7)	117.6 (8)	144	225	324	441	576	729	900	1,089	1,297
117.6 (8)	132.3 (9)	162	253	365	496	648	820	1,013	1,226	1,459
132.3 (9)	147.0 (10)	180	281	405	551	720	912	1,125	1,362	1,621
147.0 (10)	161.7 (11)	198	310	446	607	792	1,003	1,238	1,498	1,783
161.7 (11)	176.4 (12)	216	338	486	662	864	1,094	1,351	1,634	1,945
176.4 (12)	191.1 (13)	234	366	527	717	936	1,185	1,463	1,770	2,107
191.1 (13)	205.8 (14)	252	394	567	772	1,008	1,276	1,576	1,907	2,269
205.8 (14)	220.5 (15)	270	422	608	827	1,080	1,367	1,688	2,043	2,431
220.5 (15)	235.2 (16)	288	450	648	882	1,152	1,459	1,801	2,179	2,593
235.2 (16)	249.9 (17)	306	478	689	938	1,225	1,550	1,913	2,315	2,755
249.9 (17)	264.6 (18)	324	506	729	993	1,297	1,641	2,026	2,451	2,917
264.6 (18)	279.3 (19)	342	535	770	1,048	1,369	1,732	2,138	2,587	3,079
279.3 (19)	294.0 (20)	360	563	810	1,103	1,441	1,823	2,251	2,724	3,241
294.0 (20)	308.7 (21)	378	591	851	1,158	1,513	1,914	2,363	2,860	3,403

Table C-1. *Continued*

Gage Reading psi (bar)	Pressure *P*, psi (bar)	Nozzle Diameter, in. (mm) 0.040 (1.00)	0.050 (1.25)	0.060 (1.50)	0.070 (1.75)	0.080 (2.00)	0.090 (2.25)	0.100 (2.50)	0.110 (2.75)	0.120 (3.00)
				Argon						
14.7 (1)	29.4 (2)	33	51	73	100	130	165	203	246	293
29.4 (2)	44.1 (3)	49	76	110	149	195	247	305	369	439
44.1 (3)	58.8 (4)	65	102	146	199	260	329	407	492	585
58.8 (4)	73.5 (5)	81	127	183	249	325	412	508	615	732
73.5 (5)	88.2 (6)	98	152	220	299	390	494	610	738	878
88.2 (6)	102.9 (7)	114	178	256	349	455	576	711	861	1,024
102.9 (7)	117.6 (8)	130	203	293	398	520	659	813	984	1,171
117.6 (8)	132.3 (9)	146	229	329	448	585	741	915	1,107	1,317
132.3 (9)	147.0 (10)	163	254	366	498	650	823	1,016	1,230	1,463
147.0 (10)	161.7 (11)	179	279	402	548	715	906	1,118	1,353	1,610
161.7 (11)	176.4 (12)	195	305	439	598	781	988	1,220	1,476	1,756
176.4 (12)	191.1 (13)	211	330	476	647	846	1,070	1,321	1,599	1,903
191.1 (13)	205.8 (14)	228	356	512	697	911	1,152	1,423	1,722	2,049
205.8 (14)	220.5 (15)	244	381	549	747	976	1,235	1,524	1,845	2,195
220.5 (15)	235.2 (16)	260	407	585	797	1,041	1,317	1,626	1,968	2,342
235.2 (16)	249.9 (17)	276	432	622	847	1,106	1,399	1,728	2,091	2,488
249.9 (17)	264.6 (18)	293	457	659	896	1,171	1,482	1,829	2,214	2,634
264.6 (18)	279.3 (19)	309	483	695	946	1,236	1,564	1,931	2,337	2,781
279.3 (19)	294.0 (20)	325	508	732	996	1,301	1,646	2,033	2,459	2,927
294.0 (20)	308.7 (21)	341	534	768	1,046	1,366	1,729	2,134	2,582	3,073

Table C-1. *Continued*

Gage Reading psi (bar)		Pressure *P*, psi (bar)		Nozzle Diameter, in. (mm) 0.040 (1.00)	0.050 (1.25)	0.060 (1.50)	0.070 (1.75)	0.080 (2.00)	0.090 (2.25)	0.100 (2.50)	0.110 (2.75)	0.120 (3.00)
Helium												
14.7	(1)	29.4	(2)	103	161	231	315	411	521	643	778	926
29.4	(2)	44.1	(3)	154	241	347	472	617	781	964	1,167	1,388
44.1	(3)	58.8	(4)	206	321	463	630	823	1,041	1,286	1,556	1,851
58.8	(4)	73.5	(5)	257	402	578	787	1,028	1,302	1,607	1,944	2,314
73.5	(5)	88.2	(6)	309	482	694	945	1,234	1,562	1,928	2,333	2,777
88.2	(6)	102.9	(7)	360	562	810	1,102	1,440	1,822	2,250	2,722	3,240
102.9	(7)	117.6	(8)	411	643	926	1,260	1,645	2,083	2,571	3,111	3,702
117.6	(8)	132.3	(9)	463	723	1,041	1,417	1,851	2,343	2,892	3,500	4,165
132.3	(9)	147.0	(10)	514	803	1,157	1,575	2,057	2,603	3,214	3,889	4,628
147.0	(10)	161.7	(11)	566	884	1,273	1,732	2,263	2,864	3,535	4,278	5,091
161.7	(11)	176.4	(12)	617	964	1,388	1,890	2,468	3,124	3,857	4,667	5,554
176.4	(12)	191.1	(13)	668	1,045	1,504	2,047	2,674	3,384	4,178	5,055	6,016
191.1	(13)	205.8	(14)	720	1,125	1,620	2,205	2,880	3,645	4,499	5,444	6,479
205.8	(14)	220.5	(15)	771	1,205	1,735	2,362	3,085	3,905	4,821	5,833	6,942
220.5	(15)	235.2	(16)	823	1,286	1,851	2,520	3,291	4,165	5,142	6,222	7,405
235.2	(16)	249.9	(17)	874	1,366	1,967	2,677	3,497	4,425	5,464	6,611	7,868
249.9	(17)	264.6	(18)	926	1,446	2,083	2,835	3,702	4,686	5,785	7,000	8,330
264.6	(18)	279.3	(19)	977	1,527	2,198	2,992	3,908	4,946	6,106	7,389	8,793
279.3	(19)	294.0	(20)	1,028	1,607	2,314	3,150	4,114	5,206	6,428	7,778	9,256
294.0	(20)	308.7	(21)	1,080	1,687	2,430	3,307	4,319	5,467	6,749	8,166	9,719

Table C-1. *Continued*

Gage Reading psi (bar)		Pressure *P*, psi (bar)		Nozzle Diameter, in. (mm) 0.040 (1.00)	0.050 (1.25)	0.060 (1.50)	0.070 (1.75)	0.080 (2.00)	0.090 (2.25)	0.100 (2.50)	0.110 (2.75)	0.120 (3.00)
Oxygen												
6.0	(0.41)	20.7	(1.41)	23	36	52	71	92	117	144	175	208
7.0	(0.48)	21.7	(1.48)	24	38	54	74	97	123	151	183	218
8.0	(0.54)	22.7	(1.54)	25	40	57	78	101	128	158	192	228
9.0	(0.61)	23.7	(1.61)	26	41	59	81	106	134	165	200	238
10.0	(0.68)	24.7	(1.68)	28	43	62	84	110	139	172	208	248
11.0	(0.75)	25.7	(1.75)	29	45	65	88	115	145	179	217	258
12.0	(0.82)	26.7	(1.82)	30	47	67	91	119	151	186	225	268
13.0	(0.89)	27.7	(1.89)	32	51	73	99	130	164	202	245	292
29.4	(2)	44.1	(3)	51	80	116	157	206	260	321	389	463
44.1	(3)	58.8	(4)	69	107	154	210	274	347	429	519	617
58.8	(4)	73.5	(5)	86	134	193	262	343	434	536	648	771
73.5	(5)	88.2	(6)	103	161	231	315	411	521	643	778	926
88.2	(6)	102.9	(7)	120	187	270	367	480	607	750	907	1,080
102.9	(7)	117.6	(8)	137	214	309	420	549	694	857	1,037	1,234
117.6	(8)	132.3	(9)	154	241	347	472	617	781	964	1,167	1,389
132.3	(9)	147.0	(10)	171	268	386	525	686	868	1,071	1,296	1,543
147.0	(10)	161.7	(11)	189	295	424	577	754	955	1,179	1,426	1,697
161.7	(11)	176.4	(12)	206	321	463	630	823	1,041	1,286	1,556	1,851
176.4	(12)	191.1	(13)	223	348	501	682	891	1,128	1,393	1,685	2,006
191.1	(13)	205.8	(14)	240	375	540	735	960	1,215	1,500	1,815	2,160

Table C-1. *Continued*

Gage Reading psi (bar)	Pressure *P*, psi (bar)	Nozzle Diameter, in. (mm) 0.040 (1.00)	0.050 (1.25)	0.060 (1.50)	0.070 (1.75)	0.080 (2.00)	0.090 (2.25)	0.100 (2.50)	0.110 (2.75)	0.120 (3.00)
Oxygen										
205.8 (14)	220.5 (15)	257	402	579	787	1,029	1,302	1,607	1,945	2,314
220.5 (15)	235.2 (16)	274	429	617	840	1,097	1,389	1,714	2,074	2,469
235.2 (16)	249.9 (17)	291	455	656	892	1,166	1,475	1,821	2,204	2,623
249.9 (17)	264.6 (18)	309	482	694	945	1,234	1,562	1,929	2,334	2,777
264.6 (18)	279.3 (19)	326	509	733	997	1,303	1,649	2,036	2,463	2,931
279.3 (19)	294.0 (20)	343	536	771	1,050	1,371	1,736	2,143	2,593	3,086
294.0 (20)	308.7 (21)	360	562	810	1,102	1,440	1,822	2,250	2,722	3,240

SCFH = 0.47 L/min = 0.0282 SCMH, 1 SCMH = 16.67 L/min = 35.461 SCFH

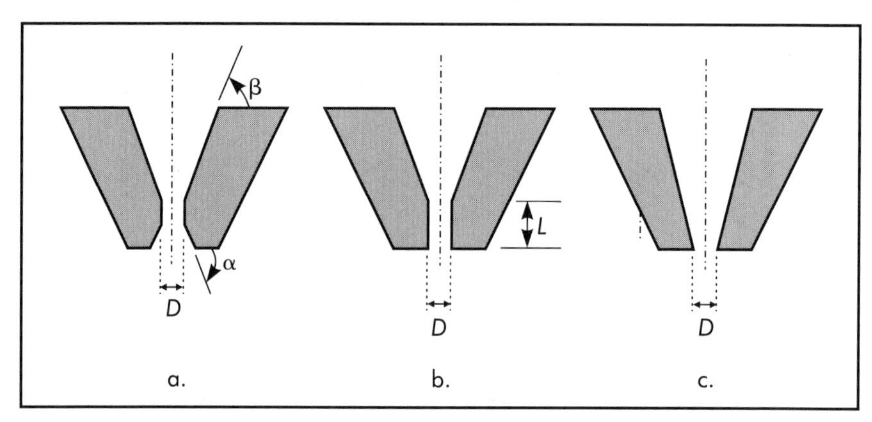

Figure C-1. Three axis-symmetric nozzle geometries: (a) Laval type with a converging-diverging section and smallest cross-section of diameter D; (b) capillary orifice of diameter D with a straight segment of length L, which is generally ≧2 × D; (c) convergent nozzle with orifice of diameter D. The capillary and convergent nozzle types are the most widely used for laser cutting.

pressures to yield a "choked" supersonic flow output without unwanted normal and oblique shock wave development. However, within this narrow range of stagnation pressures, the pressure at the workpiece and the mass flow rate are optimum compared to nozzle types (b) and (c). All three nozzles are axis-symmetric and, therefore, for simplification of the fluid-transport equations, can be considered as generating steady one-dimensional compressible flow up to the nozzle exit. Downstream of the nozzle, the gas flow also can be considered axis-symmetric. Viscosity will be neglected in the derivations except where deemed helpful. All gases will be considered ideal gases according to:

$$P = \rho\, rT \tag{C-1}$$

where:

P = gas pressure
ρ = gas density
r = ratio resulting from the ideal gas constant, $R = 8.314\ J/K$-mol ÷ molar mass equivalent of the gas
T = gas temperature

ISENTROPIC FLOW AND SPECIFIC HEAT COEFFICIENTS

Appendix A explained that gas particles (atoms and molecules) carry internal energy in the form of electronic, vibrational, and rotational energies in addition to translational energy related to thermal agitation of the particles. The internal energy, U, of each molecule and atom depends only on temperature, T, not on static pressure, P, or volume, V. A physical quantity known as an entropy, S, of an ensemble of molecules can be interpreted as a measure of the agitation's randomness or "disorder." If a system represented by 1 mole of an ensemble of molecules is thermally isolated (adiabatic process), then entropy can be defined in differential terms by the Gibbs relationship (Fox and McDonald 1985):

$$T\,dS = dU + P\,dv = dH - v\,dP \tag{C-2}$$

where:

T = gas temperature
S = entropy of an assembly of molecules
U = total internal energy of 1 mole of the ensemble of molecules
P = static pressure
H = a physical quantity known as enthalpy of 1 mole of the ensemble of molecules
v = volume occupied by this mole of molecules

The quantity product $P\,dv$ represents the differential of mechanical work done by 1 mole of the ensemble of molecules. In a process in which loss or gain of internal energy is balanced by, respectively, gain or loss in work, then this leads to $dS = 0$ in *Equation C-2*. The entropy is constant; the process is said to be *isentropic*. A compressible gas flow through a laser-cutting nozzle can be considered in first order approximation, an isentropic process. The following development from *Equation C-2* leads to important characteristics of ideal gases in an isentropic flow, summarized in *Equation C-6*.

$$dH = C_p\,dT \text{ and } dU = C_v\,dT \tag{C-3}$$

where:

C_p = specific heat coefficient at constant pressure
C_v = specific heat coefficient at constant volume

Combined with *Equation C-2* for an isentropic flow:

$$0 = C_v\,dT + P\,dv = C_p\,dT - v\,dP \quad \text{(C-4)}$$

solving the two equalities of *Equation C-4* for dT yields:

$$\frac{dP}{P} = -\frac{C_p}{C_v}\frac{dv}{v} = -\gamma\frac{dv}{v} \quad \text{(C-5)}$$

Assuming that C_p and C_v are constant, an easy integration yields:

Pv^{γ} = constant, and for an ideal gas,

$$\frac{P}{\rho^{\gamma}} = \text{constant} \quad \text{(C-6)}$$

where:

γ = a ratio defined by the specific heat of the gas at constant pressure $C_p \div$ specific heat of the gas at constant volume C_v

Degrees of Freedom

The equipartition theorem attributes the same amount of internal energy for each degree of freedom of a particle—translational, rotational, and vibrational. The degrees of freedom are associated with the internal energy of a particle. As such, translational energy represents thermal agitation in random directions of the molecules and atoms, leading to collisions among them. This should not be mistaken for the kinetic energy of the ensemble of molecules and atoms associated with gas flow. A simple statistical thermodynamic derivation (Chahine and Devaux 1976) shows that the average translational speed of particles at temperature, T, is given by:

$$\overline{v} = \sqrt{8rT}$$

which is higher than the speed of sound as will be shown in the next section.

An atom has only three translational degrees of freedom. It does not have vibrational or rotational degrees of freedom. A molecule composed of N atoms generally has $3N$ degrees of freedom, among which are three degrees of freedom for translation (one for each Cartesian axis in a three-dimensional space). It also generally has three degrees of freedom of rotation (one about each Cartesian axis in a three-dimensional space). Linear molecules are an exception as their atoms are aligned along one axis. Consequently, the rotation about this axis of the molecule contributes negligibly to the internal energy (negligible inertia), so it is not considered a degree of freedom of rotation because no atom changes place in the rotation. For these reasons, linear molecules are considered to have only two degrees of freedom of rotation. The $3N$-6 or $3N$-5 remaining degrees of freedom are vibrational degrees of freedom as summarized in *Table C-2.*

Specific Heat

A statistical thermodynamic derivation of the partition function of a system of particles shows that each rotational degree of freedom contributes $1/2rT$ to the internal energy for each mole of gas and each translational degree of freedom contributes $1/2rT$ to said internal energy (Anderson 1982; Chahine and Devaux 1976). The real contribution of vibrational energy per mole of gas can be derived by a similar statistical thermodynamics calculation as a

Table C-2. Number of degrees of freedom for atoms and molecules

Number of Degrees of Freedom	Atoms	Linear Molecules with N Atoms	Non-linear Molecules with N Atoms
Translation, n_T =	3	3	3
Rotation, n_R =	0	2	3
Vibration, n_V =	0	3N-5	3N-6
Total, $n_T + n_R + n_V$ =	3	3N	3N

function of temperature, assuming each vibrational mode can be approximated as a perfect harmonic oscillator vibrational mode:

$$E_v = rT\left(\sum_{i=1}^{n_V} \frac{\frac{\varepsilon_i}{kT}}{e^{\frac{\varepsilon_i}{kT}} - 1}\right) = rT\sum_{i=1}^{n_V} Z_i = \frac{1}{2} rT(2n_V\ Z) \tag{C-7}$$

where:

E_v = internal vibrational energy
r = ratio resulting from the ideal gas constant, R = 8.314 J/K-mol ÷ molar mass equivalent of the gas
T = temperature
n_V = total number of vibrational degrees of freedom *(Table C-2)*
ε_i = quantum energy levels of the fundamental modes of vibrations directly associated with the molecule's vibrational degrees of freedom
k = 1.38 10^{-23} J/K, the known Boltzmann constant, which can be related to R by $k = \frac{R}{\aleph}$ with $\aleph$ = 6.02 10^{23}, the Avogadro number

The term sum in parentheses in *Equation C-7* can be called:

$$n_V\ Z = \sum_{i=1}^{n_V} Z_i$$

where:

$$Z_i = \frac{\frac{\varepsilon_i}{kT}}{e^{\frac{\varepsilon_i}{kT}} - 1}$$

are dimensionless numbers between 0 and 1 and so is their average, Z.

Note that when $kT \langle\langle \varepsilon_i$ for each mode i (this is the case at room temperature for most gas molecules), then $Z_i \approx 0$ and $Z \approx 0$. That is, the contribution of vibrational degrees of freedom i, individually and as a whole to the internal vibrational energy of *Equation C-7*, is negligible. Whereas when $kT \rangle\rangle \varepsilon_i$ for each mode i (high temperature), then Z and $Z_i \approx 1$. That is, the contribution of each vibrational degree of freedom to the internal energy approaches rT. *Figure C-2* illustrates examples of N_2 and CO_2 vibrational modes. *Table C-3* gives known molecular vibrational quantum energy levels for different molecules. Similarly, the electronic energy levels, ε_{el}, are so large that even at metal-vaporization temperatures of several thousand Kelvin, $kT \langle\langle \varepsilon_{el}$. This explains why electronic energy's contribution to internal energy is neglected.

The internal energy per mole of gas is given by:

$$U = \frac{1}{2} rT (n_T + n_R + 2Z\, n_V)$$

and

$$C_v = \left.\frac{\partial U}{\partial T}\right|_V = \frac{1}{2} r (n_T + n_R + 2Z\, n_V) \tag{C-8}$$

where:

n_T = number of translational degrees of freedom
n_R = number of rotational degrees of freedom

For an ideal gas, it can be demonstrated that $C_p - C_v = r$, thus yielding (Fox and McDonald 1985):

$$C_P = \frac{1}{2} r (2 + n_T + n_R + 2Z\, n_V) \tag{C-9}$$

and

$$\gamma = \frac{C_P}{C_v} = 1 + \frac{2}{n_T + n_R + 2Z\, n_V} \tag{C-10}$$

Equation C-10 gives γ for a pure gas. For a mixture of pure gases it can be derived that the equivalent molar mass, m, and heat capacity ratio, γ, of the mixture as a function of molar mass m_i, heat-capacity ratio γ_i, and molar fraction, x_i, of each pure gas composing the mixture is:

$$m = \sum x_i m_i \tag{C-11}$$

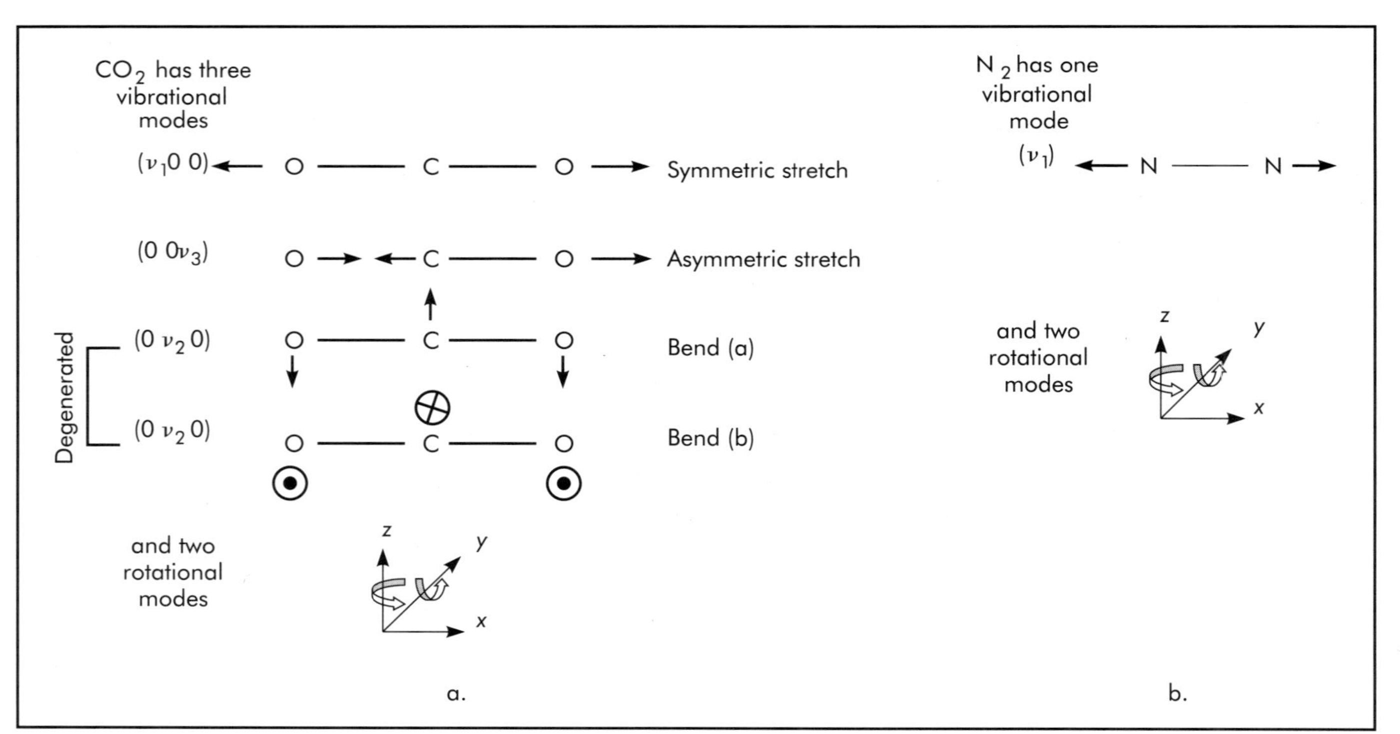

Figure C-2. Rotational and vibrational degrees of freedom: (a) CO_2 has four degrees of freedom of vibration resulting in three modes of vibration. The bending mode of vibration is degenerated in that both degrees of freedom have the same vibrational energy. Being a linear molecule, CO_2 has only two degrees of freedom of rotation. (b) N_2 has only one degree of freedom of vibration (a stretch) and two degrees of freedom of rotation.

Table C-3. Vibrational energy of fundamental modes

CO_2	N_2
Four vibrational degrees of freedom yielding three vibration modes Symmetric stretch, v_1, 1,333 cm^{-1} Asymmetric stretch, v_3, 2,349 cm^{-1} Bend, v_2, 667 cm^{-1} is degenerated (that is, two degrees of freedom)	One vibrational stretch mode 2,331 cm^{-1}

Note: The energy-equivalent unit cm^{-1} used in spectroscopy is the unit for the inverse of the wavelength. It is equivalent to 1.99 10^{-23} J or 1.23 10^{-4} eV. For order of magnitude sake, 1 cm^{-1} is equivalent to 1.44 K temperature difference.

and

$$\frac{1}{\gamma - 1} = \sum \frac{x_i}{\gamma_i - 1} \qquad \text{(C-12)}$$

Table C-4 displays values for m and γ for different assist-gases, assuming that assist-gas flow for laser cutting generally occurs at room temperature represented by $Z \approx 0$ in *Equation C-10.*

Table C-4. Critical point characteristics for different assist-gases

Gas	m (g)	γ	$\frac{P^*}{P_0}$	$\frac{\rho^*}{\rho_0}$	$\frac{T^*}{T_0}$	$\frac{a^*}{a_0}$
O_2	32	1.40	0.528	0.634	0.833	0.913
N_2	28	1.40	0.528	0.634	0.833	0.913
H_2	2	1.40	0.528	0.634	0.833	0.913
Air (80% N_2 + 20% O_2)	29	1.40	0.528	0.634	0.833	0.913
CO_2	44	1.40	0.528	0.634	0.833	0.913
Ar	40	1.67	0.487	0.650	0.749	0.865
He	4	1.67	0.487	0.650	0.749	0.865
Water vapor, H_2O	18	1.33	0.540	0.630	0.858	0.926

* = Critical physical quantity

Speed of Sound and Mach Number

In an ambient atmosphere, sound waves are pressure waves of air that propagate and eventually strike the tympanic membrane of the ear. If the frequency of a wave is between 20 Hz (bass) and 20 kHz (high pitch), humans can hear its sound provided that the amplitude is audible enough. Below 20 Hz is infrasound, which is inaudible to humans. Above 20 kHz is ultrasound, also inaudible to humans, regardless of amplitude. The speed, a, at which a sound propagates in a medium is equal to the square root of the differential of pressure with respect to density at constant entropy (Fox and McDonald 1985):

$$a = \sqrt{\left.\frac{\partial P}{\partial \rho}\right|_S} \tag{C-13}$$

where:

a = speed at which sound propagates in a medium
P = gas pressure
ρ = gas density
S = entropy

For an ideal gas governed by *Equations C-1* and *C-6*, it can be easily deduced that:

$$a = \sqrt{\gamma r T} \tag{C-14}$$

Mechanical information such as density, temperature, and speed can propagate at the speed of sound. For example, sonic devices use sound waves to detect cracks in welds by measuring density gradients. Highway patrols use radar emitting sound waves that reflect from a moving vehicle, precisely measuring the speed of that vehicle. However, radar measurement is impossible if the target is moving away from the radar faster than the speed of sound. In ambient atmospheric air, the speed of sound is approximately 1,138 ft/s (347 m/s).

The Mach number of a particle in motion is defined as the ratio of its speed to the speed of sound:

$$M = \frac{V}{a} \tag{C-15}$$

where:

M = Mach number
V = speed
a = local speed of sound

$M < 1$ indicates a subsonic regime, while $M > 1$ indicates a supersonic regime. The term hypersonic describes supersonic regimes in which $M \geq 5$.

Quasi-one-dimensional Isentropic Gas Flow

Most nozzles used for laser cutting exhibit an axis-symmetry feature which, when neglecting friction, allows quasi-one-dimensional gas flow (the thermodynamic physical quantities of the gas only depend on one Cartesian coordinate). Consider a gas flowing through the arbitrary segment of nozzle depicted in *Figure C-3*. The governing conservation equations for continuity, energy, and momentum render the following differential equations.

Continuity conservation expresses the conservation of mass flow rate coming in versus going out of the control volume:

$\rho_{in} V_{in} A_{in} = \rho_{out} V_{out} A_{out}$, which in differential form can be written as $d(\rho VA) = 0$. This leads to:

$$\rho V dA + \rho A dV + A V d\rho = 0 \tag{C-16}$$

Conservation of momentum leads to:

$$A dP + A V^2 d\rho + \rho V^2 dA + 2 \rho V A dV = 0 \tag{C-17}$$

where:

A = nozzle cross-sectional area
P = static pressure
V = speed of the gas flow
ρ = gas density

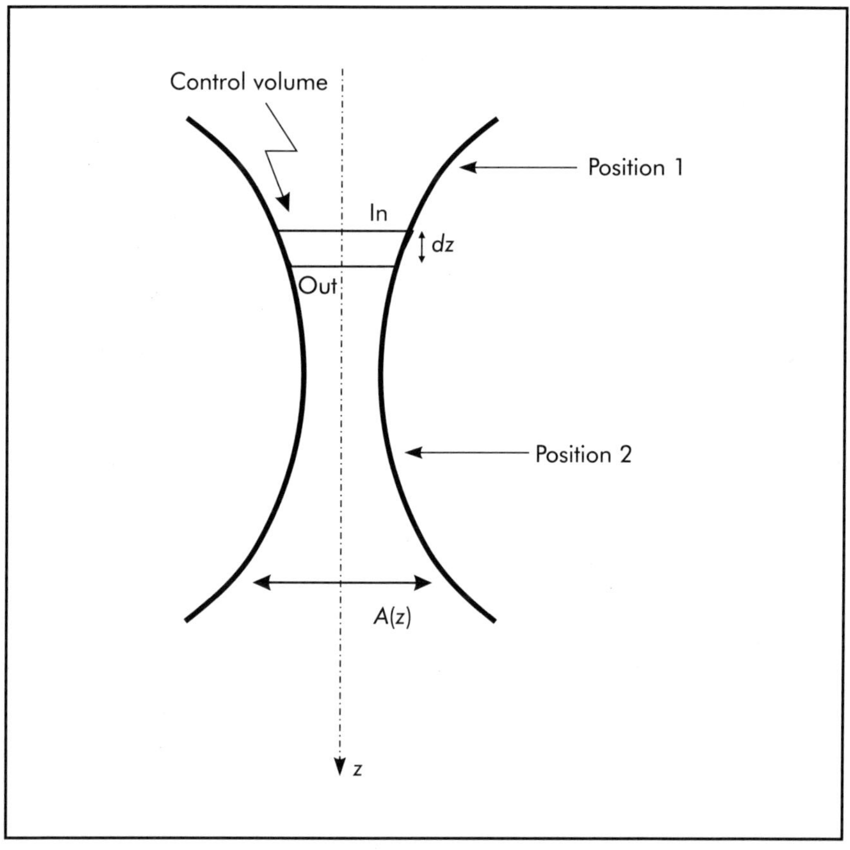

Figure C-3. In this axis-symmetric convergent-divergent nozzle, a control volume is represented by its entry cross-section A and width dz. The thermodynamic characteristics of the gas are compared coming in and going out of the nozzle. The flow of gas is indicated by the arrow of the z axis. Neglecting friction, the thermodynamic characteristics depend only on the variable z and, therefore, there is quasi-one-dimensional flow.

Conservation of energy per mole is given by:

$$H_{in} + \frac{1}{2}V_{in}^2 = H_{out} + \frac{1}{2}V_{out}^2$$

where:

H_{in}, H_{out} = enthalpy going in and coming out of the control volume in *Figure C-3*

In differential form this can be written as $dH + \frac{1}{2}d\left(V^2\right) = 0$, leading to:

$$C_p\, dT + V\, dV = 0, \text{ that is,}$$

$$\frac{\gamma}{\gamma - 1} r\, dT + V\, dV = 0 \tag{C-18}$$

Careful manipulation of these equations coupled with *Equations C-1* and *C-6* allows extracting interesting characteristics of gas flow as follows. Multiplying *Equation C-16* by speed, *V*, and combining it with *Equation C-17* leads to the known Euler equation:

$$dP + \rho\, V\, dV = 0 \tag{C-19}$$

For isentropic flows, *Equation C-6* can be written as $P = C\rho^{\gamma}$ where:

C = absolute constant

Combined with *Equation C-19* it yields:

$$\left(\frac{P}{C}\right)^{\frac{-1}{\gamma}} dP + V\, dV = 0 \tag{C-20}$$

Integrating *Equation C-20* between arbitrary position 1 and position 2 along the *z* axis yields:

$$\frac{\gamma\, C^{\frac{1}{\gamma}}}{\gamma - 1}\left[P_2^{\frac{\gamma-1}{\gamma}} - P_1^{\frac{\gamma-1}{\gamma}}\right] = \frac{1}{2}\left[V_1^2 - V_2^2\right] \tag{C-21}$$

Replacing $C^{\frac{1}{\gamma}}$ by $\frac{P_1^{\frac{1}{\gamma}}}{\rho_1}$ and using the ideal gas *Equation C-1* yields:

$$\frac{a_1^2}{\gamma - 1}\left[\left(\frac{P_2}{P_1}\right)^{\frac{\gamma-1}{\gamma}} - 1\right] = \frac{1}{2}\left[V_1^2 - V_2^2\right] \tag{C-22}$$

where:

a_1 = speed of sound at position 1

Consider a case in which position 2 represents the stagnation condition in the nozzle chamber where the gas resides at relatively high stagnation pressure, $P_0 = P_2$, and speed $V_2 \approx 0$. The subscript "1" can then be omitted in *Equation C-22*:

$$\frac{P_0}{P} = \left[1 + \frac{\gamma - 1}{2} M^2\right]^{\frac{\gamma}{\gamma-1}} \tag{C-23}$$

From *Equations C-6* and *C-1* comes

$$\frac{P_0}{P} = \left(\frac{\rho_0}{\rho}\right)^{\gamma} = \left(\frac{T_0}{T}\right)^{\frac{\gamma}{\gamma-1}}$$

leading to:

$$\frac{\rho_0}{\rho} = \left[1 + \frac{\gamma - 1}{2} M^2\right]^{\frac{1}{\gamma-1}} \tag{C-24}$$

and

$$\frac{T_0}{T} = 1 + \frac{\gamma - 1}{2} M^2 \tag{C-25}$$

Equations C-23 through *C-25* are key to characterizing quasi-mono-dimensional, isentropic, inviscid, compressible gas flow through a nozzle as a function of Mach number. They apply whether the nozzle geometry is convergent-divergent, capillary, or just convergent as depicted in *Figure C-1*.

Area-velocity Relationship

To derive a relationship between Mach number and nozzle cross-section area, use the continuity equation, $\rho\, V A$ = constant, and manipulate the Euler equation (*Equation C-19*) by rewriting it as follows:

$$\frac{dP}{\rho} = -V\,dV = \frac{dP}{d\rho}\frac{d\rho}{\rho} \tag{C-26}$$

Since the flow is isentropic,

$$\frac{dP}{d\rho} = \left.\frac{\partial P}{\partial \rho}\right|_S = a^2 \text{ (the square of the speed of sound), yielding:}$$

$$\frac{d\rho}{\rho} = -M^2\frac{dV}{V} \tag{C-27}$$

Combining *Equation C-27* with the continuity *Equation C-16* results in the area-velocity relationship:

$$\frac{dA}{A} = \left(M^2 - 1\right)\frac{dV}{V} \tag{C-28}$$

The area-velocity relationship reveals that if the flow is supersonic downstream of the nozzle exit, it can be deduced that: 1) $M = 1$ at the throat of the nozzle (minimum cross-section area with $dA = 0$); 2) $M < 1$ upstream of the throat; and 3) $M > 1$ downstream of the throat (Anderson 1982). For converging and capillary nozzles, the throat coincides with the nozzle exit. This has been confirmed by calculation involving the numerical method of characteristics under different throat conditions. However, experimental density profile measurements in supersonic free jets tend to reveal that the $M = 1$ throat condition is not fulfilled on a perfectly flat plane section, but rather on a slightly spherical convex surface bulging out from the throat (Mombo Caristan et al. 1989).

Critical Conditions

If the superscript "*" indicates a critical physical quantity at the position where M would become equal to 1 if the flow was to be supersonic, then A^* coincides with the cross-sectional area at the throat of a convergent-divergent nozzle or at the exit of a capillary and convergent nozzle (see *Figure C-1*). The following relationships are obtained by manipulating the conservation equations—the isentropy *Equation C-6* and *Equations C-23* through *C-25*.

$$\frac{A}{A^*} = \frac{1}{M}\left[\frac{1+\frac{\gamma-1}{2}M^2}{1+\frac{\gamma-1}{2}}\right]^{\frac{\gamma+1}{2(\gamma-1)}} \quad \text{(C-29)}$$

$$\frac{V}{V^*} = \left[\frac{(\gamma+1)M^2}{2+(\gamma-1)M^2}\right]^{\frac{1}{2}} \quad \text{(C-30)}$$

and

$$\frac{P^*}{P_0} = \left(\frac{2}{\gamma+1}\right)^{\frac{\gamma}{\gamma-1}} \quad \text{(C-31)}$$

$$\frac{\rho^*}{\rho_0} = \left(\frac{2}{\gamma+1}\right)^{\frac{1}{\gamma-1}} \quad \text{(C-32)}$$

$$\frac{T^*}{T_0} = \left(\frac{2}{\gamma+1}\right) \quad \text{(C-33)}$$

$$\frac{a^*}{a_0} = \left(\frac{2}{\gamma+1}\right)^{\frac{1}{2}} \quad \text{(C-34)}$$

Equations C-29 and *C-30* do not apply to capillary nozzles. *Table C-4* lists numerical values for the critical ratios of *Equations C-31* through *C-34* for common assist-gases at low stagnation temperature (close to room temperature).

Whether the critical conditions are met at the throat or not depends on the stagnation pressure, P_0, and the downstream ambient pressure, P_a. If P_a is the ambient pressure outside the nozzle, and P_{exit} the static pressure right at the nozzle exit, then the following condition must exist to generate supersonic flow:

$$\frac{P_0}{P_a} \geq \frac{P_0}{P_{exit}} \geq \frac{P_0}{P^*}$$

This enables the extraction of the condition to have a supersonic flow with M at least equal to 1 at the nozzle exit from *Equation C-31*:

$$\frac{P_0}{P_a} \geq \frac{P_0}{P^*} = \left[\frac{\gamma+1}{2}\right]^{\frac{\gamma}{\gamma-1}} \quad \text{(C-35)}$$

With the condition of *Equation C-35* fulfilled, M increases from 0 in stagnation conditions to 1 at the throat position where the cross-sectional area of the nozzle reaches a minimum: the flow is "choked." It is impossible for the flow starting from rest in the stagnation chamber to accelerate to $M = 1$ at a position upstream of the position of the minimum cross-sectional area. For capillary and converging nozzles, the throat coincides with the exit plane. At this exit plane, $P_e = P^* \geq P_a$ regardless of the value of the ratio:

$$\frac{P_0}{P_a}$$

as long as *Equation C-35* is satisfied. In other words P_e increases when P_0 increases, but

$$\frac{P_e}{P_0} = \frac{P^*}{P_0}$$

remains constant per *Equation C-31*.

Downstream of the throat position, the Mach number increases either in the diverging section of a converging-diverging nozzle or in free atmosphere with a capillary or converging nozzle. Upon exit from the nozzle, due to the supersonic nature of the flow colliding with ambient air, two shock waves develop. A lateral shock wave starts at the lip of the nozzle exit and a frontal shock wave called Mach disk closes the lateral shock downstream of the nozzle. Together, these shocks form a shock barrel as depicted in *Figure C-4*. Shock waves are discontinuities characterized by a sharp gradient in density. Inside a shock barrel, no mechanical information from the ambient atmosphere can be communicated to the gas because it is flowing faster than the speed of sound. This is called the *zone of silence*. The gas-flow characteristics in the zone of

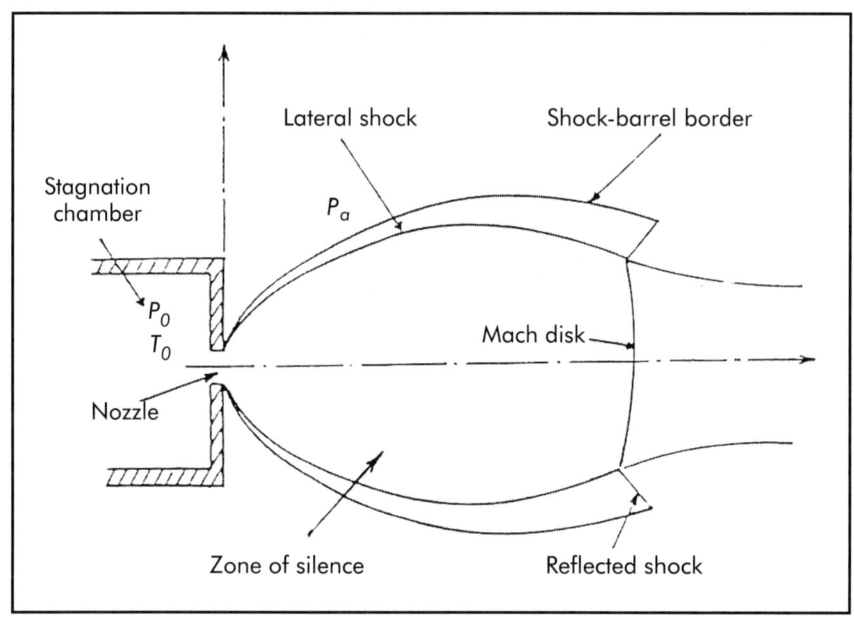

Figure C-4. In a supersonic free flow, a shock barrel is delimited by a lateral shock and a downstream frontal shock called Mach disk. Shock waves are discontinuities with a sharp gradient of density. The reflection of the lateral shock against the Mach-disk shock creates an oblique reflected shock.

silence are independent from the value of P_a or any mechanical information outside the zone of silence.

Supersonic-flow shock waves reflect upon collision with any type of physical discontinuity, whether it is another shock wave or the edge of a kerf on the workpiece (Anderson 1982). The result is an oblique wave that can divert gas flow from where it was initially aiming and disrupt cutting performance. *Figure C-4* shows that eventually the reflection of lateral shocks against Mach disks generates a downstream, quasi-periodical, barrel-like structure of shocks. Evidence of this phenomenon was shown while plotting dynamic pressure as a function of nozzle standoff distance downstream of a laser-cutting nozzle exit at constant stagnation pressure (Powell 1998; Fieret and Ward 1986). The measured dynamic pressure at the workpiece exhibited a quasi-periodical pattern due to the reflections of quasi-periodical Mach disks upon the lips of the Pitot tube used for measurement.

Figure C-5 illustrates plots of dynamic pressure at the workpiece versus nozzle standoff at constant stagnation pressure and the dynamic pressure at the workpiece versus stagnation pressure at constant nozzle standoff distance. The plots in the figure are consistent with experimental measurements from the reference (Powell 1998). It is therefore recommended that the nozzle standoff distance be shorter than the distance x_M of the first Mach disk to the nozzle exit. This distance cannot be derived analytically. However, Pitot-tube measurements (Ashkenas and Sherman 1965) confirmed the optical strioscopy experimental results (Bier and Schmidt 1961) that indicated the ratio:

$$\frac{x_M}{D}$$

where:

D = nozzle throat diameter, which depends only on the ratio P_0/P_a

An empirical equation accurate for P_0/P_a between 15 and 17,000 has been established (Ashkenas and Sherman 1965). This empirical equation will be used as an approximation when P_0/P_a is smaller than 15:

$$\frac{x_M}{D} = 0.67\sqrt{\frac{P_0}{P_a}} \tag{C-36}$$

SUBSONIC FREE FLOW

If the condition of *Equation C-35* is not met, gas flow will remain subsonic downstream of the nozzle throat and nozzle exit. *Figure C-6* summarizes static pressure, P_e, and Mach number, M_e, at the exit of the three types of nozzles—converging-diverging, capillary, and converging. In the subsonic regime, the static pressure, P_e, at the nozzle exit is always equal to the ambient static pressure, P_a, and the gas flows mainly in straight streamlines out of the nozzle if the flow is laminar. If the flow is turbulent, less dynamic pressure flow is applied at the kerf of the workpiece and

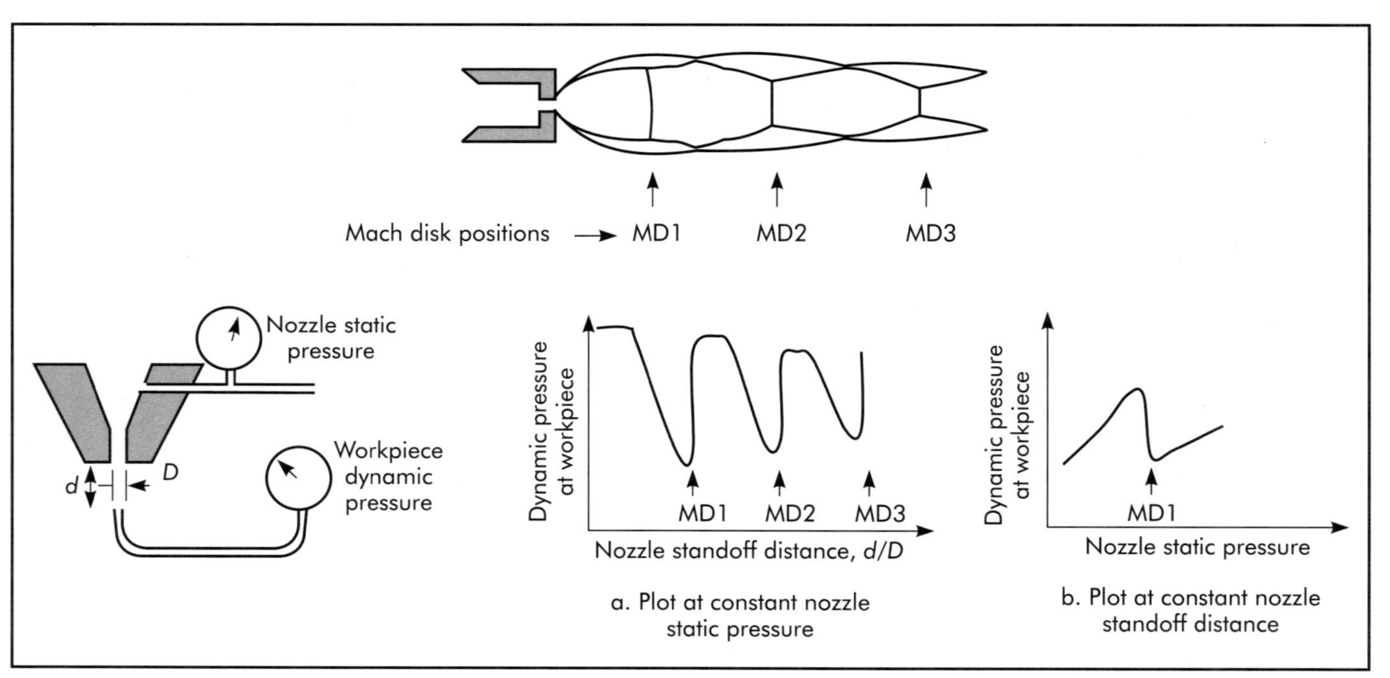

Figure C-5. At high stagnation pressure, the reflection of a lateral shock against a Mach disk creates quasi-periodical, barrel-like structures. (a) Pitot-tube experiments to measure dynamic pressure of the assist-gas on the workpiece versus nozzle standoff distance, d, *exhibit quasi-periodical features (Powell 1998) indicative of the quasi-periodical Mach-disk shock reflections against the entry lips of the Pitot tubes. (b) These reflections yield reflected shock waves that may translate into either a sharp increase in measured dynamic pressure upon their entry into the Pitot tube, or a sharp decrease if the reflected wave deflects flow away from the tube entry.*

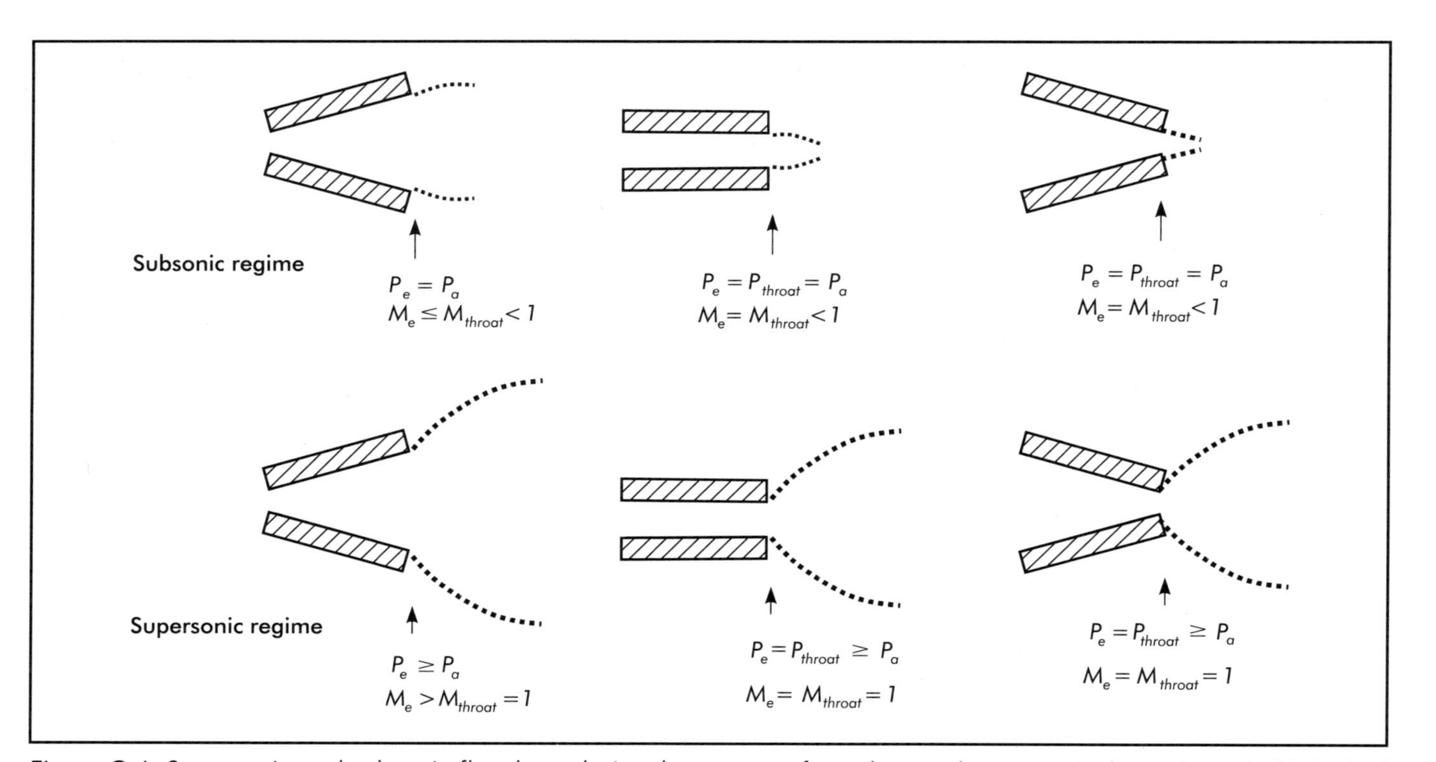

Figure C-6. Supersonic and subsonic flow boundaries downstream from the nozzle exit are indicated in a bold dashed line for converging-diverging nozzles (left column), capillary nozzles (center column), and converging nozzles (right column). P_e *is the static pressure in the exit plane;* P_a *is the ambient back pressure; and* P_{throat} *is the static pressure at the nozzle's throat.* M_e *represents the Mach number at the exit plane and* M_{throat} *the Mach number at the throat.*

possibly different cutting performance results. The Reynolds number, Re, helps distinguish the turbulent from the laminar regime and is given in the general case at the nozzle throat by:

$$Re^* = \frac{\rho^* V^* D^*}{\mu^*} \qquad \text{(C-37)}$$

where:

μ^* = viscosity (so far neglected) of the gas given the throat conditions

And in the case of the capillary of length, L (Fox and McDonald 1985):

$$\frac{L}{D} \approx 0.06 Re \qquad \text{(C-38)}$$

The gas flow is considered turbulent as soon as Re^* becomes larger than about 2,300. By order of preference to avoid turbulent flow, a capillary nozzle should be chosen over a converging-diverging nozzle; and a converging-diverging nozzle over a converging nozzle.

FLOW RATE DERIVATIONS

Supersonic Regime

A mass flow rate can be calculated as being equal to the product $\rho\ V A$. Continuity *Equation C-16* states that $\rho\ V A$ is a constant regardless of where it is calculated along the nozzle. For a supersonic gas flow of molar mass, m, through a nozzle of throat diameter, D, mass flow rate is calculated at the critical point where $V^* = a^* = (\gamma r T^*)^{1/2}$ by using *Equations C-32* to *C-34*. This yields (all variables are in the international system of units):

supersonic mass flow rate =

$$P_0 \frac{\pi D^2}{4} \sqrt{\frac{\gamma m}{R T_0} \left(\frac{2}{\gamma + 1} \right)^{\frac{\gamma+1}{\gamma-1}}} \qquad \text{(C-39)}$$

or

$$P_0 \frac{D^2}{\sqrt{T_0}} \underbrace{\sqrt{\frac{\pi^2 \gamma m}{16R} \left(\frac{2}{\gamma+1} \right)^{\frac{\gamma+1}{\gamma-1}}}}_{\alpha_{sup}} \tag{C-40}$$

This confirms that in the supersonic regime, the mass flow rate does not depend on the ambient atmosphere type, pressure, density, or temperature. Numerical values for α_{sup} are given in *Table C-5* for common assist-gases. Translating the mass flow rate into a volume flow rate is achieved by dividing the mass flow rate by the density, ρ. As the mass flow rate is invariable regardless of which position it is calculated from, the volume flow rate changes depending on which position ρ is calculated at.

Standard Volume Flow Rate

A *standard volume flow rate* is defined as the flow rate under standard temperature and pressure conditions, namely $T \approx 80°$ F (300 K) and $P \approx 760$ torr (1 bar). In standard conditions, 1 mole of any gas occupies 0.8 ft^3 (22.4 L) of volume. The standard volume flow rate is deduced in standard cubic feet per hour unit (1 SCFH = 28.3 L/hr = 0.47 L/min) as being:

supersonic volume flow rate (SCFH) =

$$P_0 \frac{D^2}{\sqrt{T_0}} \underbrace{\times 2{,}236.64 \times \sqrt{\frac{\gamma}{Rm} \left(\frac{2}{\gamma+1} \right)^{\frac{\gamma+1}{\gamma-1}}}}_{\beta_{sup}} \tag{C-41}$$

Numerical values for β_{sup} are given in *Table C-5* for common assist-gases.

Table C-5. Parameters α_{sub}, β_{sub}, α_{sup}, and β_{sup} for known assist-gases

Gas	m	γ	α_{sub}	β_{sub}	α_{sup}	β_{sup}
O_2	32	1.40	0.13	11,472.69	0.03	2,969.18
N_2	28	1.40	0.12	12,264.82	0.03	3,174.19
H_2	2	1.40	0.03	45,890.75	0.01	11,876.72
Air	29	1.40	0.12	12,051.50	0.03	3,118.98
CO_2	44	1.40	0.15	9,783.94	0.04	2,532.12
Ar	40	1.67	0.12	8,675.14	0.04	2,816.12
He	4	1.67	0.04	27,433.20	0.01	8,905.35
H_2O	18	1.33	0.10	16,414.92	0.02	3,888.93

The relative percent variation in mass and volume flow rates can thus be derived as a function of relative percent variation in P_0, T_0, and D:

$$\frac{\Delta(\text{flow rate})}{\text{flow rate}} = \left|\frac{\Delta P_0}{P_0}\right| + 2\left|\frac{\Delta D}{D}\right| + \frac{1}{2}\left|\frac{\Delta T_0}{T_0}\right| \tag{C-42}$$

If less than 5% tolerance in flow-rate variation is acceptable for the stability and repeatability of the laser-cutting process, then it can be reached with a relative 10% temperature variation, a relative 2.5% nozzle-diameter variation, or a relative 5% pressure variation.

Subsonic Regime

To derive the mass flow rate

$$\frac{d\ mass}{dt}$$

in the case of a subsonic flow, calculate:

$$\frac{d\,mass}{dt} = \rho AV = \frac{P}{rT}AV = PAM\left(\frac{\gamma}{rT}\right)^{\frac{1}{2}}$$
$$= PAM\left(\frac{\gamma}{rT_0}\left(1+\frac{\gamma-1}{2}M^2\right)\right)^{\frac{1}{2}} \tag{C-43}$$

leading to:

$$\frac{d\,mass}{dt} = P_0 AM\left(\frac{\gamma}{rT_0}\right)^{\frac{1}{2}}\left(1+\frac{\gamma-1}{2}M^2\right)^{\frac{\gamma+1}{2(1-\gamma)}} \tag{C-44}$$

Using *Equation C-23* to eliminate M produces:

$$\frac{d\,mass}{dt} = P_0 A^*\left(\frac{2\gamma^2}{\gamma r T_0(\gamma-1)}\right)^{\frac{1}{2}}\left(\frac{P}{P_0}\right)^{\frac{1}{\gamma}}\left[1-\left(\frac{P}{P_0}\right)^{\frac{\gamma-1}{\gamma}}\right]^{\frac{1}{2}} \tag{C-45}$$

Since for subsonic flows, $P_e = P_a$ (see above), it can be deduced that:

subsonic mass flow rate =

$$\frac{P_0 D^2}{\sqrt{T_0}}\sqrt{\left(\frac{P_a}{P_0}\right)^{\frac{2}{\gamma}}-\left(\frac{P_a}{P_0}\right)^{\frac{\gamma+1}{\gamma}}}\times\underbrace{\sqrt{\frac{m\pi^2\gamma}{8R(\gamma-1)}}}_{\alpha_{sub}} \tag{C-46}$$

and consequently,

subsonic volume flow rate (SCFH) =

$$\frac{P_0 D^2}{\sqrt{T_0}}\sqrt{\left(\frac{P_a}{P_0}\right)^{\frac{2}{\gamma}}-\left(\frac{P_a}{P_0}\right)^{\frac{\gamma+1}{\gamma}}}\underbrace{\times 3{,}163.087\times\sqrt{\frac{\gamma}{mR(\gamma-1)}}}_{\beta_{sub}} \tag{C-47}$$

In all equations, the international system of units is used to obtain a result in kg/s for mass flow rates. The volume flow-rate equations contain a numerical conversion factor to obtain a result in SCFH units even though all other physical quantities are expressed in international system units.

The subsonic flow rates depend on ambient atmospheric pressure, P_a.

Table C-5 provides parameters α_{sub}, β_{sub}, α_{sup}, and β_{sup} for common assist-gases. Volume flow rates for common assist-gases are derived in *Table C-1*.

It is informative to derive the relative percent variation in mass and volume flow rates as a function of relative percent variation in P_0, T_0, and D. In the subsonic regime, the relative variation regarding P_0 and P_a is slightly more complicated. However, for simplification, the following inequalities can be obtained by assuming that atmospheric pressure, P_a, is constant:

$$\frac{\Delta(\text{flow rate})}{\text{flow rate}} = \underbrace{\frac{1}{2}\frac{\gamma-1}{\gamma}\left[1+\frac{1}{1-\left(\frac{P_a}{P_0}\right)^{\frac{\gamma-1}{\gamma}}}\right]}_{F_0}\left|\frac{\Delta P_0}{P_0}\right| + \frac{1}{2}\left|-\frac{\Delta T_0}{T_0}\right| + 2\left|\frac{\Delta D}{D}\right| \tag{C-48}$$

$$+\underbrace{\frac{1}{2}\frac{1}{\gamma}\left[1+\gamma+\frac{1-\gamma}{1-\left(\frac{P_a}{P_0}\right)^{\frac{\gamma-1}{\gamma}}}\right]}_{F_a}\left|\frac{\Delta P_a}{P_a}\right|$$

For subsonic flows, factor F_0 increases while factor F_a decreases when P_0 decreases to approach P_a (limit of the no-flow condition). In fact, $F_0 = 1 - F_a$. When P_0 increases to reach the limit of supersonic regime transition given by:

$$\frac{P_a}{P_0} = \left[\frac{2}{\gamma+1}\right]^{\frac{\gamma}{\gamma-1}}, \text{ then } F_0 = 1 \text{ while } F_a = 0$$

Assuming that P_a is constant:

$$\begin{aligned}\frac{\Delta(\text{flow rate})}{\text{flow rate}} &= F_0\left|\frac{\Delta P_0}{P_0}\right| + \frac{1}{2}\left|-\frac{\Delta T_0}{T_0}\right| + 2\left|\frac{\Delta D}{D}\right| \\ &\geq \left|\frac{\Delta P_0}{P_0}\right| + \frac{1}{2}\left|-\frac{\Delta T_0}{T_0}\right| + 2\left|\frac{\Delta D}{D}\right|\end{aligned} \quad \text{(C-49)}$$

If a 5% tolerance is needed, it can be reached with a relative 10% temperature variation or a relative 2.5% nozzle-diameter variation, or more than 5% pressure variation. For numerical reference with O_2 assist-gas of 1.5 bar, that is,

$$\frac{P_a}{P_0} = \frac{2}{3}, F_0 \approx 1.4488 \text{ while } F_a \approx -0.4488$$

REFERENCES

Anderson, J. D. 1982. *Modern Compressible Flow*. New York: McGraw Hill.

Ashkenas, H. and Sherman, F. S. 1965. *Proceedings of the 5th Rarefied Gas Dynamics Conference*, vol. II, p. 84. J.H. de Leeuw, ed. New York: Academic Press.

Bier, K. and Schmidt, B. 1961. "Zeitschrift fur angewandte Physik." 11, pp. 493–500. Germany.

Chahine, C. and Devaux, P. 1976. "Thermodynamique Statistique." France: Dunod Universite.

Fieret, J. and Ward, B. A. 1986, June. "Circular and Non-circular Nozzle Exits for Supersonic Gas-jet Assist in CO_2 Laser Cutting." *Proceedings of the 3rd International Conference on Lasers in Manufacturing*. Paris, France.

Fox, Robert W. and McDonald, Alan T. 1985. *Introduction to Fluid Mechanics*. New York: John Wiley & Sons.

Mombo Caristan, J. C., Philippe, L. C., Chidiac, C., Perrin, M. Y., and Martin, J. P. 1989. "Measurements of Free-jet Densities by Laser-beam Deviation." "Rarefied Gas Dynamics (RGD): Physical Phenomena," Vol. 117, *Progress in Astronautics and Aeronautics*. Washington, DC: American Institute of Aeronautics and Astronautics (AIAA).

Powell, John. 1998. *CO_2 Laser Cutting*. New York: Springer Verlag.

Index

A

B

C

D

E

F

G

H

I

J

K

L

M

N

O

P

Q

R

S

T

V

W

Y

Z